Tak Paris

The
Burning Ground

authorHOUSE™

1663 LIBERTY DRIVE, SUITE 200
BLOOMINGTON, INDIANA 47403
(800) 839-8640
WWW.AUTHORHOUSE.COM

For the purpose of anonymity, some of the names in this book have been changed. This is to maintain their dignity and privacy.

First published by AuthorHouse 09/27/05

ISBN: 1-4208-7290-7 (sc)

Printed in the United States of America
Bloomington, Indiana

This book is printed on acid-free paper.

Acknowledgements

My sincere thanks to Arthur Morgan and Carol Gray, who sifted through reams of early manuscripts, to make *The Burning Ground* a reality.

Special thanks to my mentor Dave Ball and Faye, whose wisdom and hospitality was always greatly appreciated.

Finally, due to overwhelming support and love, my heartfelt thanks to my wife Anja. Her critical eye for detail was invaluable, during the final edit of *The Burning Ground*.

Dedicated to Dr. Douglas Baker, my spiritual teacher and task-master; without whose guidance, encouragement and wisdom, the contents of **The Burning Ground** would never have materialised.

'To know, to will, to dare and to be silent'

CHAPTER 1

'This is the cabin service director. Cabin crew; doors to automatic and cross check; stand by for the safety demo at your door positions.'

Whilst fiddling with my personal TV screen, I caught a glimpse of the ground engineers de-icing the wings for takeoff. It was 6am on the 10th January 2000 and it was very dark. The outside temperature was minus 20 degrees Celsius and Almaty International Airport, Kazakhstan, resembled the icing on an elaborate Christmas cake. The terminal building, which had been struck by lightning just a few weeks earlier, looked like it was cloaked in a huge, supernatural, ebony shell. Black carbon fronds punched through the shell and reached skywards in adoration of the crystal clear, starry sanctuary.

The full moon's lunar light focused its beam, searing the awesome Tien Shan mountain range, scattered with alpines and amazing glaciers. The floodlights fought a losing battle with the elements, as they tinkled like dim fairy lights on a festive tree. The runway, engulfed in freezing fog, disappeared before my eyes and beckoned our aircraft into a mystical union with the divine. Stark figures of ground staff and army officers with layers of clothing and heavy coats huddled around the aircraft as if it was a massive bonfire. The intermittent puffs of hot air bellowing from their mouths and the occasional slight movement were the only signs that these were living beings; somehow existing in this God forsaken ice arena.

'Please make sure your tables are folded away, your seats are in the upright position and your armrests are down. Your seat belts should be securely fastened and your hand luggage securely stowed in the overhead lockers or under the seat in front of you.'

I was used to the safety and security ritual because I was cabin crew. This time though, I had been on holiday and I was a passenger on my way back to London.

'Cabin crew, please take your seats for takeoff,' said a monotone voice through the PA.

The crew scurried to their positions and strapped themselves in. It was 21st century technology versus Mother Nature. A few moments later the cabin chimes sounded and the interior cabin lights went out. I peered out through the porthole to be confronted by an exquisite, icy extravaganza. The frost on the window had made the most beautiful and intricate designs; minute patterns of divinity in perfect balance and harmony. With this spectacle, I lapsed into a reverie and we glided off the tarmac and into the deep, dark womb of the celestial mother. In that state of complete bliss, the eternal cosmic questions flowed into my consciousness.

'Who am I? Have I lived before? Will I survive death to live again?'

Well, I knew who I was at least. Chris Kasparis, astrologer and British Airways worldwide air steward, on the Heathrow fleet. My astrology column in 'Contact', our crew magazine, had made me famous with the cabin crew and infamous with the establishment. All my finely tuned talents as a serious astrologer were grossly undermined. For the magazine I created my own astrological style, geared just for our cabin crew lifestyle and mentality. It was a zany blend of sexual innuendoes, crew jargon, alliteration and just a lot of fun. It was, however, astrologically correct, and it contained hidden wisdom. Cabin crew would not believe me when I told them it took me 48 working hours to complete. They thought I took it from the *Daily Star* or *The Sunday Sport!* It really was a scream and a great morale booster. I would often use the column to poke fun at myself.

'When I was a serious astrologer my spiritual guide was so pure, now I've got one who's a sex maniac,' I once wrote.

During my reverie I could hear 'ching, ching, rattle, rattle'. It was the all too familiar sound of the drinks trolley turning out of the galley and into the cabin.

'Good morning madam, good morning sir, May I offer you a refreshment?' chirped the stewardess to passengers a few rows ahead. Despite feeling exhausted, I slowly surfaced from my withdrawal and was greeted with a beaming smile from the stewardess, who knew I was crew.

'So what brings you to Almaty? It's not exactly a hotspot holiday destination,' she asked, in a mildly sarcastic tone and with a chuckle in her voice.

'Wouldn't you like to know?' I said, in an enigmatic manner. 'I've got a Kazakh girlfriend out here, with legs up to her armpits and a mini skirt the size of a BA scarf.' We both had a laugh as she tinkled off to the next passenger, with a gorgeous glow and a gregarious manner.

The meal trolley with stewardess in toe trundled towards me. God, I hadn't even looked at the menu yet. All was well though. Being cabin crew I was served what was left. It beat making choices so early in the morning. Within an hour I had finished breakfast. A hot towel promptly followed as my tray disappeared into the dark recesses of the trolley. In seconds the lights were dimmed and I was tucked in as snug as a bug in a rug.

I pulled out a book that was given to me by a medium I had met through a mutual friend a week before. It was called 'How to Meet and Work with Spirit Guides' by Ted Andrews. It was a small paperback, part of a series of 'How to' spiritual books. The whole meeting with the medium still puzzled me. I've been a New Ager for 22 years, but I like to think I keep a practical head and treat most things with a healthy dose of scepticism.

'I had to embrace this spirit realm,' she advised me, and added that I should 'open my mind up and just accept'.

Most of the content seemed practical enough and kept in line with traditional 'Ancient Wisdom' teachings. After reading the first few chapters I was prepared for spirit guide contact. Preliminary exercises outlined methods of deep relaxation, breathing techniques, visualization and guided imaging sessions. To this day I really don't know why I got the urge to try out the imaging session up there. I was always taught, being at the right place at the right time, magic can be experienced. Well, 35,000 feet up in the air in a pressurised metal tube travelling at 500 miles an hour seemed to be the right place at that time. I was always one to do weird things.

I had memorised the contents of the guided imaging session and I was ready. But I had to create the right environment. The in-flight entertainment radio channel had just the remedy. Soothing sounds of nature, the sea, gulls, the swishing of wind and delicate ethereal melodies. Within minutes, I was in the recline position, earphones on and surrounded by cushions and blankets. The preliminary scene was set.

I had to imagine myself in a harmonious, natural environment with emerald green, grassy glens, sweet aromas and wildlife meandering to and fro. In my mind I strolled aimlessly to a clear area. The space was my sacred altar, where I would experience spirit contact in a safe haven. I had to visualise an energy emerging from a golden ball of light, opening up like a flower to reveal my guide. Communication was possible in this state of awareness. I had to ask questions and wait miraculously for responses. It was all very weird and a bit far-fetched. But I was told, 'go with the flow. Open your mind up and just accept'.

That was all there was to it. You could vary the journey according to your imaging.

I centred myself and within the darkness of my mind I envisioned a seascape: crashing waves and sea gulls chattering in the wind, balanced effortlessly in the elements. The sun's rays soothed my back as I walked through a luscious, dew drenched meadow. The waft of freshly cut grass, fragrant flowers and apple blossom hung tantalizingly in the sweet air. I felt the swish of the meadow brush past my legs. An opening led to an immaculate garden where an emerald lawn stretched out in front of me. Bumblebees buzzed around and butterflies glided to and fro caressing beautiful wild blooms. I entered the space and surrounded the garden with elm and oak trees. I felt safe and secure, knowing the Old Ones protected my sacred sanctuary. I walked to the centre anticipating the discovery of a stone to sit on. There was no stone. Instead, a white medieval tent with the Pendragon flag flying on a central flagpole, jutted out like a tooth from a milky gum. I walked up to it and pulled the fabric back. Wao! To my amazement I encountered an exquisite, ornate, golden throne decked with lions heads on either side as armrests.

Well there is no stone for me, I'm meant to sit on this! I thought. I sat down on the throne and began to visualise a pathway zigzagging up a mountain. Then completely out of the blue, an Egyptian High Priestess's head shrouded by a mass of black matted hair, loomed out from the darkness of my mind. It was crowned with a high headdress. A golden necklace adorned with jewels hung from her long, slinky neck. Her deep brown Nubian features and piercing brown eyes seared my face.

Wow, this isn't supposed to happen, but go with the flow, I thought. Then a voice shouted out from the void *'Akhenaten'*. It was so loud it thundered and vibrated in my ears. I was then hit in the face by a pungent, forceful jet of heavy incense, which made me cough and splutter violently. I was in shock.

'This wasn't supposed to happen. It wasn't in the book,' I shouted. I managed to centre myself after a short time.

'What do you want of me?' I asked. I was flashed an image: a **massive bottle of champagne cascading down a stepped waterfall.**

Somehow, I knew what it meant. All was peaceful and quiet now as I drifted into a semi-conscious dream state. As the dream unfolded, I am chatting away to some friends in a street, suddenly I felt myself moving off the pavement. A few inches first, and then a few feet. I felt strange but excited about my new gift. I was in total control, could levitate at will and control my movements.

The scene changed in the dream. I'm floating above a large auditorium; it felt like the inside of the Greek Orthodox Church in Glasgow, where I was born and grew up. I looked down and my eldest sister Angela is giving a sermon. She saw me flying above her. Then, that voice from the void thundered, 'who are you?' I wanted to answer, but the words just would not flow. The word on the tip of my tongue was **Christos.**

I managed to hover out above the auditorium and headed for the exit. I approached the large gothic archway, which led downwards via some steps and outside to the street. I was aware of a presence on my right side; some thing or someone was tugging at my heels. I slowly turned around and to my utter amazement; my grandparents on my father's side were standing there, arm in arm, full of life, fit and beaming *with light. They had passed over within a few years of each other, some time after my father died. I suppose seeing my father pass over so young contributed greatly to their demise. But, there they were, smiling at me and embracing my aura. It was definitely as real as you and I. Their colours were so vibrant, their vital energies sparkled and their youthful appearance confirmed what most clairvoyants have stated.*

The body is renewed at physical death; we discard the physical shell, which is like a heavy overcoat, especially if the body is disease ridden at death. The remaining human consciousness, the human light body is released and rejuvenated. We exist as pure energy in our subtler bodies, the astral or emotional body being the next garment we view the outer and inner world through.

'Yiayia, Pappou, is it really you?' I shouted and reached out my arms. They just smiled at me with eyes shining like moonbeams. Their spirits penetrated my heart and gently embraced my whole being with love and light. They were alive; they had survived death! They were there for me and for the rest of us, forever! It was then I became aware of another presence, this time over my shoulder on my left side. As I slowly turned around, I felt an intense aura of brilliant light and love sear my face.

'Oh my God, Oh my, God, Papa, Papa,' I shouted, falling to my knees in adoration, despair, elation and confusion. It was my dear Papa. He shone like a beacon of light. My emotional body was blasted apart. I was in a million pieces and each fragment was a holographic image of my dear Papa. He just stood there as proud as ever. He was in an immaculate back single-breasted suit, pure white shirt and a crisp black tie. His chest was muscular and inflated and his chin high in a regal pose. He was a Leo through and through. He had a heart of pure gold, adored my Mama and all seven of us. Even in the inner worlds he had not changed. He died at the age of 36. Tears cascaded, ripping deep chasms down my pale face. The pool of sobs flooded all over my body as if I was being baptized in spirit. I grabbed him around his legs and clung there from his trousers, in lament, looking up at his stern, expressionless face.

'Why did it have to happen? Why did it have to happen? It wasn't fair, it wasn't fair!' I wailed and wailed uncontrollably.

That moment felt like a million years had come and gone. It was suspended in time and space. There was no time, no space, there was just this reality, the here and now. I felt as if I had been swallowed up by a big black hole, where there was no beginning and no end. I waited for a response...not even a murmur echoed back from that void.

Was he mad with me? Had I gone against my Greek Orthodox religion? What had I done wrong? I was a good boy; I went to church every Sunday; I became an alter boy. I was dedicated and so good that my Mama had contemplated sending me to Greece to become a novitiate. I took communion each Sunday. There I was in my white silky robes, in front of Pater Athinagoras. The chalice cup raised above my head and the chink of the holy spoon against the side, a sign that communion was imminent. I took the soft, silky, crimson cloth emblazoned with a gold Byzantine cross, whilst opening my mouth to receive the Lords' Blood and....

'Ladies and gentlemen, this is the first officer speaking, sorry to wake you; I hope you had a pleasant rest and managed to get some sleep. We will be landing in 30 minutes, the weather in London is as expected for this time of year, showery, intermittent spells of sunshine. The outside temperature will be a cool, one degree Celsius. Thank you and good morning.'

I emerged from my encounter and opened my eyes to the beaming and welcoming smile of my stewardess.

'Good morning Chris, I trust you got some rest; cup of tea?'

Still in awe of the vision, with my mouth poised to take Holy Communion, I gratefully received this terrestrial blessing. I supped on a great cup of English tea and I was glad to be 'on the ground', in the capable and warm hands of the crew. I was on my way home.

But was the experience real? Had I imagined the whole thing? I had a lot of brooding and pondering to do. One thing I do know for sure, I opened my mind up and just accepted that other dimensions existed. I followed the imaging session and embraced my dearly departed family and was introduced to ***Akhenaten***, my spirit guide.

CHAPTER 2

The terminal that particular morning was dead. The ground staff hung around chatting, as if they were a band of thugs loitering at a street corner, waiting to be moved on. With my luggage in toe, vodka and caviar reeking from my duty free bag, my mind glided back to my imaging session.

I had to tell someone, but whom? Who could I trust? Who would understand? We were a close family, but for God sake, we were Greek Orthodox. If it got out, my Mama would kill me; I'd be excommunicated, she'd be excommunicated. I would bring shame to all my family and my family's family. I would be dammed eternally.

Doti and Aki? No, they had become Born Again Christians. Mickey and Georgie? No, they were born again materialists. Elli? No, she understood but was a nervous wreck. My eldest sister Angie? Yes, she would believe me, she was *in* the experience; she was in control. She was my saviour, I thought with glee and relief.

Angie was a slick chick of the sixties. One of the original flower people, a fanatic Beatles fan, a hippy, an artist, a rebel; she smoked dope and drank Newcastle Brown by the bucket. She was the family's black sheep, until I changed that. Angie somehow blamed herself for my father's death. Maybe I could release her from her torment and self-torture. God just to see her face when I tell her Papa's not dead. He's just in a kind of waking sleep and he's waiting for us all to pass over, to be a family, united again, after all the anguish. I ought not to tell her about the stern, misgiving and disapproving visage he was wearing. That would finish her off.

'Can I see your passport sir? Mm, doesn't look like you now, does it?' said the puzzled and bemused control officer.

'Where's the moustache and you've lost so much weight?' He had a point; I had changed so much after I joined BA.

'You should see my ID,' I said. 'All my colleagues gape with disbelief every time they see it. I tell them it was my previous life.' That was not too far from the truth. He had a sense of humour, most don't, but I was home and it showed. I left him with a slight after smile as he changed persona, slipped into official mode and robotically demanded the next passport.

I had to get a coffee, I was tired and jet lagged; I desperately needed a caffeine injection. My body, displaying severe withdrawal symptoms, begged for a strong stimulant. Whilst sitting supping my beverage, my mind and body mellowed. The waft of freshly ground coffee, the squish, froth and bellow of the cappuccino machine, sent me slipping into an altered state.

I was back home in Glasgow, Scotland. It was Sunday night. My Yiayia was brewing a Cyprus coffee on the stove. There I was, 12 years old and just reached puberty; my tender voice lost to an intermittent, gravelled, gruff of early adolescence. I was pleading with my Mama not to send me to high school with short trousers on again.

'Mama, it's not fair,' I cried in desperation. 'All the other kids are taking the micky out of me.'

It was bad enough being Greek, a 'bubble and squeak'. They used to tease all the time.

'Hey, is your Ma a darkie?' the kids would jeer and sneer, to the encore of the class. I had great sympathy for the 'Pakies' because I had acquired Pakie status and my best friend was one. Life was cruel at that time, very cruel indeed.

We had my aunt Loula and my cousins round for lunch after church. Sunday was always a family affair. It was part of our cultural bonding, especially in a foreign land. My cousins were staying the night. We were having a wail of a time, pillow fighting in our pyjamas. Our laughing and screaming drowned the sounds of the adults next door. They were playing 'Spastra', a typical Greek card game played mainly by women on Sunday evening or any evening after the domestic responsibilities were despatched. They were chuckling and cheering as each team won a hand. The whole household was deeply content, but in one foul swoop of fate, all that was to terminate abruptly.

'Dring-dring! Dring-dring! Hello, who's speaking?' There was a long, ominous and unnerving void.

'Oh Mother Mary, Jesus Christ. My husband, my husband.'

A tidal wave of emotion raged from my Mama and swept over the whole household, swamping our laughter and destroying our young spirits forever. My Papa was dead.... our Papa was dead. We could not believe it; it was not true; someone's got it wrong. He was an athlete, a boxer, he was as strong as an ox, he was invincible; our Papa was Superman. Strange thing though, the night before, he called up. He was in an unusually melancholic mood. He wanted to talk with each of us, one by one. He even asked my Mama to make the baby cry, so he could hear him one last time. He somehow sensed divine intervention was going to change his life, and ours, forever, and it did. The following night he was gone.

On reflection, he suffered from severe asthma and had been hospitalised on a few occasions. But that was in the past, he was fit and healthy now. The fateful, cruel call was from his uncle in Brighton. Papa had been working as a waiter and a Greek dancer in his club. That particular dark night of the soul, he suffered a fatal asthma attack, which resulted in a cardiac arrest. He was dead at 36 years old. My Mama was a widow at 30. He left seven of us orphaned, the youngest being only 12 months old. Yes, life was hard and cruel. What kind of God could allow this injustice to happen? It was a family fate line we all had to experience, for some obscure reason, which I could not begin to comprehend.

Papa was a good man. He married my Mama and raised my eldest stepsister and brother as if they were his own. He loved us all equally. He was hard working and his friends loved him. He had a heart of gold; but he was dead, taken in the prime of his life.

There I was now, standing in front of a packed, sombre congregation drenched in black, with my sorry siblings. Aki, the little one in his pram, playing innocently with his dummy, was a bundle of pure love and joy. His gargling and chuckling, was an extreme anti reflection of the turbulent, torrents of emotion, spewing from the mourners. My poor Mama stood there, dressed in black from head to toe. Clouds of deep despair bellowed from her tormented soul as she wailed, orchestrating the band of woeful players. What a performance. Do you know professional mourners are sometimes hired to get the congregation going and keep them all fired up? Needless to say, we didn't need their services; Mama and the others were doing a great job.

Papa was laid out ahead of a procession of seething, ebony-clad isles. A sober black box shrouded his heavenly body. A solitary, floral cross, decked the box. It was our cross, his beloved kids' cross, which we all had to bear so sadly. I knew what had happened in my mind, but my Papa was still alive in my heart.

'Kirie Eleison, Kirie Eleison, Kirie Eleison,' echoed angelically from the sombre, frail figure of Pater Athinagoras as he emerged from the Holy Altar. His normally cheerful demeanour was deeply saddened by the loss of my Papa. He had performed this ceremony many times before; he was used to it. It was his job; he had to be detached, but he wasn't. The wafting scent and sight of frankincense cut through the tense air as he frantically swung the incense holder around in defiance of the sorry spectacle before him. My poor Mama, a wretched figure, supported on both sides, spewed out one almighty cry after another, before falling to her knees in submission and exhaustion. She had collapsed in a bundle on the floor with my Aunt and Yiayia trying to revive her with Eau de Cologne. The sweet scent battled frantically against the heavy, musty frankincense, as if they were in mortal combat and the prize was my Mama's soul. Mama blasted and bellowed; she had come round, gasping and groping for air. The nightmare was still brewing and the worst was still to come. It was all too much now. Everything became engulfed in a deep, foggy blur around me. The funeral passed me by as if it was a film in fast forward. Thank God it was all over. My 12-year-old body and mind went into spasm and shock. I was in a void; a vacuum had swallowed me. I was in limbo. Nothing was real to me any more. It took years to get back to normal, but I was scarred deeply for life.

'What now? What's life going to offer me now?'

Angie had left the roost. She'd had a shotgun wedding at Gretna Green, the Scottish marriage haven for 'quickies'. She had set up home with her fellow 'flower power' lover, Mike. My eldest brother Mickey was working away and he was courting.

'Was it my destiny to fill my Papa's shoes? How could I? It was not fair, I was only a boy.'

Needless to say, I grew up very quickly. I had four young souls to look after and my dear Mama, who pined uncontrollably, for years, like a faithful dog who had lost its master. Many times I would be abruptly awakened at the crack of dawn by her wails and laments for my beloved Papa. One particular night, she was panting and gasping for life. I heard my voice shouting during her fight for breath.

'Taki, Taki, Taki!' Then a stale silence loomed ominously in the air. I bolted to my door, ran what seemed a marathon in slow, deliberate motion, shouting 'Mama, Mama'. It echoed around my ears, drumming up images of what I might find when I got to her room. Like a raging bull, with adrenaline pumping on overload, I smashed the door open. My Mama lay there lifeless and listless, like a rag doll that had the stuffing wrenched from it.

'Mama, Mama, wake up, wake up!' I shouted as I shook her violently. I was only 13 years old. I should not have to deal with life and death. Not at 13. I grabbed the Eau de Cologne, drenched her nose and mouth with it and proceeded to give her the kiss of life, whilst praying for someone to help. I had seen it done in a film, but this was no act, this was for real.

Splutter, splutter, ah, ah. She took one almighty gasp for air and shouted, 'Stevie, Stevie, Stevie', my Papa's name. She regained consciousness, lashing out into thin air in a frantic, frenzy of grasps. My heart pounded so hard and loud against my chest I thought it was going to explode like a grenade, into a mass of shrapnel.

'Mama, Mama, Mama, it's me, Taki,' I cried uncontrollably. 'Are you all right?' I shouted and gently hugged her wretched frame.

'Taki, Taki, Taki! Stevie, Stevie, Stevie!', she wailed and groped frantically at chimeras in the scented room. In seconds she had calmed down. I cradled her like a newborn baby in my arms;

her black nightdress was like a shroud, laced around her head and shoulders. She was 'in her body' again, perched up in bed, sighing and taking in normal breaths. The sun's early morning beams danced around the window ledge and darted though the minute space in the curtains and through into the room. Dawn was crackling in blinding flashes, bringing a ray of hope for a new day ahead. I opened the window to a glorious encore. Apollo was there, a golden orb of light, warmth and sustenance. His partner, a gentle, sweet Zephyr in this early morning symphony, danced graciously to his magical melodies. I took in a deep breath of life as I sensed the Solar God's gift on my pale, innocent and relieved visage. It was great to be alive after that scrum in the dark.

I often wondered what my Mama saw during that eventful evening. She never said and I never asked. I know my Papa came to her in spirit. What they shared, God only knew. She was changed for good from that evening onwards. Strange thing though, my father's boxing name was 'Steve Apollo'. Maybe it was a coincidence, or a message from the other side. The new day dawned, spawning a new phase in our lives. Mama was back better than before, with new hope for a brighter future for us. She was a fighter, but there were other days of drama. She put on a brave face under that black shroud she wore and soldiered on for our sakes. It was customary to wear black as a sign of respect. Mama wore black robes for almost 10 years. It seemed like an eternity. I can't remember her in anything else. The shock of my Papa's death had buried all my recollections of her dress sense, as well as my memories of my Papa. I had deleted all but a few, blurred, broken fragments, which play back, mysteriously, to haunt me, like a series of misplaced images of someone else's childhood.

The years ahead were rapidly smelting me into a man. Glasgow was a searing crucible, blasting fragmented, white-hot molten shards daily, in a Plutonic underworld. Murders, rape, gang warfare, slashings and racism were all ingredients in this seething, unwholesome cauldron. It was the way of life here. We had to make the most of it. It was my Pappou's idea to settle here. In the late 40s, after the war, boatloads of Cypriots emigrated to flee their beloved isle of Aphrodite. She was a barren goddess bereft of opportunity then, not the heavenly paradise of good food, drink, sea and sunshine she is now. Droves came seeking their fortunes in the land of opportunity, glorious England. I often burst my sides with laughter when I think of this Cypriot anecdote about the exploits of Kybro's emigration to England.

Once there was a Cypriot village simpleton called Kybro. He was listening to a conversation between his friends in the village cafenion.

Stavro said to Kosta: 'Do you know what they say about life in England, Kosta?'

Kosta, grinning like a Cheshire cat, his gold teeth gleaming and his eyes sparkling said, 'I know the streets are full of dance halls and lovely ladies wanting Cypriot boyfriends.'

'Yes,' laughed Stavro. 'But they also say that the streets are littered with money that grows on trees!'

Kybro's face lit up. 'Well, I'm taking the next ship out of here!'

Kybro's family gave him the fare and he took the ship to England. As he walked off onto the dock, he saw this bulging bundle of money on the pavement. He stooped to pick it up, hesitated for a moment and said to himself: 'I don't want to start collecting yet; I've just arrived. I'll go and have some fun with the girls first,' and he kicked the wad of notes into the gutter. 'I will start collecting tomorrow.'

Pappou Toffi was a Cyprus lace salesman. They were all Cyprus lace salesmen in the beginning. Even the multi-millionaire hotelier, Rio Stakis, had his humble beginnings in Kato Dris, a lace village in the Lefkara area. They eventually set up home in Glasgow. Rio created his empire and my Pappou frittered away a fortune on gambling and women. He did all right at selling, but he loved life too much and lived it to the full.

After years of humiliating racist and physical attacks on us, my Pappou vowed to take the whole family back to Cyprus, our safe haven, some time in the near future. He had saved some money and started to build a house in Alethrico village, on land handed down to him by my great-grandfather.

One final bloodbath my brother Georgie and I witnessed was the last straw. It was 11 o'clock on a Saturday night and the moon was full of menace. We had gone down to pick up the first edition of the Sunday Mail from a stand just off St George's Square. The city that particular evening was like a seething, smouldering, red-hot volcano. All it needed was a spark to trigger an awesome explosion of anger, revenge and sheer sadistic violence. Celtic had just beaten Rangers to win The Scottish football league again. Rival gangs were gathering ranks on either side of the square. It looked like the Coliseum. Massive sculptured lions flanked the four corners. Gigantic Roman pillars dwarfed hoards of hungry spectators waiving bottles and chip packets high above their heads. They stood there, wooing and coaxing the gladiators into action. The pubs spewed out hoards of revellers onto the square. The stench of sickness and sheer brutality ranked in the volcanic atmosphere. Bottles exploded like Molotov cocktails and cans of beer swished like dynamite through the dark of night. Taunts, jeers, patriotic songs and battle cries raged between the 'Fiennians' and the 'Orange Boys'. We knew how to handle ourselves, we were streetwise, but this was out of our league. We ducked into a dingy, dark alleyway, running the gauntlet through winos and crimson ladies, with the echoes of all hell letting loose in the background.

'Die ya Feinnian bastard!'

'Ya fuckin cunt!'

Swish! The flash of an open razor glinted against the moon's sadistic beams; the sickening flush of bright, red blood sprayed from that pale face, into the sardonic air.

'Ah, my face! Ya bastard. You've slashed my face!'

We ran as fast as we could, hearts pounding, blood boiling and breath bellowing, until we reached home. The tussles, screams and battle cries of that massacre still haunt me to this day. Yes, this close shave was the last straw.

Soon afterwards, at 17, I was bundled into my Pappou's car, suitcase in hand. I was off to seek my destiny in sunny, safe, Cyprus, the land of my fathers.

CHAPTER 3

My Pappou had made the epic trip, to and from Britain to Cyprus every year for as far back as I could remember. His smart, sturdy and powerful, two-litre Austin Morris was a brilliant wagon. It was dependable, roomy and durable, which fit my Pappou's personality exactly. He was a typical, old-fashioned Cypriot male chauvinist. Proud and arrogant as 'Punch', but he had a big heart and was always supporting lost causes. Indeed, my Yiayia Angelica could characteristically be 'Judy'. She was always on the receiving end of my Pappou's anger and frustrations. My Yiayia was a deeply religious woman, sensitive, caring and protective, but with the conviction of a true Cypriot matriarch. She was a victim and a saint to put up with my Pappou's explosive outbursts. It was a normal Cypriot marriage in those days.

After an uneventful 10 days on the road through Europe our car ferry terminated at Limassol docks. Pappou was a regular traveller. He knew all the officials and customs officers, which was always an asset, especially in a small republic like Cyprus. We headed out of the port for Alethrico village, Larnaca, into a sickening stench of death that saturated the whole island's aura. Everywhere you looked, massive billboards, posters and flags, depicted horrific images of a bleeding Cyprus wrenched in two. Virginal white banners slashed with the gaudy, red words, **'I Won't Forget'**, looked like blood-drenched bandages over gaping wounds. With guns goading, bombs blasting and women wailing, the beautiful Isle of Aphrodite was yet another pawn in the 'Cold War' chess game. It had become another ravaged rape victim of power politics.

It was a year or so after the sadistic and barbaric invasion of the island by Turkish forces. They had usurped at least 40 per cent of the northern territories, half of the capital Nicosia and Famagusta, the premier holiday hotspot of the island, as well as hundreds of towns and villages. I couldn't believe it. It wasn't possible. Who could allow this to happen? Pappou didn't warn nor prepare me for this colossal carnage, callousness and national mourning. It was like jumping from the fat into the frying pan. I was expecting Cyprus as I had imagined it: my saviour, a sunny, safe haven and a paradise, not this battle-torn, bludgeoned hellhole. The whole countryside was littered with rows of makeshift tents and temporary shelters. Hoards of broken, young and old women, and mothers drenched in black, spirits smashed and humbled into submission, lined up for food and water rations. Children dangled like rag dolls on their mother's tunics. Their pure little, angelic faces, stained by the blood of war, had lost their innocence in an act of terror. Every family had lost a papa, an uncle, a brother, their possessions, a home and their beloved island.

Images of my Mama, blackness of despair, pain of love lost and anguish of life in Glasgow exploded in my head. Genocide, rape, blood and Cypriot black widows flashed before me, merging in a macabre kaleidoscopic screen. I slouched into a deep state of withdrawal, my only escape, as Pappou's car protected us from the elements. His sad, sullen and silent persona mirrored the horrific aftermath we were driving through. Yes, this was the land of my fathers, my destiny and my sunny safe haven!

'Taki, Taki, lovely to see you, my lovely grandson,' shouted my Yiayia Angelica, with arms outstretched and a broad, beaming smile. The car door creaked open. I was still in a semi-sleep state as I melted into my Yiayia's warm bosom and merged with her comforting aura.

'Yiayia, Yiayia, It's great to see you. I've missed you so much. How are you?' I said, glad to be home at last. I walked arm in arm with her through the hallowed archway of sweet-scented Jasmine.

17

Its purifying aroma released my tormented soul and prepared me for entry into her sublime and humble village house.

The house was like a photographic mausoleum dedicated to our family tree. Boughs branched out from great, great grandfathers, great-grandmothers and great aunts. Fronds of uncles and aunts and twigs of nieces and nephews spread over the walls like a vast tapestry of human life. Old village dressers, kitchen cabinets, village chairs and an antique table, decked the quaint, colourful, but sparse little kitchen. Two bulbous, terra cotta vats full of water collected from the village well, hugged the old, wooden worktop.

An old four-poster, cast iron and brass bed, flowing with the finest, white linen Cyprus lace, took pride of place in the main bedroom. It was a reminder of a decadent past, full of the pomp and splendour of Imperial Britain. The waft of mothballs intermingled with Eau de Cologne gently laced the air. Speckles of sunlight danced tantalisingly around this deeply pleasing place. Candle lights in the sacred altar, dedicated to our relatives, flickered and flashed in adoration as they mirrored the spirits of our loved ones on the other side. My soul mellowed and my emotions soothed in this divine parlour.

After a brief walk around the remainder of the house we sat at the table in the kitchen, chatting about the family. Yiayia was making Cyprus coffee on the old stove. In no time I was relaxed and content. Not long after, I was led to my bedroom. She loosened my clothes, cuddled and kissed me and put me to bed as if I was a wee boy again. My childhood memories flooded back in waves of nostalgia as I drifted into a deep and peaceful slumber.

A few hours later I surfaced feeling relaxed and rejuvenated. Alethrico village life was a far cry from the intense struggle and stress of life in Glasgow. I walked down the dusty old dirt road, where every household gave me a warm welcome and invited me in for some refreshment. Memories of running the gauntlet in Glasgow's slimy lanes, dodging winos and bottles, faded into oblivion as I was bathed in the hospitality of the village folk.

Alethrico had grown considerably to accommodate a steady influx of refugees. The village was saturated with strange faces laden with traumatic emotional lines that mirrored their distressed souls.

The government was doing its best to re-house them in Turkish homes, ramshackle old barns and small-corrugated shelters, but aid was slow and insufficient. The village folk all shared the responsibility of helping out as best they could. As the sun set on the horizon, slowly disappearing behind 'Stavrovouni', the sacred mountain monastery of The Holy Cross, my heart went out to the thousands of misplaced folk. Greek Cypriots, Turkish Cypriots, Armenian Cypriots and even British Cypriots were made refugees in their own land. How could it happen in this deeply spiritual island? I asked myself.

Cyprus had a long and chequered history; won, lost, plundered, sold, annexed; it was always in demand because of its strategic position. Mycenaean Greeks, Phoenicians, Romans, Crusading English and French, Venetians and Ottomans… all had come and left their ancient sites, temples and churches on the island. The Stavrovouni monastery, which professes to possess a piece of the crucifixion cross, was built by Saint Helena in 327 AD. It was originally a sacred pagan temple site, one of many established by the early Cypriots. The goddess Aphrodite was venerated and worshipped there, on Mount Olympus, hundreds of years before. Even to this day, some pagan rituals are still practiced, albeit under the umbrella of the Greek Orthodox Church and unknowingly by the general public.

My Yiayia knew everything about the church. She was a season ticket holder. Religiously, every Sunday and every day of special worship, she would be the first one there and the last to leave. In retrospect I must have inherited my Yiayia's commitment to religious life and interest in the unknown, even if my spiritual world was very different to hers.

I had accompanied her to church one crisp Sunday morning. Winter was setting in, but the sun's ray's still shone brilliant in the bright, crystal clear sky. Blood red and 'Barbie' pink Bougainvillea splashed vibrant rainbows against virginal white village houses. Sacred pomegranate bushes lay pregnant; some bursting with fertility, as their tiny, ruby-red, crystalline, fruit bombs, exploded in adoration of Aphrodite. Church gospels echoed in the ethers; bells gonged in unison and Pater's ecclesiastical shrills and chants beckoned the believers to his sanctuary. It was a normal service, but with the exception of my Papa's annual remembrance celebration. Yiayia had made the traditional offering of, 'Prosforo', blessed, freshly-baked bread and 'Kollifa', which was a mixture of boiled wheat, nuts, sesame seeds, sugar and pomegranate seeds. It had its roots in pagan rites of passage and was used to appease the soul of a loved one who had passed over. These offerings were given to the congregation, who blessed the soul of the deceased as they tucked into the religious treat.

It was such a lovely late morning that we decided to walk back. We passed house after house, enjoying the sweet citrus aromas of orange and tangerine blossom that hung tantalisingly in the air. Lemon trees bulged with a bulbous, bumper crop of bright yellow grenades and the tiny, tangy flowers exploded into bloom. Rose bushes, the glory of each garden, glowed gregariously in the brilliant sun, their scent wafting for miles. They are the 'masters' of the plant kingdom, you know. They are prefect beings in the terrestrial realm.

'Good morning Angelica, God bless Stevie's soul and may he rest in peace,' said my aunt Rita.

'Thanks Rita, and God bless the souls of your loved ones,' replied my Yiayia. After waving goodbye to Rita, I was gasping to ask Yiayia about her perception of the afterlife.

'Yiayia, can I ask you something about our religion?'

'Yes Taki, as long as I can answer you. What are you interested in?'

'Well, you know, we remember my Papa's death each year and we light our altars to honour our loved ones, who have passed over,' I said in a philosophical tone.

'Yes,' she answered, in her all knowing voice.

'One night, I went to my Mama; she was in a dreadful state, screaming, hallucinating and shouting my Papa's name. I tried so hard to revive her, but it was the old Eau de Cologne trick that eventually brought her round. Well, I didn't ask her what she saw then, but after a few days, we were alone and she explained what she had experienced.'

'Yes, Taki, mm.... I think we need to go inside to talk, I don't want the whole village to know our private life.'

Within minutes we entered our safe haven and the Greek coffee was on the stove. My Pappou was down in the cafenion playing 'Tavli', Greek backgammon. All was quiet and the scene was ripe for religious discussion.

'Before you go on with your story, let me tell you what the church says about life and death,' Yiayia said in an authoritative manner.

'Okay, I'm all ears,' I replied, bowing down in submission.

'When someone dies, his body is buried. Earth to earth, ashes to ashes, dust to dust. The soul leaves its body behind in the presence of two guardians. It is weighed to find out if it will go to Heaven or Hell. The Archangel Saint Michael stands with Satan's messenger, Lucifer, and they both monitor the scales. If the scales tip towards Saint Michael then you receive your pass to go through the 'Pearly Gates' to pure bliss and Heaven. Then, at the 'Second Coming', all God's children will be raised from their graves to live again, reborn in the light of the 'One God'. But if the scales tip towards Lucifer, then your soul will be damned forever. You will never escape Hell, and you'll never come back. Does that answer your question?' she said in her religious fervour.

'Not exactly, you say nothing survives death and the soul goes to Heaven or Hell. Well, Mama had a vision that night. My Papa's spirit came to her and told her not to mourn and cry anymore. He also said it was the will of God that he should be taken. He said never question God's will, just accept it. He said we were special, all seven of us and she was to live for us, because he lived through us. He assured my Mama he would be there for her, always, and when she passed over, he'd be there to help her through the transition from physical life to spirit life.

'Don't dwell on the past and don't go into depression, he said. He told her it held him back from passing from the spirit world into the light. From that day on, she was a changed person.'

'Oh my God, oh my God, Taki, don't tell anyone about this. I'm sure your Mama was hallucinating. It was the stress that brought it on, I'm sure,' she retorted, as if I had been talking blasphemy.

'Yiayia, I've got something else to tell you. Sit down and I'll put another coffee on,' I said in a persistent tone. 'Well, when I was a lad, just after my Papa's death, I must have been 13 or 14 at the time. I woke up one early morning and I was bursting as usual. I had a weak bladder and on many occasions, I'd wake up in the middle of the night, soaking wet. It was a big problem; I suppose it was connected to my papa passing over. Anyway, this particular morning I had woken up; a miracle, but I had to rush because 'willie' was not going to wait for me. With my wee thing squeezed tight in my hand, I ran towards the toilet, bursting for a pee. I opened the door and there she was, old Adams, our home help and baby-sitter. She had passed over just after my Papa. Old age I suppose. But there she was, sitting on the toilet, with nylons and bloomers down at her ankles. You can imagine the shock. Well, needless to say, I wet myself right through and in my new pyjamas. What was I going to tell Mama? She would not believe me. I got another sore ear and a verbal bashing. And there was the other time at your sisters' in Birming...'

'Jesus, Mary and Joseph! Enough. Enough! I've heard enough,' she replied. 'Right that's it, you're going to confession tomorrow; you're going to purify your soul. God help you if you tell anybody about this nonsense. You'll get us all excommunicated. I'm going to get you a new cross and an 'evil eye' pendant to warn off evil spirits.'

You can imagine how I felt. I was a freak, someone who sees dead people. According to my Yiayia I was possessed and I needed to be exorcised immediately. Maybe it was the trauma after my Papa's death. It opened my psychic powers up and heightened my perception. I knew what I saw. It was not my imagination. It was real to me. I was different, weird; I had a knowing that needed quenching. But where was I going to turn to? Who could I talk to?

Time passed very quickly, hours became days, days turned to months, and months became years. I joined a professional football club; I was quite famous. But those spiritual experiences were to stay with me, until another fateful day loomed on the horizon.

I met Elena; we got married. She was a nice Cypriot girl, a headstrong Leo with a bubbly personality. She had gorgeous, brown, curly hair, sea green eyes, an enchanting smile and good child bearing hips, which is characteristic of most Mediterranean women. Plato, Socrates and all the other Greek philosophers fascinated her.

I suppose she was spiritual in her own way. I was 21-years-old and deeply in love. We were young, idealistic and we had great plans. We had just had our wedding celebration; the party was over and we booked ourselves into a five-star hotel in Paphos. Four days in the sun, beautiful views, lovely warm sea and just the two of us; young lovers with the rest of our exciting lives ahead. Life was brilliant and it was going to get better, I promised her. I was going to whisk her off to Brighton, England. We were going to have a lovely, family home, have kids and live together to a ripe old age. We had it all planned. We were sunbathing by the poolside, sipping multi-coloured cocktails, flirting and enjoying each other's company.

'Sir, Mr Kasparis, you have an important message at reception. Would you please come immediately.' I rushed up, towel around my bronzed torso to the telephone.

'Hello, Christos here, who's speaking?' I said, in an apprehensive manner.

'Christo, it's me, Roula, Elena's mum. We've had some bad news. Can you both come back as soon as possible?'

I felt the blood drain from my face and my emotions were sucked into blackness.

'Bad news, what's happened?'

'Just get back as soon as possible. I can't talk on the phone.'

'But…'

'Christo, pack up and come to our house quickly!' She clicked the phone down and left me in limbo. What had happened? It must be serious I thought as I plodded back to the poolside.

'God, you look like a ghost. What's the matter? Is everything all right?'

'Elena, it was your mother; she wants us back in Larnaca as soon as possible. I think something serious has happened.'

'Oh my God. It's my grandfather; he's so old and frail. He's been ill for some time. Oh no, he's passed over, he's dead.'

'She never said. I pressed her but she put the phone down on me. We've got to get back as soon as possible.'

Silence reigned, during that long drive back. We both comforted each other, fearing the worst.

'But why didn't she tell you what had happened? Why had she just left it, hanging, like a sword of Damocles, waiting to fall on us as soon as we get home,' Elena cried. I suppose Roula had her reasons; she was always wise and diplomatic.

We arrived at Elena's home in Larnaca. Nothing was amiss outside. No cars, fuss or noise, just deadly quiet. We thudded the car doors shut and tip toed upstairs. The door was open; an ominous silence reeked as we entered. The house was rank with blackness; something really horrible had happened. Faces were sombre, eyes soulful and hearts hung heavy in the dense dining room.

'What has happened? Tell us what has happened,' I frantically exclaimed.

'Sit down Christo. We've got some bad news for you,' Roula said, in a sullen tone.

My heart sunk to a pit in my chest, my face sagged and my eyes glazed. I felt Elena's hand reassuringly grip mine: my only comfort at that tragic moment.

'It's your Pappou Toffi and your uncle Antony.' A long pause followed. 'They were both killed in a car accident. Your young brothers and cousin were in the back of the car. They're in intensive care; they're seriously hurt, but their lives are not in danger.'

I squeezed Elena's hand so tight it went blue. My eyes filled up. My soul deserted me for a moment. I just sat in the eerie silence, staring into space, expressionless and emotionless. I got up, steadied myself and walked to the door without uttering one sound. My mouth dried up and my tongue felt like it had been cut out. I disappeared down those dark, winding stairs and out into the stillness of the deserted street. Elena raced after me.

'Christo, Christo, wait. I'm coming with you.'

'Elena no, I have to go to the village alone. Please understand; it's no place for you,' I said in a courageous voice, hiding my true feelings. She understood, kissed me on the cheek and sullenly disappeared upstairs.

In the short journey back to the village, images of what I might find haunted me. My poor Yiayia, my Mama, my aunt Rita, our whole family was torn apart yet again.

When was this fate line going to end? How many more of my family were going to suffer? I prayed to God to give me strength to cope. I had to be strong for them. I was a man now. I had to support them. Slowly, I made my way along the road.

What timing: the happiest moment of my young life, my wedding, destroyed in a matter of minutes. How callous life was for me. I was losing all faith in God. My life had been one tragedy after another.

Needless to say, the whole village turned out to support my family. Cars clogged up the narrow road, mirroring my twisted and tormented emotions. I had to squeeze through and walk the last few steps to our house. The whole scene was deeply disturbing. I was whisked outside, bundled into a car and driven to the hospital to see my brothers. They were under sedation, thank God. Their young bodies were smashed up, but they were alive at least. In their condition they had no idea we had lost Pappou and uncle Mamma. It was all too tragic to think about.

I was left to pick up the pieces. I had to go to the morgue to identify the bodies. Nobody was fit enough to do it and it had to be done soon. The stench of death hung in the haunting air as the attendant pulled my uncle out of the fridge. He didn't even have a scratch on him: not one scratch. He lay there as if he was in a deep slumber, a sleeping beauty waiting to be awakened some other day, by the sweet kiss of a loved one.

'Yes, that's Antonis Mamma,' I said to the attendant, displaying no signs of emotions. 'Where's my Pappou?' I said, puzzled and disoriented.

'He's lying over there.' He pointed to a trolley shrouded in a white drape. I slowly approached and stepped into a pool of coagulated, deep-red blood. It was dripping from the corpse, onto the trolley and 'tip, tip, tip,' onto the floor. I froze stiff in that tense, icy tomb. I dreaded what I would find under that shroud, but I had to do it. With a cold, calculating pace, heart and mind suspended, I slowly slipped the shroud off. It was a body, a deformed human form. At first, I could not fathom out what I was peering at. It was my Pappou; he was a mangled wreck, with arms twisted and legs broken into fragments. A gaping chest wound ripped him from throat to lower tummy. His proud face, smashed into oblivion, was barely recognisable, but it was him. I had done my duty.

'Yes, this is my Pappou, Chris Kyprian,' I coldly told the attendant.

I can't explain my thoughts or feelings during the ordeal. I was there, but not in my body. Somehow I had been spared the emotion. It had disappeared into my subconscious, to return some day, with a vengeance. But that mass of dripping flesh was not my Pappou. His soul had jettisoned out of his body on impact. We were told he died instantly, at the wheel of his beloved car, where he was happy. I could not see him going any other way. He had cheated old age, senility and helplessness. Yes, he was too proud for that.

We buried their bodies side by side in the village cemetery. It was another woeful masterpiece of life and death.

I have seen him, in spirit you know. He's happy tinkering around his beloved plot in the spirit gardens, still fussing about the hosepipe and the lack of water. He's regenerated all right; full of life and he's not had to wait for the 'Second Coming' either.

That was it; I'd had enough of paradise. It was time to get back to the real world. Brighton, England beckoned me to a new life with Elena and a rosy future.

CHAPTER 4

Within a couple of weeks we were on our way to sunny Brighton on the south coast. Its popularity soared from the time of the Prince Regent, the eccentric, flamboyant Georgian royal. He set the fashions of his day in art, architecture, literature and music. His most prized innovation was The Royal Pavilion, a masterpiece of new thinking. It was a kaleidoscope of styles: a gaudy mix of sheer extravagance, pomp and splendour. The exterior was a tantalising cocktail of eastern promise, dressed with domes, turrets and towers. There was a masterful dash of western cynicism, creating just the right balance. It was all lit up like an Arabian fairy castle. The pavilion seemed to flash multi-coloured, rainbow rays and searing bolts of iridescent light from its mystical aura.

Elena was bowled over by its presence; her excitement and exuberance reflected my mood. It was great to be back in this cranky and alternative coastal Mecca. Flickering lights flashed back childhood memories. I remember a family holiday, when my Papa had just passed over. Mama wanted to treat us, to smooth over the tragic phase. What an impact it made on me.

Bright blue skies, blasts of sea air, gulls screeching and screaming like Spitfires during the war. Two Victorian pleasure piers jutted out like erect phalluses, in union with the sensuous sea, the womb of all life. Vast stretches of pebble beaches hugged the coast, hemming in rows and rows of gleaming Regency apartments. Old biddies lined up in there hundreds on stripy deck chairs, with their hairnets harnessing brightly coloured silver locks under their straw sun hats. Some in a state of deep relaxation flashed their sombre granny pants airing between their thighs; their stockings stood at half mast around their vein mottled, blotchy legs. Silly, old geezers in their ridiculous, traditionally English, handkerchiefs tied around their heads and in their string vests, proudly sat next to them. What an anti-climax!

It was a far cry from Glasgow and our sad existence there. Within minutes of arriving at the coach station, my uncle Vic and 'Big George' met us. The restaurant they owned was minutes away, in the heart of The Brighton Lanes.

'Welcome back Taki,' said Big George, throwing his arms around me. His deep, soulful eyes glazed over with a mix of elation and despair. My Pappou was George's godfather and my Papa's best friend. His pitiful persona reflected the loss in my heart.

'George, listen I'm not trying to be disrespectful in any way, but I've put the skeletons in the cupboard for now. I want a fresh start. This is Elena; Elena this is Big George and uncle Vic.'

'Hi, pleased to meet you. Christo has told me a lot about both of you,' Elena politely replied.

We got the formalities out of the way, made our way to the restaurant, had dinner and were shown to our maisonette. Elena was in awe of the place. It overlooked Brighton Square, the hub of the social wheel. Glorious shopping, antiques, designer boutiques, bars, high-class restaurants and quaint little coffee houses saturated the area. She was in her element. It was a typical Leo environment, bursting with hustle and bustle. It was Brighton's playground for the elite; a glamorous jet set scene and she absolutely adored it.

Within days, I had started working in the restaurant and Elena had commenced an OND in hotel and catering management. We had all the trimmings of a materialistic life: money, great prospects and good health. Our future happiness seemed to be all planned for us. It was too good to be true and our lives were to change dramatically.

One night, I woke up in a cold sweat from a traumatic dream experience. I was shaking all over with blood pumping through my veins and my heart thumping against my ribcage. My lungs bellowed for breath. I felt like I had been mortally wounded. I was in complete shock. I thought of waking Elena, but I dare not because she was a major player in the vision and I was confused and disoriented.

It was an ancient Greek temple setting. Pristine, white, Doric columns stretched skywards, disappearing into the mists. Heavenly statues decked the pleasure dome. Frescoes of gods and goddesses in regal poses flanked the walls. Young, scantily dressed lovers, frolicked, flirted, drank and danced. Satyrs plucked alluringly on lyres, each sensuous strum sending the pantheons into euphoria. Dionysus, beloved master of music, lust and intoxication, lorded over this orgy of gratification. My focus caught the chimeras of a couple in a four-poster bed, draped in blood red and wine satin. Their silhouettes, intertwined in ecstasy, swayed in tune with the orchestra of lust. Lewd laughter, screams of pleasure and gasps of orgasms gushing, pounded in my groin. I had to see behind the veil. Who was in the shadows on those semen soaked, satin sheets?

Whoosh... the music ground to an abrupt halt: finely tuned instruments squawked and squeaked. The pleasure palace, drowned by the drone of dying melodies, faded in the background and a spotlight seared the sickening scene. There she was, Elena, with a sardonic smirk and a sarcastic stare, peering straight at me. Her loathsome lover's face concealed in her bosom, hiding his identity. The sordid sight of two bodies still entwined in the aftermath of lust filled me with rage, revenge, disgust and betrayal. I lunged at him, and in a moment of sheer frenzy, the glint of a dagger flashed into my chest. With an agonising groan, blood gushing from a gaping wound, I collapsed into Elena's sex splattered body. In intense pain I lapsed into unconsciousness and woke up from that wicked ordeal.

Who was he? The dream hid his face. Why didn't it reveal the adulterous bastard? How could she do such a thing? I could never forgive her. It was sick; I was sick. I dare not tell her. She would think I was crazy. But what did it mean? Was it only a dream or was there more to it? I came slowly to my senses, cuddled up to Elena and slid back into a deep and satisfying slumber.

I woke quite relieved and refreshed, but that experience quaked in my heart. As we sat at the breakfast table the sun's rays glinted through the Wicca blinds, sending strobe-like flashes around our space. It reminded Elena of a classmate she had met.

'Christo, you will never believe who is in my class at uni,' she said in excitement.

'Go on then, shock me,' I said sarcastically, taking very little notice of her.

'It's another Greek Cypriot, from Limassol. He's a refugee, who lived in Famagusta, Stellios Pavlou.'

'God, that's a coincidence, isn't it,' I answered nonchalantly.

'Do you know he's a mystic. He spends most weekends at a place just like a Kibbutz, in Potters Bar, Hertfordshire. A guy called doctor Douglas Baker runs it. You ought to hear Stellios talking astrology and metaphysics, it's fascinating,' Elena said in an intellectual manner. She always thought she was an intellectual. She loved anything out of the ordinary, eccentric and radical. She was a cut above the rest; sitting there on her throne, chin tilted skywards and posh posture, the mark of exquisite, social etiquette.

'Mmm, you must invite him down one night for dinner. I'd like to meet him.' I said in my Scorpionic, investigative tone. 'Tell him to come down tonight if he can. I've got the night off.'

'All right darling, see you later.' With a lightning kiss on my cheek, she bounced out of the door, skipped down the stairs, singing a Greek love song, and disappeared into the square. She was a real, bubbly kitten, full of life and innocence. She left me pondering on this boy Stellios. Who was he? Why has he crossed our path? He might have answers to my questions. Astrology, mysticism, metaphysics, it all intrigued me, deep down, but I didn't really know why. I suppose it was my inquisitive nature.

Thud! Thud! Dring! Dring! The door reverberated, echoing my name in the ethers.

'Christo. Are you ready? We're opening in five minutes. Get downstairs now,' shouted uncle Vic. He was a stickler for timing.

'Coming,' I shouted, adjusting my tie and mind into work mode.

It was a busy but uneventful day. Elena was back early. She bounced into the restaurant for afternoon tea.

'He's coming tonight. Stellios is coming tonight,' she said and tucked into a slice of homemade baklava.

'That's great. We'll have to get some Cypriot specialities from the deli. I'll get the Keo beers in too. I'm sure he'll be as homesick as you, Elena. At least the food will warm his spirit and soul.'

'Brilliant idea, we'll do kebabs too. Real pork, salad, parsley, chopped onion and pitas, mmm... now that will be a real food fantasy worth savouring,' she said, licking the syrup oozing from the glucose explosive.

The mood was set with dim lighting, scented candles, flickering flames, incense and soothing music. The dining room had the perfect presence for culinary ecstasy, mystical masturbation and spirit materialisation. The table, overflowing with a delicious array of multi-sensory, gastronomic delights, dazzled the space.

Dring dring, 'Christo, he's at the door, will you welcome him,' Elena shouted and went to a mirror to touch up her makeup. She was a real glamour girl; everything had to be perfect. I don't know what I expected, but as I opened the door, this waif stood there, laden with a rucksack, green canvas coat and crinkle cut jeans. A balaclava hid his head. He looked like a terrorist.

'Hi, I'm Stellios, you must be Christo,' he said in English, with a heavily tainted Greek accent. As I shook his hand, he swished off his balaclava to reveal a mop of golden curls. His pale visage shone angelically in the light, climaxing with a broad smile and a flash of pure, white teeth. As I peered into his deep, brown, soulful eyes, I knew him. His presence touched my soul, sending shivers down my spine and tingling all over my body.

'Come in, come in, let me take your coat and bag,' I said, still dazed and slightly overwhelmed by the impact he had on me.

'Stellios, great to see you, I'm glad you made it. Come and sit down,' Elena said in her warm and gregarious manner.

Whilst hanging the garments, I knew he had come for a reason. I sensed something, but I could not put my finger on it. It wasn't a jealousy thing. He just wasn't Elena's type. What was he after, this dazzling Adonis, with his golden mop and unassuming manner? Money, work, friendship or was there an ulterior motive? It puzzled and intrigued me, but I should keep an open mind, I said to myself. The suspense was killing me as I heard their voices, chattering and laughing in the background.

After our feast we sat around the glowing hot embers of a real fire. Sparks, blue, flickering flames and golden red flashes warmed our bodies and mellowed our souls. It conjured up memories of a distant primordial past: ritual worship, shamanic trance and dreamtime. There we were, three sparks of individuality, united by some unseen force. Our destinies forged together in a cauldron of suspense and uncertainty.

'Elena, you don't mind making a Greek coffee for us?' I asked, in my 'can you leave us, so I can probe this guy manner'. She got the message and merrily cleared some plates and disappeared into the kitchen. This was my chance to put him on the spot and give him a good roasting.

'So Stellios, I hear you're interested in astrology and things. That's a bit risky being a Greek Orthodox, isn't it? I think it's all crap and a load of mumbo jumbo,' I said in a penetrating and derogatory way. I thought he would be flustered by my unprovoked attack. Instead, he paused for a moment, collected his thoughts and eloquently replied.

'Well, to tell you the truth, that's what I thought in the beginning. But I put all my prejudice and religious conditioning to one side and allowed my mind to embrace different ideas. There was a bookshop in Limassol, owned by Mr Stylianos, my first mentor, which provided me with spiritual books. He was in his 60s, a rebel and a member of a secret, elite, mystical group, centred in Nicosia. He introduced me to the teachings of an occultist called doctor Douglas Baker. He…'

'Now just hold on there, that's Satanism and the Devil's work, isn't it?' I retorted in an abrupt statement.

'That's what most uninitiated people think, and it's very far from the truth. The occult is labelled with this stigma because Hollywood and sensational thriller writers equate it to dark, satanic, evil forces. In fact, an occultist is an individual who understands and uses natural, unseen forces, for the good of all humanity and mankind. He serves a code of pure, spiritual, ethics that includes selfless humanitarian service, unconditional understanding of all religions and universal love. He embraces ancient wisdom such as the reincarnation of the human soul and karma; knowing that life is eternal and undying.'

Stellios rattled off many more ideas in his philosophical fervour. I switched to altered state mode, with a dribble of his drone echoing in the cave of my mind. He was right; I knew he was right. He was genuine and inspired. His voice played distant past life memories on my heart and soul strings. We were a heavenly duet, drawn together to play another master part in this terrestrial ball. Which dance had we started? Were we to learn new steps? Or had we to go over past lessons?

'There we are boys,' Elena said, entering with a tray of coffees and cakes. 'You wouldn't get better in the best cafenion in Larnaca.' Her bubbly entrance bounced the spiritual banter into a cheery 'tittle tattle' of nostalgia and good humour. We laughed at Stellios corny Greek jokes and his stories before the time came for him to leave. I gathered his stuff together and led him to the door.

'You know, I've helped organise a lecture in the area for Dr. Baker in a fortnight. It would be great if you could come. Then you can hear it from the horse's mouth.'

'I'll have to think about it and get the time off. I'll let Elena know soon. Bye bye, it was nice to meet you,' I said. Before he turned to leave Elena kissed him on both cheeks. With a swish of his bag over his shoulder he melted into the misty, night sky. He left me with a head full of dangling loose ends, bulging knots and frayed fragments of the night's mystical tapestry.

CHAPTER 5

It was 6pm and the night ahead promised to be inspiring and illuminating. Stellios had just called to say the lecture was set up and to meet him at The Old Ship Hotel at seven. It was within walking distance so we decided to take the scenic route through The Lanes and by the fountain.

'Come on Elena, you're not going to a fashion show for God's sake. Hurry or we'll be late, again.'

'I'm just coming Christo. You know I always like to dress up where ever we go. I want you to be proud of me,' she answered from her boudoir. Well, she appeared in an ethereal, violet, flowing gown, a multi-coloured throw and a bandanna enveloping her gorgeous, curly locks. She looked like a real New Age traveller. All that was missing were a few body piercings, dreadlocks and a spliff lingering on her bottom lip. She was the epitome of alternative lifestyle. She loved the glamour and glitz of the whole affair. To her it was one mega masquerade, a class act and a drama to be lived, if only for a night. I was the exact antithesis. I wore a cool, sober suit, shirt and tie. I felt like a trussed up turkey for the oven. We were like 'chalk and cheese'.

The dusk had slowly started to blanket the seashore. It mellowed as it merged with the luminous, full moon's peeping face. Gusting sea zephyrs enticed the sprites of sparkling froth into frenzy. Gulls skydived through the ethers, bombing unsuspecting prey. The swish, cackle and screech of each plunge, echoed in our ears as we approached the fountain. The sound of its gentle trickles and soothing, translucent sprays, merged with our mood. Three bronzed, blue-green, pouting, dolphins graced this divine chalice, gushing a cleansing aqua aura into the heavens. Cascading fonts and spraying sparkles tantalised the celestial sphere. A silvery, ethereal gown enveloped her mysterious body, spinning a web of betrayal, intrigue and illusion against an indigo blue, starry backdrop. That ecstatic foreplay lingered in my mind as we glided into the outstretched arms of Stellios embrace. He had been anticipating our arrival and was pacing up and down like a caged, neurotic wildcat.

'It's great to see you. I'm glad you could make it. It was getting late and I was a little worried that you would not come,' he said in an elated but relieved fashion. My senses were still buzzing from that mystical orgasm, but I felt an uneasiness slowly swamp me. Stellios nervousness and anxiety puzzled me. Why was he pacing to and fro at the door? Why was he under so much pressure? I felt his tense aura swoon in relief at the sight of us.

'We decided to meander by the fountain. You know how enchanting it is against the night sky,' Elena said, as he led us into the lecture hall.

People were milling around the bookstall and tables. Chairs were decked out theatre style and a solitary, phallic rostrum penetrated the twin isles. The air was heavy with the scent from joss sticks and soothing New Age music echoed to the murmur of the crowd.

'Hi, you must be Chris, Stellios friend. My name is John, pleased to meet you. Stellios has told me a lot about you,' John said in a broad Yankee accent. He had a beaming face surrounded by a full beard.

'Nice to meet you John, It's my first time to one of these lectures. I hope I find it interesting, otherwise I'll demand my money back,' I said in an abrupt and probing manner.

'You do know it's a free public lecture don't you. Didn't Stellios tell you?' John answered in a puzzled and bemused way. He glared at Stellios.

A moment of tenseness loomed in the air. Stellios face mirrored John's frustrations.

'Only joking John, I'm sorry, but I'm always a bit of a tease. You'll get used to my humour eventually.' He lit up with laughter and shook my hand furiously.

'God, you really had me going. I thought you were going to be one of those hecklers we get, trying to disrupt the status quo.' He led us to our seats.

The crowd were a colourful, mixed bag. Punk rockers sporting spikes and Mohican-style, multi-coloured haircuts took the front line. The 'fluffy bunny' brigade, students, serious intellectual types and an array of old-aged pensioners more at home at the bingo hall, filled the mid section. At the back, a group of clean-cut, sober suited men and women conspired amongst themselves before the room slowly hushed to a steely silence.

A tall, broad, heavy set, authoritarian figure, thundered in from the flank, taking the room by surprise. He was dressed for battle, with a brown and beige suit, starched shirt and razor sharp tie. He stood there, military style, like a sergeant major, looking at his sorry new recruits. His clear, direct and masterly voice called for attention as he centred himself on the rostrum.

'My name is Dr. Douglas Baker. Tonight's lecture will be on the subject of reincarnation. Please do not interrupt me during my discourse. You may ask questions at the end of the lecture, if you please. My books and tapes on the subject and related topics are on sale at the table. Please feel free to buy any items as my lectures are always self-funded and non-profit making,' he said, preparing his notes, markers and easel.

The sea of faces directed their focus and calmed their minds, ready for the exposition.

'The soul of man is immortal and its future is the future of a thing, whose growth and splendour has no limits.

'This is one of the three great truths of ancient wisdom.'

The appetiser wetted our taste buds, but I felt a wave of disapproving energy seethe from the back. This oozing broth bubbled and bellowed indignation as doctor Baker eloquently elucidated example after example of the survival of the soul after physical death.

The punks rapturously applauded one of his theories. He said that they were all reincarnations of North American Indians who chose to incarnate here because their souls could not bear to go back to the USA. The pain and injustice they experienced there was too overwhelming. He had struck a note with the youths and they exploded into cheers, chants and war dances. Nobody tried to contain them as they revelled in the recognition of their true identity. Someone really understood them and respected them. It was brilliant to see such a show of appreciation from this bunch of social degenerates.

The intellectuals were fascinated by his theories on child genius and super-giftedness; he used Mozart as an example, stating that he had many previous lives as a musician. Goethe, the German mystic born a peasant, had lived before, as a philosopher. The older generations warmed to his theories, which stated that we would all be united in love, when we pass over. He said our friends and families would all be there to welcome us into this new dimension. There was no death, only change of state. I could see reassured faces and much of the audience held hands, reinforcing their vows of everlasting love.

'Right, that's enough. We've heard enough blasphemy and Paganism. You must stop this heresy now. You are Satan's emissary, a dark lord, brainwashing the vulnerable. This is not Christian, it's not in the Bible and it's certainly not God's teachings.'

The whole back of the room was in outrage. The seething mob had erupted and they wanted Baker's blood.

'Ladies and gentlemen at the back, I can tell by your comments that you are all God fearing, good Christians. I compliment you on your dedication to your faith and commitment to your doctrine, but it was you lot who crucified Jesus Christ. You chose him to die. You condemned him to death in the company of thieves and robbers. And further more, I bet you all masturbate and that's not very Christian is it.'

The whole room erupted in laughter. Young, old, male, female, weird and starchy were united in their unanimous support of doctor Baker. The fuming, fundamentalists scurried out of the room, heckling, bible bashing and shouting scripture and damnation to the encore of the crowd. I was on fire, my enthusiasm liberating my spirit. The mood was contagious; what an impact he had made. Even the fluffy bunnies applauded Dr. Baker's crudeness, recognising the victory he had won. The room slowly soothed and he brought the lecture to a close.

The enthusiastic crowd swamped the table. Books, tapes, posters were consumed by the dozen. They were all hungry for spiritual food. Eventually the room emptied until just a few remained. Stellios helped the other lads pack up, while Elena and I bought some books.

'Did you enjoy the lecture, or are you here to demand your money back?' John said in a broad, beaming, sarcastic smile.

'Give me a ringside seat next time John. I'd be happy to pay extra to see it all again,' I said making out a cheque.

'Is that order to eat in or take away sir?' John shouted in his Californian cackle.

He appreciated my sense of humour now and was getting his own back.

'You must come up to Claregate when you have a spare weekend. I'd like to show you around. We have guest accommodation if you need to stay,' John said, in a happy and sincere manner.

'I'd love to John; it's really kind of you to invite us. I'll let Stellios know when I'm off. I'll really look forward to it.'

The enigmatic doctor disappeared but I wanted to talk more, much more. He was an eccentric recluse; a brilliant orator and he knew his stuff. It was unusual to find a medical doctor, scientist and Bachelor of Arts who was also an authority on metaphysics, healing and astrology. His credentials were impeccable, not like the many quacks with dubious letters tagged onto their names.

I scanned the room to see where Stellios was. I wanted to thank him for inviting us to this wonderful, inspiring and entertaining evening. I caught a glimpse of him in a heated debate with two figures that were concealed in the shadows.

Who was he talking to? Why all the subterfuge? What were they conspiring between them?

I stole close to them with my Scorpion radar on red alert. I could sense Stellios aura being bombarded by bolts of piercing questions. His armour was paper-thin. His tinny, limp cacophony was drowned by wave after wave of a gruff grilling by his interrogators.

'Stellios, is he coming to Claregate or not?'

'Well, I didn't have the chance to....'

'Excuses, fucking excuses, I told you to talk to him. Stellios, you are fucking useless. Yet again you've disappointed me. I don't know what to do with you, I really don't.'

'John spoke to him. Didn't you John?' Stellios exclaimed in desperation.

'I told you to do it. Jesus fucking Christ man, I told you to do it.'

'John, what did he say? Did you ask him? Did you find out any more about him?' The voice from the void ranted.

'It's okay don't worry. He's coming. I've got him wrapped around my little finger. He's easy meat,' said John in a commanding tone.

'Stellios, next time I tell you to do something and you pass the buck, you'll be out. Do you understand?'

'I'm sorry. It won't happen again,' Stellios said in a whimper.

The aura around the gang was a swirling mass of dark browns and grotty greens. It reeked of usury, conceit and blackmail. I was being set up. But who was in the shadows? My first reaction was to confront the conspirators, but I needed to know more. My steely, super sleuth side took control. I was in a strong position now. I knew what they didn't. I knew their game and I could play it my way. I needed to get to the bottom of this quagmire.

As I stole away, I could hear Elena's laughter and giggles echo in my ears. There she was, bless her, surrounded by an audience of amorous admirers. She was the centre of attention and she loved it.

'Come on Elena, let's go.' I pulled her away from her fan club. 'Have you seen Stellios? We need thank him for inviting us.'

'There he is, Christo, over there.' She pointed to the exit. As we walked towards him, he waved off a car into the murky, night fog, which had descended in minutes. It was so thick that it blanketed the sea front in a ghostly mantle.

'Stellios, it was brilliant. What a great turnout and all those lovely people. God you're really lucky to have such good friends. I envy you,' Elena chirped.

Stellios face fashioned a muddled mix of surprise, elation, shock and despair. His nerves were on tenterhooks and he was sweating profusely. He did not look well at all.

'Yes, wasn't it great? Dr. Baker's reaction to the hecklers was brilliant. He's such an inspiration to us all. I've heard this lecture so many times, but it still fires me up,' he answered, brushing aside his morbid demeanour. Signs of normality returned to his face. His tense aura faded, rosy cheeks blossomed and the bounce was back in his step.

'Come on, let's go for a coffee,' he said and ushered us to the bar.

It was late, however and I had work in the morning so we said goodnight and left to make our way home. Elena cackled on and on as we walked, huddled together, back to the pad. My only thoughts were engaged in planning my next move. I needed to play Stellios both ways. If I were clever he would not suspect anything. The lecture opened up a hornet's nest in my head. I was poised to take the plunge into the depths of a spiritual quest. The way ahead seemed perilous, full of uncertainty and treachery, but the whole thing intrigued me. I was eager to study and explore the ancient teachings. My whole perception of life was changing. Explanations of my mystical experiences were in my grasp, but I needed to be extremely vigilant. Maybe there was a price to pay. Would it be worth the sacrifice? I was willing to give it my best shot. I never did anything in half measures. This was the ultimate challenge and I was up to it.

CHAPTER 6

My mind and emotions were engaged in a tug of war. The lecture opened up a dichotomy of conspiracy and spirituality. I dare not tell Elena of Stellios double-dealing. I had to keep it under wraps for the moment. What strategy should I adopt? Should I trust Elena? She may be part of the set-up. It was strange how they hit it off so well and then there was that dream. How could I forget that experience? My plan needed much thought and contemplation. I had to sleep on it for the moment.

'Elena, you don't mind putting a cuppa on do you? My head is still in the clouds and my mind feels as if it has gone through a mangle.'

'Well, you haven't said two words since we left the lecture, Christo. Wasn't it brilliant? I can't wait to go to Claregate. It's so exciting isn't it?' Elena's voice echoed above the sound of cups rattling and the kettle whistling. The screaming sound of steam sparked off a searing, high-pitched sound in my right ear. The haunting words, 'Beware of the Ides of March' echoed in my head, plunging me into a sickening vision of a bloodthirsty mob, slashing and stabbing their unsuspecting, pathetic victim.

Swish, whoosh, swish… Shimmering blades slashed through the murderous air, forcing a fountain of blue blood to flood from gaping wounds.

'Ah… Ah… Et tu Brutus,' the last gasping groans belted out of that pale visage before them as the victim sank into a vermilion pool of spite, venom and vengeance.

'Here you are, darling. What's wrong? You look like you've seen a phantom. Are you okay Christo?'

I was in shock and shaking like a leaf; I was still trapped in that sickening scene. My hand whacked the teacup she was offering me. It shattered on the marble table, sending razor sharp shards all over my face. I ended up buckled in convulsions. Searing hot tea splashed my contorted torso. I wailed throwing punches violently in thin air, as I re-enacted the sordid scene. Within seconds I came round in Elena's warm, soothing bosom. My eyes rolled and the high-pitched screech in my ear tingled into a gentle caress and melted into infinity.

'Christo, Christo, are you all right? Wake up, wake up,' she shouted frantically. 'What happened? I only left you for two minutes. It's like you were possessed by a demon. Bloody hell, you scared the shit out of me.' Elena never, ever swore. She must have been terrified.

'Elena, please leave me alone. You're crushing me. Give me some space, for God's sake, I need air, I need air,' I said and pushed away from her stranglehold.

'All right, all right, calm down. It's all right now. I'll get you a glass of water. You just stay there and don't move, okay,' she said in a commanding way before rushing off.

I had time now to explore my thoughts. Ever since meeting Stellios, I've experienced the weirdest things. I'm being plagued by vivid dreams, illuminations, premonitions and now unprovoked visions. What's happening to me? She was right. I do feel as if I am being possessed; dragged into an infernal dance with unknown partners for reasons that totally escape me. I had to be rational and keep my wits about me. Who knows where it was leading, but the stakes were getting higher and higher. That old, bloody kettle: whistling and wheezing. It was to blame. I told her to get rid of it. No, she had to hold onto it. It was a present from her mama. It had sentimental value and it's presence brought nostalgia oozing out of that screeching spout every time she made a cup of tea. But what was that high-pitched sound? Why did it bring on the attack? Could it be some sort of warning of danger? Was something trying to protect me? All these questions ricocheted around my skull.

'Here you are darling. Your colour is coming back, thank God. Look at you; you're soaked to the skin. Quick, get out of those clothes; you'll catch your death. I'll get your gown from upstairs.'

I almost did catch my death anyway, I whispered inwardly. Minutes later I was sitting by the fire with a hot cup of tea in my hands, gazing into the soothing, flickering flames.

'Well, aren't you going to tell me what happened then?' Elena probed. I paused for what seemed an eternity. What could I tell her? I thought. I'll tell her the truth. No you can't tell her; she may pick up alert signals and before you know it, she will spill the beans to her accomplices. She's not really part of this, is she? How could she be? She was so naive, green and shallow. She just wanted to be noticed and worshipped as a goddess. On the other hand, she could be another Mata Hari, full of deceit, lust and self-interest. I could not be sure.

'Elena, listen, it was nothing. I was tired, the lecture, the excitement, I don't think I ate before we left. You know how it is,' I said rather unconvincingly.

'Well I'm off to bed. I don't believe you. Something happened. You don't just lash out like that; like a madman, for no reason,' she spouted and trundled off upstairs.

She left me alone with my memories. Fleeting flashes on that inward eye flickered in unison with the fire sprites and danced around the bonfire of my mind. I must have dozed off on the sofa and slept there all night.

I woke from a heavy, uninterrupted sleep and called out to Elena. After a while, I realised she had got up early and disappeared without even saying goodbye. I looked at the clock; God it was ten to nine. Uncle Vic would be bashing hell out the door any minute. I swished the blind to reveal our staff huddled outside, waiting for someone to let them in. They were waiting for me! I had forgotten all about it. I was on an early and I should have opened up at eight thirty. I opened the window and threw them the keys, apologising profusely for sleeping in.

'I'll be down in a few minutes guys. Put the coffee machine on and rustle up some toast. I'll just throw on some clothes. I'll be down in two ticks,' I shouted.

The day passed slowly, business was dead. I had lots of time on my hands. Vic and George took the day off and I was in charge. I took the opportunity to do a bit of reading so I picked up 'The Jewel in the Lotus'. It was Dr. Baker's first major book, a synthesis of The Seven Pillars of Ancient Wisdom. It postulated certain hidden keys which, when understood, would lead to union with your higher self, your *daemon*. The acts of study, meditation, service work to humanity and keeping a spiritual diary were paramount in the process of spiritual development. My mind devoured page after page, just as if I had known these ancient truths in a past life. A whole range of tantalising subjects whetted my taste buds. Esoteric astrology, esoteric healing, the psychology of the seven rays, the chakras, esoteric anatomy, dream symbolism, astral projection, the menu was endless.

Elena danced and chirped her way up the spiral staircase, planted a big kiss on my cheek and cuddled me.

'Hi gorgeous, what's cooking good looking?' She said in an amorous tone, as if we had made passionate love the night before. I was surprised by her mood and vitality. It was all very strange indeed.

'Brilliant day Elena, I've been studying Dr. Baker's book. It's so inspiring and down to earth. He's a real genius: an initiate or something.' I babbled on and on reciting what I had digested.

'Christo. You'll never guess? We've been invited to Claregate. John called Stellios to tell him about a workshop on the seven rays. It's planned for next weekend. We have to go, Christo, we have to go,' Elena said gushing like a big kid.

'I've just been reading about the seven rays. It's fascinating stuff. I'd love to…'

'Christo, Christo, there's more. Dr. Baker wants to do your rays and calculate your astrological chart. Isn't it wonderful?' She sounded very excited.

'I'll have to talk to the bosses to get the time off. I'm due a few days leave anyway, and it's not as if we're busy, is it.' I was buzzing with zeal. This was it, the start of my spiritual quest. An audience with Dr. Baker, I could not wait. But, hang on a minute.

Let's be sensible about this. My razor sharp intellect interrupted my passions and cut me down to size.

'Beware of the Ides of March. Beware of the Ides of March.' The bewitching voice was back and the high-pitched siren seared my inner ear once more. Who was it? What was this signal? Could it be my *Daemon*? It was baffling me, but I knew I had to go into the furnace to find out.

I called my uncles and arranged the weekend off. I was so excited, though I tried not to let my enthusiasm carry me away. I had to be aware of hidden agendas. I decided to read up on the rays before the analysis. I wanted to go there with a little knowledge, at least. I did not want to make a fool of myself.

The Jewel in the Lotus described the origin, history and application of the rays. According to the doctor's teachings, the seven rays are a manifestation of light, colour, energy and vibration. They stem from a galactic source that some call God Consciousness. When white light is focussed on a clear prism, it disperses into the seven colours of the spectrum. The rays filter from their divine source to man in a similar fashion. They enter our consciousness via the astrological signs and planets, impacting upon us through our physical, emotional, mental, personality and soul bodies. The rays are further categorised by their source energies. One, three, five and seven are 'will' rays and embody will and power to certain degrees. Equally, two, four and six are classed as 'love rays', expressing love and wisdom in varying vibrations. It was a unique psycho-spiritual approach, which included endless co-relations to chakras, crystals, endocrine glands and more. What an honour it was to be a guinea pig in the ray workshop, I thought. It was deeply interesting and meaningful.

By now my appetite for knowledge was so obsessive I felt withdrawal symptoms when I could not feed my hunger. As the weekend approached my energy levels were on overload. I borrowed uncle Vic's red convertible Jag and arranged to pick up Stellios on the way. You wouldn't believe the expression on his face when we glided up the pokey, wee lane to his drab digs. His eyes shone like pound signs, just as if he'd hit the jackpot. Maybe it was too close to the truth.

'Cor! Christo. I didn't realise we were going by limo. I would have dressed up for the occasion if I had known.' He was clearly overwhelmed. I could almost hear the little cogs in his cranky mind grinding gold and spinning silver as he gleefully looked forward to the Claregate reception. He had done well. He had delivered the goods. He was going to be rewarded for a change.

'Stellios, isn't it exciting, a beautiful day, clear blue skies, sun shining and a brilliant weekend to look forward to,' Elena shouted over the roar of the engine.

'Yes, it should be a great weekend. We are expecting a good response.' Stellios donned his balaclava, concealing his golden locks and his intentions. Halfway there I decided to pull into a service station. Elena wanted to powder her nose and I wanted to interrogate this little conspirator.

'So Stellios, How does Claregate make a living? It must be so difficult to keep a college running and house full-time students there. How do they cope?' I thought I'd go for the jugular and gauge the response. Stellios quite flustered by my directness, stuttered and fluffed his nervous dialogue.

'I'm not really sure; you'll have to ask John. They produce books, posters and tapes, which they sell, I suppose,' he replied, racking his little grey cells. That's never enough to cover costs, I thought. I knew there had to be other, more lucrative, ways to bring in funds.

'Mmm, they must need to sell a hell of a lot of books and they cost money to produce. What about the labour, that must be expensive?'

'The group provide the labour in return for lodgings and teaching. It's part of their service work to humanity. There's also a steady flow of helpers like myself. We offer our services when we can,' he said, in a more convincing manner.

'How many students live there? The accommodation must cost a bomb.'

'Well, there are two girls and about 12 lads. Oh, there's Mr and Mrs Mac, but they live out. They take care of the gardens,' Stellios answered.

'To keep more than 12 people fed and watered each day, seven days a week costs a fortune Stellios. How do they do it?' I pressed. 'The organisation and planning must be a real challenge.'

Before Stellios could reply, Elena emerged from the shops with a bag of refreshments for us.

'All ready to go boys? I got some munchies to keep you going,' She swished her slinky, bronzed legs into the big cat. Stellios welcomed her cheery intervention and sank thankfully back into the safety of his protective balaclava. As I eased the car out of the service station, my thoughts sped ahead to Claregate. It all seemed idyllic: esoteric teachings, community life and self-financing and self-sufficient approach, all set in rural Hertfordshire. What more could any spiritual aspirant wish for? It was all too good to be true. There must be a catch somewhere I thought. There must be a price to pay for this package of paradise.

CHAPTER 7

A fter a couple of hours we hit the Great North Road leading to Potters Bar. Stellios pointed out the last few directions and we turned into the driveway leading to Claregate. The setting was very serene. Mature conifers searched skywards and swayed in adulation of the multi-faceted, colourful shrubs. Dense deciduous bushes looked like an emerald mantle on a dining table, as they draped their lush, green foliage over freshly laid, red brick, garden walls. Quaint smatterings of blood red geraniums battled vibrant ochre and blushing pink snap dragons for the sun's glancing, golden rays. An ivy bush stretched its scrawny fingers, searching for the next cranny to creep in to. It hung like an unfinished tapestry over the old school house. Elegant stained glass, bay windows flanked the virginal white, Victorian porch. Two flea-bitten looking cats, rock and rolled around the driveway, like a ball of hay in a whirlwind, scattering dust and debris into the air. You could almost hear the innocent, angelic voices of little children, chuckling and chattering in classrooms while others gleefully hopped down stair after stair, on their way to the green for their morning break. As the door beckoned our entry, John mysteriously appeared on the step.

'Oh what a pleasant surprise. I did not expect to see you at all. I'm looking for Steve and Jeremy. They always hide away when we have visitors. Stellios, you don't mind calling them, you should know where to find them, after all they're your friends.'

Stellios sprang from the back, as sharp as a jack-knife, eager to obey John.

'I'll ferret them out for you John. I know exactly where they are,' Stellios said, with a glint in his eye and supporting a cheek-to-cheek grin.

'They need to set up the lecture hall properly. DB will be arriving shortly and you know what he's like if it's not perfect, don't you,' John shouted as Stellios bolted around the back.

'Nice car Chris. Come in and I'll introduce you to Linda and Claire.' He turned and shouted. 'Linda! Claire! Chris and Elena have arrived! Oh, by the way Chris, don't forget to give Linda your details. She needs to calculate your horoscope for DB to interpret in the workshop.' Two women appeared from the kitchen.

'Hi there, Chris, Elena, this is Claire and I'm Linda. Pleased to meet you; we're glad you could make it. Stellios has told us lots about you. Come in and make yourselves at home. Cup of tea or coffee?' Linda said in a broad Yankie accent. She motioned with her hand and led us to the dining room.

'That's brilliant, we're gasping. I'll have a coffee and Chris drinks tea,' said Elena. At that moment I staggered forward feeling faint and in shock.

'Oh my God, quick girls, Chris has just collapsed! I need some water and a cold compress now,' Elena frantically shouted.

'Christo, Christo, wake up. Are you all right?' she shouted and cradled me in her bosom. I could see them trying desperately to revive me. I was out of my body in a kind of conscious state observing the frantic scene. I was above myself. It was chaos. I had bashed my head on the edge of the table as I fell. Blood spewed from a gash, but I knew it was not serious. It was that bloody hallway. I'd seen it before; I knew the place. It was a kind of deja-vu experience.

It was set up as a film studio. They had recently shot a scene for a film about reincarnation. There it was, adorned in Greek Doric columns and statues of gods and goddesses. Frescoes of youths hunting and drinking draped the walls. Golden urns and platters overflowing with fruit graced opulent tables. Lush animal skins were draped over chaise longs and invited the bodies of sensuous mortals. Blood red and purple drapes swished around that lewd lair. The stench of blood, debauchery and…

'Ahh, Ahh, give me air. I need air, quick,' I gasped, as I was propelled like quicksilver back into my physical body. I slowly regained consciousness only to find myself deep in the clutches of *her* adulterous arms. It was that awful waking nightmare I had dreamed in the flat. This was it; the sordid act took place here. But why? It made no sense at all.

'Leave me alone, leave me alone,' I demanded throwing Elena away and startling the girls. They scattered like skittles all over the floor.

'What the hell's happened here? Oh my god. Quick, someone fetch the medical kit,' John shouted. We were lying in a bundle on the floor with furniture upended and smashed crockery all around us. It looked more like the aftermath of a bar room brawl, rather than the Claregate dining room.

'It's okay John, it's nothing serious, Chris just had a fall and knocked himself out. He's grazed his head, but I'm sure he'll live to fight another day,' Claire said in a reassuring and commanding way.

'It happens sometimes. It's the energy of the place. Sensitive people just can't adjust to the vibrations when they first enter. It impacts their aura and sends them into a kind of catalepsy.'

By this time I was being comforted, reassured and calmed by the gentle caresses of Elena.

'You know, he's been acting strange for some time now. He's had a series of weird dreams, visions, premonitions and uncontrolled outbursts. He sometimes scares the hell out of me,' Elena said, still in shock.

'I'll talk to you after about it, Elena. The important thing is that he is okay. Look, all his colour is back,' Claire said as she stroked my brow and dabbed the graze with iodine.

'Now Chris, this is not going to hurt. It'll nip just for a moment. I'm sure you'll be fine. Anyway, you're our guinea pig today. We must have you fit and healthy for the slaughter,' she laughed. 'I'll give you some rescue remedy. In fact, I think we all need some. Here Elena, open wide.' She administered two or three drops on our tongues and knocked back the rest herself. It was a Bach flower remedy, which was a panacea for all types illness and great for treating shock.

Claire knew just about everything. She had been at Claregate for years. Dr. Baker had met her whilst touring the states. In actual fact this is how he met John and Linda. They were very close and were the backbone of the community.

'How are you feeling now, Chris? Are you okay, or do you need to rest a little?' Linda said in a soulful way.

'I feel fine Linda. It must have been the drive and all that fresh air.'

'Good, now what's your time, date and place of birth,' she said, a form at the ready.

'I was born on the 13th of November 1956, at 4.55am, in Glasgow, Scotland.'

'Mmm, that explains your experience today. The Moon, Mercury and Neptune are in Scorpio at the present. They are conjunct your sun sign. The Moon is a kind of trigger, it creates a response; Mercury rules the head and Neptune can cause lapses into unconsciousness. Scorpio rules sudden, unexpected influences, which can cause crisis. It also rules cuts, grazes and bloodshed.' She had the whole situation wrapped up exactly. I was amazed and impressed.

'Furthermore, it points to a day of deep, psychological probing and inner revelations. A kind of rebirth will take place, which will widen your knowledge and stir you spiritually.'

Well, I could not have picked a better day for my initiation. First an unconscious swoon, then a bash on the head and an out-of-body experience. I was given a dose of rescue remedy and now a doctor will start probing and prodding my inner life. I was not quite sure what I was letting myself in for. But I knew I should keep my wits about me. Strange things were happening all around. The students all looked so genuine though, brilliant auras, calm and serene and extremely knowledgeable. Maybe that cocktail of mixes could be lethal? My god, she could have spiked that remedy. Was it really rescue remedy, or some drug to brainwash me with? I was getting a bit paranoid; maybe I was overreacting. I wish I could hear that comforting, laser signal now. But *he* had deserted me in all this confusion.

I could hear lots of footsteps in the hallway. The place was buzzing with activity. Stellios and the boys were doing last minute preparations to the room. People were mulling around, casually chatting and exchanging ideas. Young, old, cranky and starchy, fluffy and serious, they had one thing in common, they were here to see the 'Man' perform. With a crash of the doors, two Alsatians charged at us as if we were a flock of sheep to be bullied into a pen. The entourage appeared, marching behind Dr. Baker.

'I'm here. Does anybody need me? Wolf, Poppet, leave the guests alone, you've already been fed,' he shouted. He flicked off his cap, threw it on the stair post with the poise and accuracy of a pro basketball player and skipped upstairs into the office. As the door closed behind him, I saw that his lieutenants had gathered.

Claire and Linda ushered the group into the lecture hall.

'Ladies and gents, please be seated. There are more seats at the back if needed. Steve put some more seats out. It looks as if we'll need them today.' Steve was a tall spindly, figure, all arms and legs. He kept on falling over himself and causing chaos wherever he was. God was he clumsy. Stellios faffed around him in a nervous jitter, chattering, fidgeting and scratching just like a wee monkey. They always hung around together, those two. Elena and I were led to our seats at the front. We had all the privileges: orange juice, mineral water and iced glasses. We were treated like royalty. Elena loved every minute of it, as you can imagine. As I turned around I saw at least 30 people settling into their seats. Chakra charts, ray psychology posters, astrology charts and a massive print of the OM, the sacred Sanskrit symbol for God, graced the walls. Rows and rows of spiritual books lay dormant on gleaming white shelves. At the side of the stage a large armchair took pride of place. It was *his* throne. Tucked to the side stood a small table, flushed with a white cloth. A petite vase of fresh flowers, a jug of orange juice, mineral water and his notes, lay waiting for the maestro. The easel and rostrum jutted out in front of one, solitary chair… my chair. My thoughts blanked and my emotions churned in my tummy as he made his entrance. He was in casual mode, with an open-necked, red shirt overflowing his khaki-coloured chinos; slippers lingered on his feet. He gave me a steely stare and a contrived smile as he introduced the workshop.

'Ladies and gentlemen, It's nice to see a good few familiar faces, and of course, many new ones. I have a courageous young man today; he's going to be my guinea pig. Aren't you Chris?' He turned to me.

'Yes Dr. Baker, I've been looking forward to it all week. I've read up on the rays and I'm prepared,' I said in a loud and confident manner.

'I hear you had an accident in the dining room. I hope you did not damage any of my antique chairs,' he said, peering over his glasses with a laser sharp stare.

God, he's started analysing me already. I sensed it. I knew he was trying to put me on the spot.

'Listen, never mind that old pile of sticks. I hope you're insured, look at my face. I'll be onto my lawyers as soon as I get back.' I deflected his attack and put out a brilliant counter attack. The whole room buzzed with anticipation. Steve looked at Stellios. Both were in shock and shrugging their shoulders. Nobody had ever traded punches with DB and won. He just stared straight at me with those brown, bear-like, pool ball eyes and gave out one almighty laugh. Then he jotted something down in his notes.

'Well, at least you've got balls. I like that in a man,' he said, acknowledging my defence and sense of humour. I caught sight of John winking at me and chuckling. He knew what I was like; he had sampled my wit.

'Well, you'll have to ask Elena about that,' I replied. Elena's face turned crimson.

'What are you waiting for? Come on up here, it's your show now,' he said and waved me forward.

'Ladies and gents, please give a warm welcome to Chris Kasparis. Chris is 24-years-old. He's a Scorpio with Libra ascendant and his Moon and Mars are in Pisces. He has therefore the Fourth Ray through Scorpio, the Third Ray through Libra and the Sixth Ray through Pisces. All are influencing his ray makeup. We will begin to probe his early childhood first to establish his emotional or astral ray.'

After a series of deep, searching questions and answers, he ascertained I was a sixth ray astral, but rapidly changing into a second ray. The sixth ray is deeply sensitive and highly emotional. It is linked to Mars and the sign of Pisces. Its energy is devoted, sacrificial and sometimes blind. Yes, I could accept that. All my childhood stuff: the death of my father, devotion to my mother and siblings, and my sensitivity. It was all uncannily true. He told the audience that due to the years of dealing with emotions, my astral body had grown to a degree of detachment. The second ray qualities of compassion and unconditional love were streaming forth in abundance. This ray of love and wisdom is highly recommended in discipleship.

'Now, Chris, we are going to analyse how you are deal with things mentally. We know there is a fourth and third ray influencing you.'

After a whole host of questions, he established I had a fourth ray mind, but again changing rapidly into a fifth ray. The fourth ray embodies the qualities of art and harmony through conflict via my Scorpio sun sign. Certainly in the past I had felt that by resolving conflicts I had learned so much, I had valued the experience, no matter how hard it had been. Now, I can stand back, analyse and prioritise my thoughts. I have a more critical, fifth ray approach, but I still retain the sensitivity and artistic temperament of the fourth ray. It was an unusual combination, but again, in spiritual development, you need a good fifth ray to sift though all the falseness and illusion.

'Now, let's look at Chris's physical body. That's the easiest ray to establish. Well, he's not a first ray; thin, nervous and hyper is he? He could be either a third ray or a seventh ray physical. Just look at the way he's slouched in that chair. He's really comfortable looking isn't he?' The group nodded in agreement.

'Are you a sporty type? Do you like camping, fishing and walking? Are you always on the go? Elena is that what he's like?' he spoke as if he was firing a volley of machine-gun bullets at her.

'Yes, that's what he's like all right. Always on the go. Into everything that moves,' she said in embarrassment.

'He must be a third ray physical. Is he really untidy then, with all that activity?'

'No on the contrary, He's always organised and tidy. He has to be for his job. He has to manage a thriving, busy, up-market restaurant and coffee house.'

'Mmm, what have we here then group?

'A possible seventh ray physical. They love organisation, are always tidy and need to have order and ritual in everything they do. They are sporty and also love the sun and get tremendous energy from it. Elena, is he a sun worshipper?'

'Look at him; he's always out in it, even in winter. He can't get enough of it. He can stay hours in it and not feel drained.'

'Well, what a mix we have here. It's not that straight forward, is it? I'll tell you, he's a 3/7 physical isn't he?'

By my analysis so far, my whole life was changing. I certainly felt a major rebirth going on. It was all very strange indeed.

'Chris, I'm now going to probe your personality ray. This is the body of consciousness that synthesises the three personality energies; the physical, emotional and mental rays.'

He proceeded to fire question after question at me. I returned my answers as if we were engaged in a furious tennis match. After a while, he ascertained my personality ray.

'Mmm, Chris it looks like you're heading rapidly towards a first ray personality. It always strives through challenge, is blessed with will and power and uses direct force, if necessary, to push things towards completion. You can be ruthless and demanding, but you need to harness and focus this energy positively and use it in service to humanity.' He had me all stitched up and he was right.

'Last and the most important ray is the soul ray. Chris, why do you think you're here on earth? Is there a purpose for you?'

I did not need time to think. I knew my inner self.

'I'm here to serve, to teach and to heal. I have a deep inner urge to help humanity. I know I have an important role to play. I trust my inner self to help me find it and express it.'

'Well, group, he's a second ray soul, isn't he? What a brilliant ray complement. My only advice to you is focus your energies into spiritual channels. It won't be easy; you'll have to let go of the trappings of the material world first. Then, after integrating your personality and channelling its energies in line with your soul's purpose, you will be serving teachings to the masses, instead of food.'

He wrapped up the workshop in minutes, and shot to the door to be welcomed by his beloved dogs.

'Going back!' he shouted, and he bundled past the door with the dogs in toe, into a waiting car.

That was it. I was left there, sitting on stage, my life shared by everyone in the room. Now, I knew how film and pop stars felt. I had no secrets, no privacy any more. My life had been made public. It was even on tape for the records and would be offered as lecture material.

I was shattered. Linda showed us to our room and I crashed out immediately. I even missed diner. Elena went without me, but I needed the rest and I had a lot to think about.

CHAPTER 8

'Wake up Christo, breakfast is in an hour. God, you must have been exhausted yesterday. I had a really interesting chat with the girls last night.'

'Elena. All right, all right, just give me a few minutes. I've just remembered a fragment of a dream I had last night. A scroll. Yes, that scroll at my feet. My God, it's coming back to me. Elena, I think it's really important. Listen,' I said and sat up. I bolstered my pillows, closed my eyes and focused my mind.

It was here, at Claregate. Two unknown women have come to receive lessons from Linda. They are extremely demanding and forceful. As Stellios, you and I join the lesson, they pull out a painting of Edinburgh castle and lay it on the table. There's something mysterious about the whole scene. The point to the painting and say,

It's very symbolic when the snow melts.'

Then, an unholy energy emerged from the painting, sending everyone into a panic. The air is thick with fear and horror as I pull out the cross I am wearing. I direct it at the energy field and focus a penetrating, pure white, laser light at it. I experience an intense zap, just like an electric shock, flow through my whole body. In a daze I run after both of you, upstairs to the landing. Stellios, who also has a cross, runs away with you into hiding. I alone pluck up courage and peer over the banister, down to the lower level. I see the women using poltergeist activity to direct a tattered, old parchment scroll up towards me. It hovers, defying gravity. I am powerless, I can't move, I am paralysed by sheer terror. It rises up above my head and furls open in mid air. I can just make out the words. They are written in an ancient script, but I can just about understand it.

You are here to serve the Will of God. You are a Christ Light worker. This is your destiny. I expect 'only everything' from you.

It was signed in my name, just like a contract. Whoosh, whish, whirl, the scroll flapped in mid air and rolled towards me, dropping at my feet. I pick it up and bolt deliriously downstairs with it firmly in my hands.

'What do you think Elena? What do you think?'

'Bloody hell! Jesus Christ! I can't believe it,' she blurted out in awe of the experience. 'It's all connected, Christo, it's all so uncanny. Listen, please listen, it's all connected. I told the girls about your strange dreams, visions and outbursts. They are convinced you're ready for soul contact. In previous lives, they said you served the Will of God. You had won the right to harness and channel The Christ Light through incarnations of devotion to The Lord's work. You served mankind, expressed unconditional love and persisted with the vision in the face of extreme adversity.'

'Mmm, that explains the light shining from the cross. Do you know what my father's real surname was, before he changed it? His surname was Christodoulou. That's Christ worker translated into English. It sheds light on my link with Stellios. He has the cross, but he ran away. He's got the potential but lacks the courage. The Scottish element is a bit vague, but I was born there. We must all be linked to Edinburgh, perhaps in a previous life. But, who were the mysterious women? And that scroll? What did *only everything* mean? It may all be a coincidence, I don't know, I just don't know anymore.'

I needed to keep a firm anchor in the real world. My rational faculties always grounded me. But all this defies the realm of logic. I had to be objective. After all, there was a conspiracy still brewing and I needed my wits about me.

'Elena, you go down and I'll have a quick shower.'

'Okay, but don't be late. John wants to show us around and Dr. Baker would like to see us later.'

I hopped out of bed into the steaming hot aqua jets. The searing sensations on my face and the moody, misty atmosphere flooded back waves of images. As I waded through my deep thoughts, the familiar Daemonic, high-pitched, tingling in my ears resonated to the water, splashing on my body. *He* was still there. *He* had not deserted me.

'I need your guidance and protection, my Daemon. My destiny lies ahead of me. It is fraught with Herculean labours. Who can I trust? Only you, who else? I am being enticed into this labyrinth. Elena, with her binding ball of string and alluring aura, has enchanted me to the gate. Had she sold her soul? What promised reward had she traded for this betrayal? You are my only salvation, my Daemon,' I muttered whilst in a semi trance-like state. I somehow sensed he was there. He was listening to me; he was in contact with me.

The sun's blazing rays shone through the skylight, animating the perfected globules of water. They slalomed down the steamy, glassy, cubicle and showered rainbow rays over my body, bathing me in iridescent lights. As this aurora penetrated my mind and body, *He* whispered a verse of the poem *Paracelsus* by Robert Browning.

> *Truth lies within ourselves;*
> *It takes no rise from outward things,*
> *Whate'er you may believe.*
> *There is an inmost centre in us all,*
> *Where truth abides in fullness;*
> *And around, wall upon wall,*
> *The gross flesh hems it in,*
> *This perfect, clear perception–*
> *Which is truth.*
> *A baffling and perverted carnal mesh*
> *Binds it and makes it all error:*
> *And to know, rather consists in*
> *Opening out a way whence the*
> *Imprisoned splendour may escape,*
> *Than in effecting entry for a light*
> *Supposed to be without.*

I had never even read it before. For some strange reason, it resonated on my soul strings and stirred me deeply. Our link was now developing rapidly. It was audio at first, but now it was overlapping into all the senses.

Symbols, poems, dreams, myths and vibrant images all charged with numinous energy were being flashed to me. Sometimes they would warn me, but on occasions they would prepare me for spiritual insights. I needed to keep a record of these contacts, a sort of spirit diary. There may be patterns of activity. I could predict *His* presence. We could create a unique dialogue, a language of spirit, which we could share and develop.

'Thud! Thud! Christo, if you are not down in 10 minutes breakfast will be cleared away. They are all waiting to see you,' Elena shouted. Her frantic cacophony ricocheted around my skull like a schizoid steel ball in a pinball machine.

'I'm coming now, okay, I'm coming now,' I said, swishing towels around my torso and searching for my T-shirt and jeans.

The room had emptied by the time I got there. Elena was still chatting to Claire and Linda. Stellios was in the kitchen with Steve washing up. I could hear their spiritual banter over the chink of cups and cutlery waltzing around the basin. The smash of a glass on the tiled floor brought their spiritual masturbation to a climax.

' Hi Linda, hi Claire. Sorry I'm late. That bang on the head, the altered state and the ray analysis must have knocked the stuffing out of me. I needed the rest.'

'What altered state Christo; you didn't tell me about that?' Elena exclaimed in a concerned manner. 'He's so secretive. He tells me what he wants me to hear. He's a typical Scorpio.'

Linda was just a slip of a lass; scrawny, bony and built like a whippet. Her lily-white face and protruding, pale blue aquatic eyes, shone angelically. She was a sensitive Pisces, but there was a potent power bubbling below, like a volcano waiting to explode. It was an interesting mix.

'It's understandable Elena. Chris is on the threshold of another dimension. It can be very confusing and disorientating. Chris, you'll have to tell me about your altered state experience,' Linda said, quickly changing the subject.

'May we congratulate you on your brilliant performance yesterday. It's the only time we have ever witnessed Dr. Baker lost for words. You really made an impact on him,' Linda said, beaming with appreciation.

'Fancy some cereal and toast? Do you take tea or coffee?' she said and pointed to the breakfast dresser.

'Help yourself Chris... Stellios, please bring Chris a mug and a plate, if we have any left. I know you Greeks like to break them, don't you,' she said, laughing out loud.

'Good morning Christo,' said Stellios. 'It's not like you to sleep in. Great rays by the way. Here you are. I'll introduce you to Steve and Jeremy later.' He wore a beaming wall-to-wall smile under his dazzling, sunny mop.

'That will be great. I'll look forward to it,' I said and tucked into my cereal.

'So Linda, Elena told me your thoughts about my experiences. I can't understand why it's happening now. I feel like I am on a tight rope, swaying from side to side with a vast, bottomless chasm beckoning me. It's driving me crazy.'

'I've been on that very same tight rope, Chris. I've felt what you're feeling. I know how frightening it is.' Her voice was reassuring. 'It's all part of your spiritual growth. It's important to meditate on it. You'll find out what it means to you. It's different for each of us.'

'Linda, I've had vivid visions, unexplainable altered states; spirit contacts and I hear strange voices in my head. Am I going nuts?'

Claire sat and listened patiently and attentively. She was absorbing the contents of my fevered mind. She was large-framed and bespectacled. Her dark brown, curly hair looked like a barrister's wig. She was a great diplomat and a brilliant counsellor. It suited her Libran personality.

'Chris, you've received the calling. Your time has come again to *Serve the Land*. Each one of us here led relatively normal lives before the calling. Linda was a student, I was a legal secretary, but I suppose deep down we were unconsciously searching for our true identity. We all have to grapple with our shadow, the unknown side of our nature. The loathsome, mythological Minotaur is a reflection of it. It stands guard, in the shadows, at the entrance to the inner realms. It goads and grapples with us, swamping us with fear, uncertainty and depression. It drains our vitality, abducts our trembling ego and draws it into oblivion. But, we must endure this onslaught, eventually realising that this grotesque monster is part of us. It's our negative self, an accumulation of all our darkest deeds, thoughts and emotions. Dr. Baker calls it The Dweller on the Threshold of Consciousness.'

She had left me dangling, suspended in mid air on the tightrope of my mind. The drop threatened to drag me deep into the bowels of the underworld. I could almost feel tongues of demonic fire licking at the pit of my soul. I sensed the clutches of that infernal entity clawing at my feverish frame and I heard hellish calls of all damnation in my head.

Her words brought the conversation to an eerie halt. Even the kafuffle in the kitchen melted into a steely silence. They had all experienced what Claire explained. You could have heard a pin drop.

'Thud! Thud! Crash! Crash! I'm here. Does anyone want me?' a voice thundered from the hallway, blasting the status quo to smithereens. Dr. Baker's familiar call echoed against the heavy artillery, trundling upstairs into the office. John popped his head around the door and beckoned me into the hall.

'Listen Chris, something important has come up. Dr. Baker won't be able to see you today. He sends his apologies, but no doubt we will be seeing you again soon. He told me to give you these books to take way with you. There's also some information on our correspondence course, which I'll give Stellios to forward to you.' His voice was trembling. 'I'll have to go, he's waiting for me upstairs.'

'John, I'm waiting; if you are not here in two minutes we'll start without you and I'll be very cross.' It was Dr. Baker's call to arms. The inner circle was in session.

'Bring Stellios up with you,' he commanded.

I could feel Stellios' aura go into shock as he was frogmarched past me. I felt so sorry for him. Deep down he was a good soul. Somehow, he's being held over a barrel. I made my mind up to challenge him on the way back home.

We did not hang around any longer. We packed our bags in an eerie silence. I knew Stellios was being grilled. Poor thing, he was so sure he'd be rewarded for bringing in his prosperous catch. As we walked through the hall all life deserted the place. Linda and Claire had scurried into their burrows. Steve and the others were hiding in the grounds. Even the bundle of cats sensed an ill wind blowing and they cowered in a corner, hair spiked, eyes pierced and fangs focused for a frenzied attack.

I loaded our luggage into the car and Stellios trudged from around the back carrying the world on his shoulders. He clambered in with his heavy aura swamping ours. I eased the car out of the drive and into a misty, murky, mid morning haze. He sat there all the way back without uttering a sound. Elena dozed off and I was left with the afterbirth of a strange but intriguing new dawn. I was adamant that I was going to clear the air with Stellios. I decided to drop off Elena first and go for the jugular while he was at his most vulnerable.

CHAPTER 9

Stellios clambered over the seats into the front. I sensed his demeanour had cleared from the heavy cloud that had engulfed him. Maybe he'd had time to hatch another plot. I could see he was desperate, but the little rat was extremely cunning too.

The seafront was shrouded in blankets of billowing mist. Crashing waves and the rustle of shifting shingle, swallowed by sweeping currents echoed in my ears. The ghostly West Pier loomed like a Dinosaur skeleton stripped bare to the bones. Blustery winds wrapped their whimpering tongues around its rusting, ochre frame, as it creaked against the menacing sky. It was the perfect time to rattle Stellios fragile cage.

'Stellios, I'm not going to beat around the bush. I know you are in cahoots with the Claregate mob. You're going to stitch me up aren't you?' I said, slashing the silence with a razor sharp attack.

'I don't know what you mean, Christo. I've got nothing to tell you.'

'Look Stellios, stop fucking about; I know you've set me up. I heard all that conversation at the lecture.

He's easy meat; I've got him around my little finger. All that abuse and emotional blackmail; I heard it all. Who was the face behind that vile voice in the shadows, anyway?'

'Listen Christo, you've got it all wro...'

'Don't insult my intelligence, you scheming little bastard!' I raged, frightening the shit out of him.

'The workshop, the ray analysis, the hospitality, your relationship with Elena. I could sense your greedy little grey cells orgasm at the thought of mega money when I pulled up to collect you in the Jag.'

'But, Christo.'

'Don't interrupt me. You were homesick; I welcomed you into my home. I fed and watered you. I trusted you and this is how you repay me, by stabbing me in the back. I had hoped we'd be friends; I felt something deep when I first set eyes on you. You touched me spiritually; I held you in high esteem. You were becoming my mentor, and now this. I just can't believe it Stellios. I just can't believe it.'

He had cowered up into a little silent bundle, slouched against the door. His eyes drooped, his pale face sagged and his sorry soul had swallowed his guilt-ridden corpse. He was ready to regurgitate his sordid story.

'Okay Christo, okay, I'm ready to tell you everything. I'm really, really sorry,' he whimpered. He sighed deeply and primed himself for the confession. 'They're holding me over a barrel. They've applied for a work permit for me, and every so often, they pull the chains. I don't want to go back to those horrible memories of the invasion. My parents are refugees; they're homeless. Famagusta lies mortally wounded, a ghost town, reeking with the stench of death and destruction. Christo you've seen it with your own eyes. I don't want to go back to that. I don't. I want to stay here and work.' His heart wrenched in two and tears trickled from those deep brown pools, flooding my forgiving soul.

'So why are they interested in me? I don't understand it. Why me?'

'You've got to believe me, they're not scheming, blackmailing, crooks. They are struggling to stay afloat. Every day they have to fight bailiffs, to quell repossession orders slapped on them. It's been like that for as long as I can remember. Somehow they always manage to pull through. You can imagine the pressure, can't you?' He rambled on and on for what seemed like an eternity.

'Stellios you have not answered my question. Why me?' I pressed.

'Well, I was asked to keep a look out for people who may be potential helpers, people with money and skills. I told them of you; I know I shouldn't have. I didn't think they would put the thumbscrews on me.'

'What's the guy's name who threatened you at the lecture?'

'That's Barry. He's Dr. Bakers' right hand man. He runs the business and leads the inner circle with John.'

'He sounds like a real thug, throwing his weight around and abusing the others.'

'Christo, he's not really like that. He's quite approachable and really helpful.'

'Stellios, open your eyes; he's a manipulating, scheming bastard, full of self-interest. He doesn't care who he tramples on in order to get results.'

'It may seem that way, but there is no personal gain involved. He tries very hard to keep the wolves from the door.'

'Stellios, I can't understand why you're defending him; after all, he's got you by the balls. What was the crisis you were summoned to attend?'

'Well, we got tipped off. Barry's got a friend in the council chambers. He told him that the bailiffs were coming on Monday morning with a writ to confiscate the typesetting machine. We have to find £1,000 to stall the demand; otherwise there goes our livelihood. No typesetter: no books. They told me to ask you if you could help. Christo, I wouldn't ask, it's not me at all, but they put pressure on me; you know how it is, don't you?'

What was I to think now? Was this a ploy to create a false sense of trust? It may all be a pack of lies and deceit. Were they really holding him to ransom over his work permit? Were they strapped for cash or were they using innocent people's donations to line their greedy pockets? And what about his involvement with Elena?

'What about Elena, Stellios? Tell me the truth. Are you having an affair with her? I'll kill you if you are, I really will.'

'Christo, she's a lovely girl, so naive and innocent. I used her to get to you, that's all. She's in love with you Christo; you're really lucky. Honestly, I had no other motives or intentions and that's the truth.'

I could see it in his eyes; he had bared his soul to me. But, how could I use the situation to my benefit? I could get him off the hook. Maybe I could apply for his work permit. Then he would be indebted to me forever. Mmm, that sounded like a good proposition. I could get all the inside information about the inner circle's activities. To be forewarned is to be forearmed, I thought.

'Stellios listen, I'm going to try to help you, but in return I want your undying loyalty, okay?'

'Okay, okay, anything you say, anything to stay in the country, anything.' He grovelled like a submissive dog shuffling along on his belly.

'Right, I need some answers. Is Dr. Baker legitimate and are his teachings inspired? Is there a source and basis for the ancient wisdom?' I rattled my questions like machine-gun fire hitting a bullet blasted corpse.

'Dr. Baker is an initiate wisdom teacher. There is something profound about him. He's in direct communication with his Daemon. He states the poet laureate, Robert Browning; the English Master works through him. He is a kind of channel for Browning's inspirational teachings.'

Wao! A whoosh of energy flushed through me, setting off alarm bells and the Daemonic siren in my ear. It was Browning's *Paracelsus* that had flooded me with light and understanding in the shower. Is Baker influencing my aura? I was utterly flabbergasted, just to think I may somehow be connected to Baker via Robert Browning. Why *Paracelsus*? He penned hundreds of poems and sonnets. Why was *Paracelsus* so important? My inadequate brain feebly submitted to a far superior force. I had to go beyond the intellect into the realms of abstract thought and intuition for answers to my searching questions. Stellios continued his exposition as my brain juggled all these mind-boggling ideas.

'This lineage of ancient wisdom teachings originated in the east. In the 1880s the Russian mystic Madame Blavatsky set up a school called The Theosophical Society. The first lodge was based in India and attracted many intellectuals of the east and west. She professed to have direct contact with Indian master teachers who initiated her in the wisdom teachings of the Hindus and Buddhists.

She wrote a treatise of doctrines that are recognised as a classical source of ancient wisdom teachings.

'Her pupils and colleagues established centres all round the world, externalising the teachings to the masses.

'Ollcott, Besant, Leadbeater, Krishnamurti, Assagioli and Alice Bailey, to name a few, further refined the wisdom. The latter founded The Arcane School and was the amanuensis of a Tibetan master teacher. Her books were published under The Lucis Trust. The Bailey teachings were the most current authority of the wisdom of the ages, until DB incarnated. He is the latest in the unbroken lineage of initiate teachers. His life's work is to establish the teachings in the language of the day. Claregate is the core centre of the teachings, which he calls 'The English Ashram'. Its purpose is to externalise the ancient wisdom in the west.'

'Okay Stellios, you've made your point. I can't assimilate all this information. I'll drive you home and I'll call you later.'

Within minutes I was outside his bed-sit. We had made our peace, but I needed time now to assess the last hours' revelations. I blanked my mind as I glided through the town. An auburn disk flashed through the indigo blue and orange veil. Apollo's chariot charged into the deep, black, sea, towards infinity. There was a trickle of traffic and a parade of pedestrians, plodding patiently along the precincts. Sea gulls dive-bombed left over fish and chip packets. They screeched and cackled in battles over the meagre carrion of the consumer jungle. All was well in this balanced eco-system. We knew our place in the master scheme of things. But what of the next frontier? That was an enigma I was wrestling with. Masters, initiate teachers, spirit guides, reincarnation, life after death, the list was endless.

I parked the car and trundled upstairs, dodging our cafe 'aristo-cat' dozing on the top step. In the safe and welcoming aura of home I sat nursing a cup of tea and brooding over the aftermath of my conversation with Stellios.

Claregate was in the shit, if I was to believe him. They were desperate, but hang on a minute, I was going to be a lamb for the slaughter. I felt the *voice of the silence* deep inside me, echoing haunting words on my soul strings.

'You are one of the chosen ones. Only everything. The calling, the calling.' I had to help. I could walk away from the whole sordid cesspool, leaving them wallowing in their own shit. Yes, you can, it's easy, just turn your back on the plotting, blackmailing bastards. They deserve it. But, I had received *the calling*; I could not escape it, even if I wanted to.

I fled him down the nights and down the days,
I fled him down the arches of the years;
I fled him down the labyrinthine ways,
Of my own mind and in the mist of fears
I hid from him and under running laughter
Up vistaed hopes I sped; And shot precipitated
Adown Titanic glooms of chasmed fears,
From those strong Feet that followed, followed after.
But with unhurrying chase,
And unperturbed pace
Deliberate speed, majestic instancy,
They beat - and a voice beat
More instant than the feet -
'All things betray thee, who betrayest me!'

The poem *'Hound Of Heaven'* by Francis Thompson resonated on my soul strings. *He* was with me; I could not betray *him*.

That was it; I had made my mind up. It all seemed absurd, but I had to help. I was a being primed for some awesome purpose. I felt it in the pit of my stomach, but I could not comprehend it.

'Stellios, hello, it's Christo; I've decided to give them a donation. I'll arrange a transfer of £1,000 to Claregate's bank account. I want you to give them the news and get their details. They will worship you. Take all the credit; lap it up Stellios. You will have their confidence; you could even be initiated into the inner circle. In return, I want you to feed me with any plans they have. Stellios don't double cross me, I'm warning you. You'll be on the next plane out of here if you do.'

'Christo, Christo, I'm so excited, thank you for getting me off the hook. Believe me, I won't disappoint you.'

'Stellios, don't tell Elena about our deal. It will be our little secret, okay? Call me in the morning, bright and early, so I can set it up.'

'Okay Christo, Before I forget; I've got a package for you from John. I think it's the first four lessons and tapes of the bachelor of metaphysics correspondence course.'

'Great, I'll look forward to starting it. Give it to Elena at uni. Right, must dash, I'm on an early tomorrow, bye.'

Strewn on the floor, with our luggage, lay the bag of books John gave me at Claregate. I just had enough energy to yank it towards me. Two books slid out onto the floor face down. I turned up the first titled Beyond the Intellect; the second was The Spiritual Diary. What a coincidence; by some weird set of circumstances, *The Spiritual Diary* was exactly how I had envisioned it. Was this another signpost of spiritual development? It outlined the system used to create a dialogue with your inner self. It formed the basis of *The Claregate Method*. It was a daily record of your efforts to make contact and understand feedback from your personal unconscious. A dedication on the preface should be an inspired poem, sonnet or saying, setting the tone of the content. Dreams, intuitions and meditations were to be recorded daily, giving timings and detailed content. Study material, inspirational writings and your innermost aspirations needed to be included. Your whole spiritual quest would be documented; the highs, lows, lull of activity, alienation and isolation. It served as a gauge stick on the path to self-realisation and progressive soul contact.

Brilliant, this is what I needed, with all the paranormal activity I had experienced. My eyelids, heavily laden with tiredness, flickered like a strobe light, flashing disordered time-frame images onto the screen of my fevered mind. It was time to hit the sack before I collapsed in a bundle on the floor. I had enough of the stuff to last me a lifetime. I should let Elena deal with this lot in the morning.

CHAPTER 10

I was up at the crack of dawn, milling over the developments of the previous day. I skipped downstairs to put a cuppa on. Last night's sprawling mess was stagnating in the lounge. I sat there, tea in one hand, as that familiar, comforting tingle began zinging in my head.

'Your country needs you!' bellowed from the depths of my being. The famous image of field marshal Kitchener pointing his finger out from the provocative war poster singled me out as it merged with my face.

'Your country needs you! Your country needs you! Your country needs you! Your time is now!'

It echoed in my ears, flashing terrifying images of war, marches and trenches. Desperate wailing, blood, gore and the rancid stench of death flooded my being. I witnessed limbs being blasted off wretched torsos, grenades, mortar fire and victorious battle-torn flags triumphantly fluttering in a hellish wild fire. Visions of bedraggled soldiers with arms outstretched, bodies racked and ruined, souls lost and dignity pounded into the dirt, blasted into my vision. A screeching high-pitch sound outside battled against the screams of hundreds of dying voices, dulling my senses and shooting me back to reality. It was the courtyard cats, locked together in carnal ecstasy. I felt as if my head was haemorrhaging. I could not cope any more. Kitchener, war, your country needs you! Was this the call to service? Or, was I really loosing my sanity?

I flicked open The Spiritual Diary at a random page to an awesome revelation. It stated that when soul contact was being established, memories and fragments of its experiences are flashed back into ones consciousness. It was like an incoherent, kaleidoscopic set of images, charged with deep emotion, thrown to the surface, to illuminate the way forward.

What did it all mean? The call to arms? Was it related to Claregate and the work there? I desperately needed to share this information with someone; otherwise I feared I would go crazy. But who? Stellios? Now that we had cleared the slate, maybe I could confide in him.

The sun's solar disk flashed its glorious orb into the square, scattering the frenzied felines through the alleyways. Its searing rays bled through the cracks of the blinds, drenching me with laser beams of brilliant golden light. As I felt that warm glow speckle my face, I closed my eyes and melted into a deep slumber, only to be awakened by my alarm an hour later. Within minutes I was up, washed, shaved and dressed. I planted a big kiss on Elena's forehead before leaping down to open the restaurant. With the swish and steam of the coffee machine I conjured up refreshments for my breakfast staff.

'Dring dring, dring dring!' The early morning foghorn blasted the fragile ethers with its horrendous belch.

'This is DB here.'

'Who?'

'Dr.Baker, Can I speak to Chris Kasparis?' What did he want, so early in the morning? I was still in the doldrums of my dream world and he's blaring like a foghorn.

'Yes, speaking. How can I help?'

'I'd like to thank you for your kind donation. You really saved us. They were going to confiscate our typesetting machine.'

'Well, Stellios persuaded me. He's a good lad. He deserves a pat on the back,' I said, bolstering up praises for my little accomplice.

'Yes, he called me this morning to tell me the good news. I gave him our bank details. He could hardly contain himself. Chris, in return for your kindness, I'm going to allow you to complete the Claregate correspondence course free of charge. If you are interested, you could even do it here. I'll provide you with accommodation and food. All you need to do in return is to help me run this place. We are preparing so many interesting projects. Videos on spiritual topics, a mini series on the life and times of *Paracelsus*, homoeopathy, publishing, teaching, exhibitions and worldwide lecture tours.'

Oh my God, *Paracelsus* again. The name kept on surfacing. This is more than a coincidence; it's got to be.

'Dr. Baker, thanks for the offer, but I'll have to consult with Elena and of course, I have commitments here.'

'Kill out ambition, but live like ones ambitions. Only everything,' he answered in an ambiguous, philosophical tone, then he abruptly severed our conversation. He left my mind grappling with these concepts. *Only everything* came ringing back like a bell tolling, calling me to arms.

The restaurant began to fill with early morning tourists and shopkeepers. The machine bellowed and belched out an endless conveyer belt of coffees. The aroma of fresh toast battled against the roasted coffee scent and sizzled among the ethers. The chitter-chatter of mindless monotony merged with the clatter of crockery. The breakfast siege was in its woes and throws as the postman, carrying my junk mail, gently converted our randy cat through the door and into touch.

The day passed by smoothly. I sat upstairs, supping a coffee and reminiscing over Dr.Baker's offer. Why did he call himself DB? I had heard the students call him that all the time? What did it stand for? Mmm, *the dog's bollocks*, I thought, chuckling out loud. Heads turned in irritation, frowning at my sudden outburst. I had disturbed the mid-afternoon, romantic twosomes, whispering and melting into each other's auras. I heard Elena's familiar shrill as she thundered up stairs, to the frayed tempers of the lovebirds.

'Christo, did Dr. Baker call you this morning? What did he want, so early? I've got the course material John gave to Stellios for us. It's really interesting. Tapes, books and diagrams, all brimming with wisdom; Christo, it's very exciting, isn't it?' She never came up for breath; she babbled on and on. I let her diffuse her exuberance while I pondered on DB's suggestions.

'Elena, do you remember the students calling Dr. Baker, DB?'

'Yes, why are you interrupting me?'

'I know what it stands for, *the dogs bollocks!*' I shouted aloud. Elena sat there puzzled. She had no idea what it meant. Slang wasn't her thing.

'Christo, that's really rude, you've shown me up again.' The poor thing was beetroot with shame and embarrassment. I was almost crying with laughter.

'Elena, it means, the best, he's the best. I might be wrong, I'll have to ask Stellios if that's what it means, *the dogs bollocks.*' I could not control myself by now. I was rolling off my chair, tears gushing and my sides splitting. Elena had deserted me; the lovebirds had flown the nest as I sat there, alone like a deranged madman with my schizophrenic laughter echoing in the emptiness. It was hilarious and just what I needed to blast away the intensity of recent events. The phone echoed in the background; a call from the pit sounded my name. It was Stellios bouncing with enthusiasm.

'Christo, it's done. I did exactly as you said. I got the praise and was promised a big pat on the back. They bought the whole thing. It was a brilliantly conceived plan and they don't suspect anything. I've got their bank details.'

'Great, I had DB on the phone early this morning, thanking me. Before I forget; Stellios, does DB stand for *the dogs bollocks?*'

'What! *The dogs bollocks?*' he exclaimed, laughing his head off. 'Could you imagine if I called him that, he'd kill me. DB is short for Douglas Baker. All initiates abbreviate their names. It's a title to honour their hard won labours.'

'Stellios, he's invited us to complete the bachelor of metaphysics at Claregate, free of charge. I'm really excited, I haven't told Elena yet. What do you think?'

'Brilliant, I am going to do it there as well, after I complete my OND. It's a hard life; don't expect results overnight. You'll have to change all your values. But, can you imagine the spiritual rewards? Direct communion with your Daemon, previous life recall, karmic gifts, animated meaningful dreamlike and ultimately, initiation into the mysteries of all life.'

'I haven't decided yet. I've got to convince Elena, and what am I going to tell my uncles. They'll disown me if I let them down. I know what they're like. They won't understand. They'll say I'm crazy, throwing away a chance to be wealthy. I've also got to be wary of the scheming clutches of the inner circle, but with your insight, we will both be okay, won't we?'

'No problem Christo, We'll stick together through thick and thin, whatever happens.'

'Listen Stellios, I'm going to talk to Elena tonight. I need her support on this matter. I'll speak to you tomorrow. Don't say a word to her about our plans, okay.'

'I promise I won't spill the beans Christo.'

'I had a strange experience this morning. I need to share it with you next time we meet.'

'Okay Christo, I'm off to the deli to get some hummus and pitas. Speak to you tomorrow.'

I wrapped up things at the restaurant, handed over my instructions to the night manager and retired for the evening. Elena was still in a mood when I walked in.

'Come on, can't you take a joke, Elena. It was a laugh, wasn't it?'

'Maybe for you it was, but it was so embarrassing. You always show me up. You know how naïve I am.'

'Oh Elena, come on, lighten up; you just haven't got a sense of humour. I spoke to Stellios earlier. I had him in stitches too when I told him what I thought DB meant.' She lightened up whilst putting the kettle on.

'Cup of tea Christo?'

'Yes okay, I'm parched after all that laughing.'

'You haven't told me why Dr. Baker called this morning. Was it important?'

'He made me a proposition.'

'What type, a business proposition?'

'He wants us to complete the bachelor of metaphysics at Claregate, full time. We'll have our own accommodation; all we have to do is work there. We'll have everything paid for. Just think Elena; in two years we'll have a bachelor of metaphysics. It will enable us to teach, lecture and instruct pupils on all aspects of the esoteric sciences. We would be well respected. Can you imagine the prestige and the honours we'd get?' I knew if I painted the intellectual picture and the prestige of a bachelor of metaphysics, she would be putty in my hands.

'Christo, you've got to be kidding. What will our parents say? What about Big George and uncle Vic; the plans for us; our own restaurant and house? They'll be devastated, they'll never understand.'

'Listen Elena, you'll finish your course in a couple of months. The restaurant is still dead at the moment. You know business; it's seasonal. We could take two years out, get our bachelors and go back to what ever we want to after. We have neither children nor a mortgage; we're relatively free. What do you think?'

'I'll have to think about it Christo. It's putting our lives on hold and we don't have any guarantees, do we? On the other hand, I'd love the title, bachelor of metaphysics. I love the study and wisdom bit, but I like my home comforts. I'll sleep on it and tell you tomorrow.'

She retired upstairs to bed. I knew I had made an impact on her. But, she loved her settled life though. The prestige of a maisonette in The Lanes, a restaurant, the luxury Jag in the drive and holidays in Cyprus. It was a major sacrifice to make. I was ready to make all the necessary adjustments. I was convinced; I was inspired. I knew what *only everything* meant now. I was ready to give up everything for the chance of initiation into the mysteries. I made myself supper and sat down to rethink the day's activities. That vision about Kitchener, his patriotic slogan, and all the horrific scenes flooded my consciousness. I stretched for the phone.

'Stellios, the morning can't wait. I need to tell you about the vision I had. It's happening all the time and driving me crazy.'

'Okay, calm down; tell me exactly what happened.'

I babbled on for what seemed an eternity. I needed his ears to bash and his comforting answers.

'Christo, sounds like you've had soul contact. You've experienced so much in so little time. Kitchener could be a previous life; you'll need to research it. No wonder you're loosing your grip on reality. I'm really surprised that you have communication with your Daemon. That takes a lot of effort.'

'What, Kitchener, a previous life? Stellios, surely it's not possible?'

'Chris, anything is possible. You may not be Kitchener now, but if you can confirm he was one of your lives, it will give you the second piece in a vast jigsaw puzzle. Each life is a fragment. A kind of holographic image of all our past, present and future lives. Our soul is the key to this patchwork puzzle. Each incarnation is seeking perfection.'

'Stellios, all these experiences are happening out of the blue, believe me. What do you know about *Paracelsus*? I've had strange premonitions and deep intuitions about him, Dr. Baker and Robert Browning.'

'Christo, where are you getting all this information from?'

'I don't know, it just pours into me from some other dimension. It's mostly when I hear *his* signal, but it's happening more frequently.'

'Browning and *Paracelsus* were DB's previous lives. It took me years to figure out and you get it through in a mysterious flash. You're tuned into a superior force, Christo, I can't understand it.'

'Stellios, I had a vivid dream, with you as a fellow Christ Light worker. You were close to me, you had similar powers, but you lacked confidence and courage to use them effectively.' I proceeded to unfold *the scroll* dream to him. He was overwhelmed by my experiences, but he encouraged me to keep an open mind. I clicked the phone down, slid upstairs to our bedroom and into Elena's warm bosom. I had the first deep, uninterrupted sleep for as long as I could remember. I suppose releasing my soul strings helped relieve me and unburden my load.

Elena woke up as bright as a bell, nudged me awake and said, 'Let's do it; it's a chance of a lifetime; we're young. Shit or bust.'

That was my saying, but I suppose she was entitled to use it, after all, she was a Scorpio ascendant. We were not going to be conventional. We were born to be bohemian, wild and rebellious, even if it didn't show on the surface.

I told my uncles of our plans. Needless to say the shit hit the fan. We were labelled social outcasts, cult members and lunatics. They would have nothing to do with us. Our parents were in shock.

They could not understand where they went wrong. We were on our own; the spiritual world beckoned us. *The Jewelled Way* lay ahead, full of prospects, pitfalls and rewards. Sacrifices would be a prerequisite on the path to spiritual enlightenment.

DB was supportive of our decision and welcomed our future presence in the English Ashram.

CHAPTER 11

Brighton's pleasure dome and the decadent lifestyle of the rich and famous faded into the depths of my mind as we made last minute preparations. We had been cold-shouldered by my uncles and the materialistic doors slammed tight behind us. What lay ahead was an adventure into unknown territory. Our idealistic spiritual life beckoned us. Were our expectations of community life, group interaction, spiritual illumination going to be fulfilled?

As we packed our last belongings into the van, a rainbow blasted its multi-coloured spectrum out from fierce, ebony clouds. This awesome sight shone bright in my heart. Aurora, the rainbow goddess blazed the heavens with hope, promise and opportunity. Menacing monstrous clouds conspired together casting devouring chimeras, which fed on doubts in the pit my soul. Winds whipped up a frenzied attack as thunder crashed and lightning zigzagged through the starry, indigo sky, like the slash of an open razor. Luna sheepishly peeped out from her shrouded shawl before retreating, too frail to battle with the elements. The heavens opened up gashing our van with shards of penetrating jets as we disappeared into infinity.

There was an eerie silence all the way there. We hardly glanced at each other or spoke. It was really weird, but understandable. I sensed Elena's aura desperately clinging onto her materialistic lifestyle. We were cruising in no man's land. She knew we were heading into a minefield, littered with uncertainty and insecurity. One wrong step would blast us to smithereens: lives scattered, hearts shattered and promises dashed. Our only aspiration was to seek our true nature in the mud of material existence. This was the ultimate gamble.

We pulled into the driveway to be met by Linda and Claire. They had not expected us to arrive in a van. I could see they had put on their official faces as they approached the vehicle.

'Hi Linda, hi Claire, it's us', I shouted as I clambered out of the cabin.

'Chris, Elena, you startled us. We didn't know what to expect. We get all sorts of whackos come in unannounced,' Claire said in a relieved manner. 'We have to be on guard all the time. Come in and I'll put the kettle on. We'll be setting up for lunch soon. I'll get the boys to take your stuff up to your room.'

'Steve, Pete, Jeremy, Chris has arrived. Please unload their van and put their belongings in their room,' she said and ushered us into the dining room.

I heard the thud, thump and bang of the doors as our life's belongings were shunted into the hall.

'I'll let DB, John and Barry know you've arrived,' Linda said in a cool, robotic fashion. 'They're busy down at *Little Elephant* planning the next filming schedule. You do know we're producing a film series don't you?' she said in a condescending manner before disappearing out of the door before I could reply.

I sensed a change in the air. It was not like this before. Something was drastically wrong. Elena sensed my uneasiness and nervously kicked me under the table.

'There we are, tea and biscuits. You'll have to excuse me for a moment; I've got a load of last minute deadlines to meet. DB needs the final draft of the next scripts. If you need anything just shout,' she said and disappeared into the office.

'Your room is the one on the landing, the medieval-looking door with the bolt, lock and chains on the outside,' she shouted from the void.

'Well Elena, welcome to Claregate; It's going to be just fine I'm sure. They must be pressed and inundated with the demands of work. That's why we're here, to help relieve the pressure,' I said, trying to reassure her. I sensed her aura cringe; I could not blame her, our welcome was really so cold and uninviting.

'Let's go and see our room. I bet it's going to be great. Claire said it's on the landing. God, a medieval door, we've got to see it, come on,' I said and pulled her up from her seat. My heart sunk to the pit of my stomach. All our personal belongings were strewn all over the hallway. They had dumped the lot and fled back to their cosy little rooms.

'Not to worry Elena, they probably didn't hear the girls properly. At least they unloaded the van for us.'

'Come on, it's exciting. Let's locate our room.' I grabbed Elena by the hand and we rushed upstairs. I pushed on the old door. It creaked and rattled as it slowly shifted from its rusty, old hinges. A waft of damp, musty air rushed out, swamping us as we entered what smelled like a dungeon. There it was; our room was a film set. The walls were drenched in dirty Hessian sacks, mock candleholders and blackened beams. The windows, latticed in multi-coloured, diamond shapes, were flanked by dingy, old, green velvet drapes. Medieval props protruded all around littering the space. Lights, cables, coloured gels and tripods decked the floor. An old, double mattress took pride of place in the centre of this medieval and techno jungle. We were expected to live in a set! It was a far cry from our luxurious Brighton maisonette.

Elena was in complete shock. She just stood there, head hanging as if she'd been sentenced for a long spell in prison. It seemed that way to me too. Solitary confinement, bread and water, chains, lock and bolts on the door. What an anti-climax. No wonder they all scampered, leaving us to fend for ourselves. They must have been so embarrassed. There must be a logical explanation for this. I can't believe it was all planned for us. Maybe it was a kind of test of detachment, I thought.

'Elena, don't worry. There must be some mistake. We'll sort it out after, promise,' I said and took her in my arms. She could not move nor speak. She just stood there, rigid and cold in my hands.

The idealised glamour of community life shattered, leaving us fragmented and broken. Our dreams of spiritual harmony, unity and group interaction were dashed in this dungeon of depression. The door creaked open, slow and deliberately.

'Hello, is anyone in here? Chris, Elena?' It was Claire's bulky frame at the doorway.

'Those kids, they never do anything they are told. Listen, I'm sorry about the room, we just shot a scene of *Paracelsus* here. We need the set to remain as it is for the time being. There may be a re-shoot or two in the near future. It's only a temporary measure, then it will revert back to a bedroom again, your bedroom. Elena, come and I'll show you our bathroom and toilet. Chris you'll have to share with the boys upstairs.'

They disappeared quite happily together, arm in arm with Elena's aura recharged and bubbly as ever. I set about bringing our stuff upstairs and bumped into Jeremy on the way up to the toilet.

'Suppose you're looking for the loo? First door on the right; Jeremy's the name,' he said. He was a strange looking lad; long blond locks, blue piercing, beady eyes, slight wiry build and dressed like a ragamuffin. To my surprise his pet rat scurried from his inside pocket onto his shoulder, his inquisitive pink nose probing the ethers and his wormy tail waving like a hypnotic cobra. Rattie looked just like his master but with more personality. Jeremy was a man of few words, no emotions and certainly no communication skills. He trotted past me with a smirk plastered over his face and Rattie snagged onto his old, holey jumper.

Elena had come back after some time. She was back to normal, with a shrill in her voice, bounce back in her step and effervescence in her sunny, leonine face.

'Christo, Claire was really sorry about the welcome. I'm happy now; She's absolutely brilliant and full of beans for a big girl. Great, let me sort our things out and you get yourself acclimatised.'

'Okay Elena,' I said, with a heartfelt sigh of relief. 'I bumped into one of the kids, Jeremy. He's weird; an albino rat scurried out from his pocket. He almost scared the shit out of me. Rattie sat there on his shoulder like a ventriloquist puppet waiting to spout off some witty comments. He was Jeremy's alter ego; he looked just like him, but he's more approachable and a lot friendlier though.'

She looked at me in disbelief as I tip toed downstairs and hopped out into the garden. I found a little suntrap and sat there, taking in my impressions of the place. Max, Claregate's fat, tabby cat crept out from the jungle, full of menace. I had taken his favourite sunspot. He just stood there, with his piercing big, brown eyes penetrating my soul. I knew what he wanted and he was not going to budge from his determined stance. I compromised by moving over; after all, it was his stomping ground. A tall, dangly, giraffe-like frame swaying from side-to-side appeared in the distance. It was Steve coming out of hiding, juggling two or three teacups in his hands whilst trying to walk. He had trouble with coordination sometimes, but he was a gentle giant.

'Hi Chris, great to see you man, moved in yet?' He looked, moved and talked like a Rastafarian, without the dreadlocks.

'Steve, I remember you. You're Stellios's mate aren't you? He's also coming up to move in next week. He told me to get you to clear the caravan out, because he's sharing with you.'

'He'll have to clear his own shit out, man. He's moved most of his stuff here already. He's so messy and so uncoordinated,' he said with a heavy dose of sarcasm and a loud laugh. Then he tripped over Max and almost somersaulting head over heels into the bushes. What a bunch of eccentrics. Talk about social outcasts, they're all here. I suppose they had to be colourful, rebellious and bohemian. I was one of them I thought, but I was different. My weirdness was on the inside.

As I made my way back to the main building, I heard a bell tolling, the rumble of stomping feet and the clatter of plates. It was the call to communal lunch. Elena popped her head out over the banister as I entered.

'Chris, it sounds like lunch and it smells so homely,' she said, in expectation of an invitation.

'Chris, Elena, come down, lunch is ready. If you don't come now this ravenous bunch will devour the lot in minutes,' Claire belted out like a foghorn.

There they were, the Claregate mob, gathered around that enormous wooden table; the one I'd had a close encounter with, last time I came here.

Its presence flooded back clear memories of my out-of-body experience, which I really did not understand.

'Come and sit down here you two and I'll introduce you to the boys,' said Claire. She was the Claregate matriarch. She commanded great respect and was the organising force around here. The room slowly trickled to a haunting silence. Faces blanked and expressions sagged, giving way to nervous twitches and fidgets. Feet shuffled, auras retracted and the occasional flicker of a nervous eyelid singled out the first victim for attack. It felt like they were going to be interrogated by this fiendish female.

'Thud! Crash! Bang!'

'Oh my God! Bloody lid! Claire, that bloody handle has come off again,' a voice stammered from the kitchen. Pete, the Claregate cook, appeared nursing his hand and blaspheming like a trooper.

'Jesus, bloody Christ! I've burnt myself again, look.'

'No chance of him getting to the next kingdom with foul language like that,' Claire blasted.

'Chris, Elena, excuse Pete's French. It's not his first language,' she said in a sarcastic tone. 'Pete is our galloping gourmet. He's always burning things: pots, pans, food and hands. He disappears into his own little dream world, forgetting things on the stove all the time. Poor thing, Pete's a brilliant writer, poet and musician, but bless; spoken words just aren't his thing this time around; he's got a terrible stutter.'

'Hi both, pleased to meet you,' he said, shaking and vibrating as if he was having an epileptic fit. He looked like he was plucked out of the dark ages. Ebony, matted hair hung down, concealing the blackest bull's eyes I'd ever seen. He had a pure white, almost anaemic complexion, and a stance like a Neanderthal. He was shabbily dressed in dirty jeans, shirt and a holey, old jumper. In contrast to his outer appearance, a searing light shone from his eyes and his soul energy flowed like manna from heaven.

In fact, as I gazed around the table, they all shone with an inner light that I had never experienced before. But, they all looked like they needed a good bath and a clean set of clothes.

'This is Steve, Jeremy, Gerald and Ron.' They all nodded in silence. There wasn't one of them who could hold a ten-minute conversation. No wonder Claregate was in the shit.

'The rest, mostly the inner circle, lunch down with DB at *Little Elephant*,' Claire said, dismissing them one by one as they scampered and scurried like frightened rats from the table.

'What is *Little Elephant*, Claire? I asked. ' I've heard you mention it so many times.'

'It's where DB lives and works. The print works is down there too. Mark lives and works there. It's where the inner circle meets and plans strategy. I'll drive you down there later; DB wants to see you,' Claire replied. She was fiddling with a wad of scripts she had typeset. 'I've got to take this lot down to him anyway.'

'Claire, remember when I passed out and hit my head on the table?'

'Yes, you said you saw yourself hovering above your body as we tried to revive you.'

'Well, I have been thinking about it. What does it mean? Was I *out of body?*'

'Have you read DB's book on astral projection?'

'No not yet, I've just skimmed through it.'

'When you have, you'll have a better understanding of the whole experience,' she said, flicking through her notes.

'I've got a few minutes spare now. I'll try to explain it to you in a nutshell. We all possess seven levels of consciousness, which can be likened to the seven ray colours and energies of the human aura. Average man functions at physical, emotional and mental levels, with very little awareness of his higher faculties. We possess a physical body that functions in a physical world called planet Earth. That's easy to conceptualise, isn't it?'

'Well I suppose so,' I said, puzzled.

'However, we also function at an emotional or astral level, in the astral world, through an astral body. This world is a replica of the physical, but in subtler form. Just think of it as where we express and deposit our emotions. Do you follow my train of thought?'

'Yes, go on. I'm just not used to metaphysical concepts like these.'

'Our astral body is alive and as energetic as our physical one, but its primary force is emotional. The astral body interpenetrates the physical body. Very similar to sand soaked with water. I won't go into the mental body and the mental world, as it's not relevant to our example. That's easy to follow, isn't it?' she said, scribbling a drawing of her exposition.

'Yes, so far so good; I can go with it,' I said, digesting her spiritual dialogue.

'Under certain stress-related conditions, the astral body haemorrhages and comes out of alignment with the physical body. When this happens we talk of the astral body projecting out of body. Hence the out-of-body experience or OOBE for short, or near death experience. An extra surge of emotion is the trigger of an encounter. It could be positive or negative energy; it does not matter. It has the same effect. What you described is an advanced OOBE. Some people witness this type of phenomena when they are anaesthetised for surgery. Some when they have suffered severe car accidents, and a few who are in the throes of a cardiac arrest. They all profess seeing themselves from a position above their physical bodies. They can hear, sense, smell and see colour a thousand times more clearer. Some say they see themselves heading towards a brilliant light, through a tunnel, then all of a sudden they are zapped back to their physical body.'

'That's exactly what I experienced: being zapped into my physical body. It seemed so weird, but so alive and vibrant.'

'It's part of our development here, to achieve controlled astral awareness at will. There are safe techniques to accomplish this phenomenon; it's all in the books.'

Dring dring. Dring dring.

'Where are my scripts? I want my scripts now, Claire!' DB's voice thundered and Claire's ears took a bashing.

'On my way now DB; I'm bringing Chris and Elena down with me. You still want to see them don't you?'

I sensed there was an atmosphere developing. They were under pressure again. We cleaned up and met Claire in the lobby, ready to be shunted off to our first private audience with DB.

CHAPTER 12

The drive to *Little Elephant* took us through the prettiest English countryside I'd ever seen. Spring was awash with all its rebirthing colours and glory. Daffodils beamed with brilliant flashes of yellow and shone like Belisha beacons. Primroses daubed in orange-pink and sweet smelling violets soothed my soul. The searing, early-afternoon sun flashed in and out of the foliage, flickering its eyelashes like a disco strobe light. The car meandered down grassy, country roads, damp, lush lanes and onto the winding dirt track leading to *Little Elephant*.

'You know the cottage belongs to Dame Barbara Cartland? Her mansion is just back there on the bend,' said Claire as we freewheeled down towards the forecourt.

'We always switch off the engines for the last few yards in case DB is in meditation. But there is another reason.'

Screech! The car swung suddenly to the right and then to the left. Claire wrestled with the steering wheel and we came to an abrupt halt.

'Bloody cats! That *Little Boy* and *Snags*, they're always chasing a bird or animal. I'm sure one day they'll be the death of me.'

All I could see was a trail of dust in the air, a mangle of paws, a flashing black and white fur ball and a tail thrashing frantically. It looked like a mini whirlwind swirling around. Then it thudded against the front door of the cottage.

We staggered out; the dogs were in a foul mood, barking and jostling for position in the hallway. DB was at his cranked, bedroom window, looking down, supporting a menacing grimace and wondering what all the kafuffle was about. So much for our sleek and silent entry.

'DB, sorry for the racket, It's me, Claire. I've got Chris and Elena with me. That bloody Snags, he always manages to cause chaos, no matter how hard I try not to make a noise.'

Snags was a miracle of the animal kingdom. He had broken his back as a kitten but had managed to survive and flourish. His coordination and balance were completely out of sync, but he had guts and bundles of personality. I suppose he was another waif and stray DB had picked up on the way.

The door catapulted open and the dogs darted towards us in a frenzied attack, only to be calmed by Claire's peaceful aura and familiar scent. John ducked his head out from the door and beckoned us into the cottage.

'Hi both, I'm sorry I was not there to welcome you; we had an impromptu meeting down here,' John said in his Californian cackle and wall-to-wall grin. 'I see you've met *Snags*. What a mess he's always in. He breaks the monotony and seriousness down here with his mad antics,' he said and ushered us into the lounge.

'Have a seat; DB and Barry will be down in a minute. Tea coffee? Lance, put the kettle on.'

I sat there amid an eerie silence and scanned the place. It was as if we had been transported back in time. The lounge was also a film set. Ancient tomes lined wall after wall; heavy, regal red, drapes dashed the diamond, multi-coloured, stained glass; a hefty old table and a leather studded, armchair begged to be occupied in the centre. Beams, medieval lanterns, tapestries and other props littered the space. The musty stench of antiquity lingered in the humid room. What were we doing in a place like this, I thought. I felt so alien and completely out of sync. Indeed, as I peered outside, a whole 14th century street scene jutted out, cleverly concealed between the cottage and a greenhouse. The whole setting was so bizarre and surreal.

I glanced at Elena's vacant visage as the door thumped open.

'You're not the only ones who live in a set. This used to be my lounge and look outside. My lovely gardens are a 14th century street scene. Change and detachment are good for the soul.'

It was DB and his trusted advisors, Barry and John. He sat on his throne flanked by his lapdog lieutenants.

'You've already met John. This is Barry; he's my right-hand man. He runs the whole organisation with the help of my inner circle,' he said, full of praise and promise.

This was the bastard who'd had Stellios by the balls. I remembered his foul mouth and manipulating and scheming presence from the lecture.

'Hi Chris, hi Elena, pleased to meet you. I'm glad to have you on board. Don't believe all that pumping up from DB. I couldn't perform my duties if I did not have everyone's support,' he said, offering his handshake. As I leant forward to acknowledge his welcome, that familiar laser sounded in my head and in a flash I was shot into another dimension.

I was in a dock, surrounded by guards. All around, rows and rows of men, floor to ceiling, were dressed in 16th century robes. The majority seethed with resentment and were after my blood. I was aware of wearing a black skullcap, a white flouncy collar draped over a black tunic and a hooded cape. I felt wretched. DB and Barry were two of the central figures orchestrating my downfall. Familiar faces loomed out of the shadows of my fevered mind. The last sweet embraces of loved ones, interspersed with images of terror, prison bars, chaplains, and damp dingy dungeons. Kingly nobles in anguish and thud!!! A horrid sound blackened my perception as the echo of a bloodthirsty mob shouted, 'Black Tom is no more! Black Tom is no more!'

There I was in a bundle, sprawled on the carpet at Elena's feet. I had fainted and they were trying to revive me.

'Christo, Christo are you okay?' Elena's comforting voice echoed in the ethers as I fought my way back from that sickening scene.

'Elena, it's okay; I'm fine. Really, I'm fine. There's very little fresh air in here and it's so hot. I need to get outside for a bit,' I said and climbed back onto my seat.

'Lance, a glass of water and a cold, wet dishcloth quick. Raise his legs in the air, it helps ease the blood circulation back,' said DB in a calm and collected manner. He knew his first aid, of course he did, after all he was a doctor.

'It's my fault; I can't stand drafts and cold weather. I never open windows in my rooms. I was brought up in South Africa, where the weather was glorious all the year round.'

After a stroll outside and a breath of fresh air we resumed our meeting. DB laid down the rules and regulations of community life. Barry and John walked us around the sprawling complex and introduced us to the lads down here. As we sat outside, supping tea and eating cucumber sandwiches, DB summoned me to the cottage. I left Elena in the company of Barry and John. She loved the attention and hardly noticed me leaving.

'Come in Chris, I want to talk to you in private before you head back,' he said, closing the doors behind him.

'Lance, I don't want to be disturbed. Don't let anyone in until I shout.'

He pulled out my file and sat there in silence perusing his notes and my astrological chart. I sat patiently; my mind was in overdrive. It was my first private session with DB. I knew we had something deep in common. That experience in his lounge blew me away. The teachings, *Paracelsus*, Browning and my altered states since meeting Stellios, were somehow all connected.

'Chris, what I'm about to tell you is personal. You must keep it in mind throughout your presence here. Understand it, analyse it, explore it's potential and embrace it, if it's right for you. The choice is yours,' he said in his metaphysical capacity.

'It is no co-incidence that you are here. You have been led here to continue your development. You have responded to the calling. We have met before, as different personalities; worked together, life after life, through the ages. We have past life karma to resolve and we are responsible for the externalisation of the ancient wisdom teachings here in the West.

Elena's role in your life was to lead you to the gateway. Your karma with her is slowly terminating; you will have to deal with it soon. It's part of your spiritual tests and trials.' He paused for a minute, enabling me to digest his views.

What was he insinuating about Elena? Did he really know my deepest fears and visions? All this crap about his karmic link with me. It was absurd, a ploy to drop my defences, a canny plan to give me a sense of belonging. After all, I had closed all the materialistic doors behind me. My family ties were loosening, my religious values were in tatters and my personal life was under pressure. On the other hand, what if it had an element of truth about it? How did he know about the calling? Did Linda or Claire confide in him? They could have. They may all be conspiring against me. He did give me the choice in the end though. It was all in my hands. I had freewill and I could exercise it at any time I wished. All these thoughts collided in my schizoid head as he shuffled through my life. Papers scattered, my chart flicked in the air and the file ended up dashed with a glass of water, he'd knocked over.

'Lance, where are my notes of Chris's ray analysis? I told you to prepare his file. Why do I have to do everything myself. Bloody kids. Lance, bring a cloth, quick.' He exploded into a thundering rage, bashing his fists on the table.

Poor Lance was his scapegoat. He was a gentle soul; he was so forgetful though and lived in his own fantasy world most of the time.

'Sorry DB, I was sure I prepared the file for you. It must have slipped my attention,' Lance said, stooping in a servile manner to mop up the mess.

'I've surrounded myself with a shower of idiots. Why! Why is it so?' he said, looking skywards. 'Bring me the notes. Oh, we'll need some tea too while you're there,' he said and waved Lance away.

God, he was so volatile and bombastic. In a split second he could erupt like a volcano, blasting the status quo to smithereens.

'Oh yes Chris, as a first ray personality, your path this life is littered with harsh challenges. It's a life of detachment, where all your materialistic values will be torn away from you. This of course depends on your willingness to change. The more you hold on, the harder it will be to release yourself from them.'

Knock knock. 'DB, I've found your notes and here's the tea,' Lance said. He placed a tray on the table and humbly withdrew, backwards, out of the room.

What was he trying to say? Harsh lessons and attachments being torn away from me? It was all in riddles. Was it his way of preparing me for my destiny? I had a lot of soul searching to do.

'Sugar and milk, Chris?'

'No, just milk,' I replied, as he piled four spoons of sugar in his cup. 'Do you know one of my strongest attachments was sugar,' he said, stirring in some milk. Now that I've beaten it, I can have as much as I want.'

What a contradiction, I thought. How can this be? I must be misunderstanding something really important.

'You'll understand it when the time is right,' he said, reading my thoughts.

'My advice to you is to prepare a spiritual diary. Read my book on it, if you have not done so already. Your diary will be your only saviour. Note your innermost thoughts, feelings, dreams, meditations, aspirations and failings. Eventually, *He* will respond, giving you hope, assurance and guidance, in your hour of need. Each one of us has to follow our own individual path. We have to harmonise our karma and fulfil our spiritual potential. However, we can progress as a group and reap spiritual rewards together. This is the Aquarian way, the New Age way. It's no good hiding away in retreat, alone, or in some monastery any more, seeking solitary withdrawal. That was the old Piscean way. We must develop group consciousness and harmony, in order to embrace the incoming energies of the New Age. I will be here for you, only if there is an answer you cannot find in the teachings. It's all there, in my books, Blavatsky's, Bailey's, Jung's, The Bible, The Koran, The Bhagavad Gita, and The Cabala. The wisdom of the ages is all around us. In nature, poetry, literature, art, music, mythology and psychology. There are many keys; don't limit yourself.

The soul of man is immortal; its future is the future of thing whose growth and splendour has no limits.

'You will experience a progressive breakdown of your personality. You will despair about your lack of will, motivation and commitment. Nothing will be the same afterwards. It will be the most challenging process you will ever live through, I can assure you.'

How did he know all these things? What was I doing? Did I really want to change that much? My personality was effective. I had command, courage, will and staying power. I was in control of my life. I was my only master. Now he tells me I'm going to go through some sort of psychological breakdown, where I lose all sense of the real world, where I'm reduced to a shadow of my former self. And for what? To toil and struggle to find my true spiritual self and destiny? It must be too much to lose, with very little practical gain. I must be mad, I thought, as he launched into another exposition.

'Lance will give you Dr. Roberto Assagioli's books, Act of Will and Psychosynthesis. His descriptions of the psycho-spiritual breakdown will help you understand the process that leads to personality integration and spiritual liberation. The tutors and I give out wisdom teachings in select classes, which you will be advised to attend. Oh, on a practical note, I want you to progressively take over Barry's duties. He will be dealing with other more pressing matters. Filming *Paracelsus* is our most important project at the moment, but as you know, the college has other projects which need constant attention.'

Finally it was my turn to speak.

'DB, I'm not sure what I am letting myself in for. Nor am I ready to relinquish my standing and personality qualities. I've fought hard to be the person I am. I've got more balls than all of your boys put together. You tell me I'm going to be reduced to a feeble, nervous wreck. What a load of bollocks! I may be green where spiritual matters are concerned, but I've met my challenges head on. This is another on the way. I don't like loosing; you have thrown down the gauntlet and I will be equal to the task.'

93

'Chris, I admire your forcefulness, courage and honesty. You remind me of myself, when I first stepped on the path of self-realisation. I need you by my side. I know you will succeed, but I cannot intervene, it's your free will; it's cosmic law.

> *Each man is his own absolute lawgiver;*
> *The decreer of his glory and gloom;*
> *The dispenser of his life, his rewards*
> *And his punishments.*

See you later at dinner.' He rose and left me sitting there with my thoughts.

'Lance, get a couple of copies of Assagioli's books and give them to Chris,' he shouted as he stomped upstairs.

The late afternoon rays flashed through the multi-coloured windows, sending a flurry of rainbows into the room. That traumatic vision came flooding back. My inner life was spilling into waking consciousness. That wasn't normal, but I had to go with it. There was a reason. *He* was giving me clues all the time. *He* was there for me.

Elena, Barry and John sat there, with the sun casting their distorted shadows on the cobbled street scene. They rose up the walls, like phantoms conspiring to swamp the quaint medieval cottages and drag them into oblivion. This surreal scene mirrored my mood and reflected my thoughts.

'Here you are Chris,' said Lance. 'Listen, don't worry, you'll make it. If I did then I'm sure you will. We've all got different personality issues you know. If you need to talk, don't hesitate to let me know. That's what the group's for.' He bobbed up and down in his trademark waddle with the books in his arms.

He was a good soul; sympathetic and caring, but too many love rays made him a real push over. Despite his nature he had a BSC in science, so he obviously had a brain under all that mish-mash.

'Thanks Lance, I'll confide in you if I need to,' I said. God, he was a real bag of dolly mixtures. At least he sounded like he enjoyed being here.

'Ready to go back Chris?' It was Claire, keys jingling in her fingers and juggling a pile of papers in her hands.

'Yes, I'm just coming.'

'Elena, let's go. It's my turn to cook tonight; you can help me. It's Pete's night off.' As she shouted, her papers went skywards. Her hands tried desperately to juggle them back but she tripped on Snags, who had found a great suntrap on the front step.

'Bloody Snags, get out of my hair; shoo, shoo!' she snapped and sent him flying.

We left Little Elephant in the late afternoon mist, as the sun sank down into the western horizon. All my thoughts faded as the solar god slipped into infinity. I needed time to contemplate on the afternoon's developments. I knew Elena would probe me as soon as we got back to Claregate. I could see it in her eyes.

CHAPTER 13

'Well, what did DB tell you? And what happened in his lounge? I suppose you just fainted for no reason at all again, like before!' she said in a sarcastic tone. 'The heat, no air, the musty stench of antiquity, DB's presence, we've heard it all; come on spill the beans.'

Elena's mortar mouth launched attack after attack on my vulnerable position. I was shell shocked, exhausted and disorientated. DB had blasted me earlier; my aura was shot to pieces, my personality was beginning to fragment and my whole life was falling apart.

'Elena, listen can we talk about this later, I really need a rest now. Anyway, what did John and Barry have to say?' I said, deflecting her volley of questions. 'Haven't you got to help Claire with tonight's dinner? She pierced my armour with a penetrating glance, threw a wobble of fits and stormed out, slamming the old medieval door almost off its hinges.

Great, that's all I need now, I thought, another emotional minefield to tread through. I suppose she had a right to know, but what shall I tell her? Oh, Elena thanks for leading me here, that's why we met. We've had a previous life together and now, we have fulfilled our karma, and it's your time to go. Nice meeting you, bye-bye, have a good life.

I heard Claire and Elena exchange laughter amidst the clatter of pots and pans. The homely aroma of sweating onions, garlic and olive oil seeped through the ethers, sending me into a reverie.

There I was, in my mama's kitchen, back home in Glasgow. She was in her black mourning attire, with her apron on, standing at our old stove. Pots popped and pans puffed; the kettle whistled and oil sizzled as the master conductor orchestrated the culinary symphony. The waft of traditional Cyprus food tantalised my taste buds while I sat doing my history homework. I had a test coming up on the English civil war.

My consciousness slipped back and forth between the past and the present. I heard Claregate's front doors thud open to the shuffle of heavy feet and the thundering shouts and jeers of what sounded like a hostile mob. Elena's voice echoed like a sweet melody in the background, drawing me back to reality.

The jeering march of the mob, echoed in the background, sweeping me back to the kitchen. There I saw my mama rustling around her kitchen drawer for the meat cleaver.

Thud! Crack! Chop! Chop! Mama started axing through a rack of pork loin. The crunch of the axe splintering through bone and blood splattering over her pristine white apron catapulted me into a sickening scene.

I was on a high platform, in a square, surrounded by battlements and castle walls. The horrendous sight of a giant, black-hooded, axe man swamped my perception. There he was, standing in front of a massive, wooden block, seasoned with the stench of stagnant blood. Flanked on either side of me were my trusted brother and a chaplain, who had given me my last rights. I scanned the populace; it was a seething sea of barbarous, bloodthirsty faces. Hellish shouts, blasphemous chants and obscenities blasted from their murderous mouths.

'Off with his head! Off with his head! Off with his head!' the mob shouted as they relished the sight of my execution.

I was drenched in a black, heavy tunic. The musty stench of my stale sweat and urine saturated the still air. The rustle of ankle and arm shackles around my bruised, aching limbs sounded like a band of percussion instruments. My weary, broken frame stooped low as I approached my executor.

'Do you have anything more to say, before you go to hell?' blasted the court magistrate.

The whole seething mob slowly melted into a deadening silence. Babies whimpered, children cackled, dogs howled and old men spat.

'Do not put your trust in princes or the sons of men, for you will surely suffer.'

I shouted as the swaying human swarm jostled and pushed for the best view. I professed my innocence and humbly bowed in appreciation of my captive audience as the final curtain beckoned.

A deadly silence loomed over the scene. The skies blackened and a gang of ravenous, carrion crows descended like dark, deadly shadows on the horizon.

My head lay on the block; the axe man's nervous, hesitant actions delayed my final moments. Then the magistrate gave the final command for my beheading.

'I hereby sentence to death, Thomas Wentworth, for treason against The Crown. May God grant you mercy and save your soul from eternal damnation.'

A clean, single, swinging blow crunched against the bone and nerves in my neck. An excruciating pain riveted though my wretched frame and as I saw my bloodied head drop into the basket.

In seconds, the mob was in uproar, jeering, chanting and celebrating.

I was catapulted back to reality by the pain and the escalating noise in the Claregate hallway. It was the boys larking around, shouting and singing. They had had a few drinks too many in the local pub.

'Ding ding ding,' rang the bell for dinner. The doors crashed open to the howl and excitement of the dogs.

'I'm here. Does anyone want me?' blasted out in the hallway. It was DB's familiar call for attention.

I was still mesmerised by the vision. My physical body spasmed and ached all over. I was in shock; my heart thumped in rage against my rib cage, my breathing bellowed and I was sweating profusely.

How can I face that lot downstairs now? Elena was like a wildcat: the boys were high as kites and I was dining with a bunch of conspirators.

Thomas Wentworth. Thomas Wentworth, who the hell was he? Why was he beheaded? What did I have to do with it? That experience back at *Little Elephant* must have triggered it. I was completely disorientated; I never for once realised the power of smell and how it releases deep memories of the past. That's why incense is used in meditation, I suppose. It stimulates recall and enhances altered states.

Thump! Thump! 'Are you coming down for dinner? You know the bell has rang. I don't want to sit at the table on my own.' Elena blasted. She was still fuming; I thought she had got over it by now; I'd heard her laughing and joking with Claire, but she was acting all the time, after all she was a Leo.

In minutes I was fresh and dressed. Elena had waited on the landing for me. She pinched my arm and gave me a horrid stare as we descended the stairway, arm in arm.

The room suddenly quietened as we were greeted by the gathering of the whole group. The inner circle flanked either side of DB, in order of rank. The outer circle, that merry bunch, sat scattered around the rest of the table. Two solitary seats beckoned my vision. We were seated in between Linda and Claire.

'You know most of the group, don't you?' DB said, scanning the table. 'Oh no, you haven't met Dick and Mike. They run the print works down at LE. Ask Dick to give you both a plain A4 pad to use as your spiritual diary. All the kids use them and we've got loads to spare.' He pause before adding, 'I hear Stellios will be joining us soon. Barry when do we expect him?'

'In a couple of days DB. He'll be shacking up with Steve in the caravan,' said Barry acknowledging Steve's Cheshire cat grin.

The faces of the entire outer circle flushed and exchanged glances. I reckon one more in the ranks was always good news. It was them against the inner circle. With Elena and I in the outer circle, they were heavily outnumbered. But there was no doubt where the balance of power was.

'I have something to share with you, so give me your undivided attention,' DB shouted and pointed to the rabble. 'Chris and Elena will be taking on the responsibility of running and organising you lot.'

I looked at Elena in amazement; he didn't tell me anything about that.

'They will have the authority to act on my behalf. I've seen a steady decline in discipline and general standards around here and it's going to stop.'

We were being fed to the lions. I felt it. What was he doing? We were to be 'piggy in the middle', a no-mans land in the community hierarchy.

'He's managed restaurants and Elena's got an OND in catering and hotel management. Barry will be relieved, to take on more of the film production.'

I could see Barry's smug little face light up. He relished the promotion and nodded like an ornamental dog in appreciation. Dick's face sunk to rock bottom and he showed his indignation by abruptly leaving the table in a huff. The room went so cold and silent you could hear a pin drop. Faces glanced at each other.

Pete's nervous stutter spluttered as he shouted, 'does that mean I don't have to do any more cooking from now on?'

'I'll leave that to Chris to decide. Oh, I've instructed him to set rosters, organise cleaning brigades and get you lousy lot into shape. We'll have famous actors and professional people coming through and I don't want you to embarrass me. If you don't like it, you know what you can do.'

You could have cut the atmosphere with a knife. Inter-community civil war hung over us and it was my task to negotiate a smooth path between them. The outer circle slowly petered away; leaving us seated with Linda and Claire holding the ranks.

'Claire and Linda have tried for years to whip them into shape, but the drunken skunks don't seem to respond.'

They looked on in relief; I felt their hearts lift and their souls sing as they glanced gratefully at each other and DB.

'The girl's will tell you all you need to know Chris. Don't take any messing. Use your will and organise this bunch. We have a heavy filming schedule ahead. Set building, costume design, sound and light engineering, not to mention our normal workload. Whip them into shape, we've got a crusade to fight out there.' He gestured towards the window. 'If you need me I'll be upstairs for ten minutes after dinner.'

I was gutted by the enormity of the task. My whole life was fragmenting. I was drifting in and out of dimensions, swamped by dreams, visions and OOBE's. My relationship was on the rocks; I was penniless; my money was all tied up here. Now he wants me to whip this unruly lot into an organised force.

We helped the girls clean and wash up. It was no mean task to wash up after 15 people: breakfast, lunch and dinner, every day, seven days a week.

'Chris don't worry, we'll help you, it's not that bad. If you've ran a busy restaurant, then this will be a piece of cake,' Linda said in a reassuring manner.

'Linda, thanks for the encouragement, but we paid staff to work for us. The boys are a volunteer force. I'll have very little leverage over them.'

'Oh, I'm sure you'll find a way; after all, you are a Libra ascendant. It brings balance, it rules diplomacy, fair play, politics and compromise,' Linda's tone was tinged with sarcasm.

Elena had not uttered a word all through dinner. I suppose she was still mad at me. I had her inquisition to come. What a first day! The welcome, two out-of-body visions and now this! I prayed she'd spare me the grilling later.

'Don't worry Christo, I'm sure we'll be okay,' Elena said reassuringly. It's not as bad as it looks. There's one consolation; we don't have to worry about making a profit.'

She had a point and I sighed with relief. 'Let's get an early night; we've got so much to plan and do. I'm sure you'll feel a lot better in the morning,' she said.

'You're right Elena. It's been a long and eventful day, a good nights sleep in our dungeon will do us the world of good,' I said, bringing a beaming, beautiful smile to her sunny face.

The dining room door thudded open. It was Dick with our diaries. He was the smartest dressed of them all. I could see he had pride in his appearance, was practical and down to earth.

'Hi both, glad to have you on board,' he said, nervously pushing his specs up onto the bridge of his nose. 'I hope you can sort that lot out. I am constantly at loggerheads with them. They are useless; there're all fucked up. I don't know why DB puts up with them. If I had my way, I'd kick them all out tomorrow. They're a bunch of messy degenerates and social outcasts; they couldn't even get a job sweeping the streets out there.' He went on and on, like a gramophone record playing the same monotonous tune again and again.

'I don't know if these will be any good to you. The esoteric is a load of bollocks. There's very little in it. You see all those fluffy bunnies sitting in yogic positions or meditating for hours. It's all a copout. Money is what matters in that world out there, not here.' He did not have a kind word to say about anyone. 'And that Barry, sneaky little rat, he's got the 'nodding dog' complex. You'd better watch him; he's a scheming bastard, he's only after fame and money. He licks ass to get closer to fulfilling his ambitions. Did you see him lap up the honours, that fucking lap dog? It was sick; I had to leave the table. I would have spewed up if I had stayed any longer.'

'Films, huh, there's no money in filmmaking. It's a glamour trip with no value what so ever. Barry, Marcus and John love it. They have visions of grandeur. The next Hollywood producers and directors, ha, that's a laugh.' He sighed for a brief moment. 'The future is in books. I've printed all of DB's and I'm reprinting the main ones. There's no future in films,' he repeated and nervously propped up his specs. 'I'll show you where the real work takes place and where real money is made, tomorrow.'

I could not get a word in edgeways. He went on and on in his neurotic babble, making out he was a cut above the rest. Eventually he left us in peace, with a head full of contradictions and two pristine diaries begging for a life story.

I turned to Elena. 'Well now we can start to document our spiritual progress. Isn't it exciting, a whole record of our life on the path to self-realisation and beyond? Let's disappear quickly before another nutter accosts us. I'm sure they're all insane or they must be on something.'

'I thought they would all be so caring, loving and supportive of each other, muttered Elena.

'It's dog-eat-dog, even in here. Maybe we've got it wrong, who knows. I've seen and felt the pressure they are all under,' I said.

'Something is working its way out in them. What it is I don't know, nor do I want to find out,' Elena said and we scurried upstairs.

What could I tell her? I was beginning to experience the changes they were all going through. Opening up your unconscious mind and maintaining a conscious existence in the real world was the ultimate challenge. At least I had Assagioli's books to help me understand the process.

Not that we should live in one world less, we must live in both worlds more, echoed in my head and I closed the door to our sanctuary behind me.

CHAPTER 14

I woke up with vague memories of the night's activities. Fragments of dream images played in my mind, but I could not quite bring them into waking consciousness. As I lay there, the sun's rays streamed through the windows. A rainbow of colours sprayed the bed, engulfing our bodies with healing light. I heard a persistent, loud scratching noise at our door. I looked at the alarm clock; it was 6am. The scratching turned into frantic clawing so I got up to open the door. It creaked open and Max pushed his head through and darted into the room. He was on our bed in no time, gnawing and purring as he settled down in his nest. It was his resting place after a night on the prowl. We had taken his bed over. He wasn't very happy with me; I could see it in his eyes.

I got dressed, took my diary and a note pad and set off for a cup of tea. I needed to get cracking on a plan of action and I wanted to set up my diary. I tiptoed downstairs into the dining room. A roaring log fire crackled in the hearth, spitting tongues of light in all directions. A warm, orange-red glow radiated around the room. What a change to the hostile environment we experienced last night. Steve popped his head out from the kitchen.

'Hey man, fancy a cup of tea? I've just brewed some,' he asked. 'Do you take sugar?'

'No thanks Steve, just milk. God, you're up early.'

'Yes, we all get up at strange times: some in the middle of the night and some in the early hours of the morning. It's recommended you know; it's all part of becoming more receptive and it reconditions your rhythms and cycles. In order to receive soul impressions, we kind of short-circuit our sleeping patterns.'

'Is it a kind of brainwashing? I've heard they use similar sleep deprivation techniques in cults, like the Moonies.'

'Well man, sort of, but it's not forced upon us. We do it if we want to. Nothing is forced upon us; we have freewill. It's all up to us; meditation, study, service work and the diary are advised and recommended. You know each discipline stimulates the opening of the higher chakras.'

I did not expect such an eloquent exposition from him. He was a space cadet, a clumsy, uncoordinated, Rastafarian look-alike. I shouldn't follow my preconceived ideas; everything around here is not what it seemed.

'Steve, what do you think about Elena and I running the place?' He shuffled awkwardly, delayed his response and reluctantly expressed his views.

'Chris man, no disrespect to you or Elena, but the boys and I have been here for years. We've taken no orders from anyone except DB and we like it that way. It all depends how it's done. I won't take any orders from a woman, no way. There is a Claregate etiquette, a kind of initiation process all newcomers must go through before they are accepted. You've got to earn your spurs,' he said rather arrogantly. 'You'll feel the energies soon enough. It descends on you like a plague, gnawing at your very core, feeding off doubts, insecurities, fears and desires. It will draw you into the clutches of demons, your demons deep in your unconscious mind. You sink or swim; the choice is yours; that's your freewill and karma. Some fall by the wayside, consumed with apathy, despair and overwhelmed by vast unconscious forces they have unleashed. They are the unlucky ones; having opened the gates, all hell is let loose. They end up on the streets, in asylums and some even top themselves to relieve the pain.'

Bloody hell, what a story; it sounded like a script from a demonic thriller. But, was he trying to frighten me, or was there an element of truth in it?

'It's the start of the breakdown, I can't understand it.'
'It's the start of the breakdown, I can't understand it.'

The Tears For Fears hit single started blaring in the background. Steve had flicked the switch of the tape recorder on by mistake as he prepared to boil the kettle for another brew. That was exactly how I felt. My personality was fragmenting, I was trying desperately to hold it all together, but that was not the answer. I had to let it go. But what would happen to me? How would I cope? I was given a task to do; I had responsibilities; I was a manager. All these thoughts ricocheted around my mind as Steve offered me another cuppa.

'Listen, take my advice, ease into life here, it's nothing you've ever experienced before, nor will you ever experience again. It will change you forever. I see you've got your diary; that's good, because it's your saving grace. Keep it religiously, talk to your inner self, it will become your personal confessional when life gets tough. It acts as a catharsis, clearing the shit of the unconscious when it's about to consume you.' He talked from the heart and from experience. I appreciated his honesty.

'Steve, do you think we could call a meeting with the boys, maybe when Stellios comes? We'll sit down and thrash everything out. After all, I'm one of you lot. I might be able to get things going for us. I don't like how things are done around here. I hate dictatorships and that's what the inner circle is. Together we could change it for the better. What do you think?'

'Mmm, well I'll consult the others and get back to you. I warn you, they don't like meetings; it sucks of authority. We are an independent bunch and we hate conformity,' he said, brushing past me with his little teapot splashing all over the hallway.

'It's the start of the breakdown, I can't understand it.'
'It's the start of the breakdown, I can't understand it.'

He left me with the fire's glowing embers. My mind was in a whirlwind. My virgin diary sat glaring at me, begging to be penetrated. I needed a poem or prose to set the vibration on the first page. A small, thin paperback book lay open, face down on the dining room table. It was titled *The Voice Of The Silence* by Madame Blavatsky. Steve must have been reading it. I turned it over and read the page he had been perusing. A passage caught my attention; that was it. It had to head my diary, it was chosen for me.

> *'Before the soul can see, harmony within must be attained and fleshy eyes be rendered blind to all illusion.*
>
> *Before the soul can hear, the image (man) has to become as deaf to the roarings as to the whispers, to cries of bellowing elephants as to the silvery buzzing of the golden firefly.*
>
> *Before the soul can comprehend and may remember, she must unto the silent speaker be united, just as the form to which the clay is modelled is first united with the potter's mind.*
>
> *For then the soul will hear and will remember and then to the inner ear will speak, The Voice of the Silence.'*

I wrote it in longhand inside and contemplated its meaning. Steve's conversation came flooding back. The Tears for Fears tape echoed in the kitchen and the door thudded open. It was Pete, bedraggled as ever, carrying a mug of stale, cold coffee and plates.

'Hi Chris,' he stuttered, 'you're up early. I thought you might have had a lie in after your long drive and busy first day.'

'Pete, I couldn't sleep, there's too much on my mind and there is so much to do.'

'Chris, take it easy, chill out, pace yourself. There is no rush; it's not like out there, in the rat race. There is time for everything. We normally meditate, write our dreams down and study in the morning before breakfast. We meditate before lunch and dinner too.'

No wonder nothing gets done around here I thought. The door thudded open again. Dick raced through, clicked the kettle on and moaned about the music playing.

'Bloody rubbish they listen to, no wonder their brains are full of shit. Where's my teapot? Jesus fucking Christ, where's my teapot? ' He ranted like a trooper for minutes before storming off. 'Bet that bastard Steve's got it. I'll make him suffer, the big…'

Pete, giggling away, nudged me in the side. 'That's our morning wakeup call. There's always a race to the teapot. Normally Dick is up first. He doesn't bother with the spiritual stuff, he thinks it's a load of crap.'

Bloody hell, what a heap of crackpots I've landed myself with, I thought.

Pete pulled out a notebook from his pocket. 'I'm writing a series of children's short stories, interlaced with esoteric meaning. There's so much garbage out there. It's no wonder the country's full of crime and delinquent kids. The stuff they are exposed to is all crude and violent. Steve's going to illustrate it for me, he's a brilliant artist.'

He passed me his notebook with pride and passion, and his big black eyes shone with excitement and anticipation. I was fixated; what a genius, he was inspired. It was brilliant and Steve's drawings were excellent; they were caricatures of Pete's masterful identities; delicate, exaggerated pen strokes, full of energy and life.

'God, Pete, it's absolutely brilliant. You've got real talent and Steve's illustrations are so ethereal. Have you got anyone interested in publishing it?'

'I'm no good at conversation. I get so nervous and I'm really shy. I close up into myself; I feel as if a bottomless pit swallows me every time I try to present it. I just can't do it. I've got a major block and it's killing me,' he said, putting his hands around his sorry head in frustration. His face lit up. 'That's why Steve's got involved. He can verbally put it together and with his illustrations, maybe we could make it work.' His aura lifted and his eyes sparkled at my appreciation of his talent. What a waste: being stuck in the Claregate kitchen, doing breakfast, lunch and dinner. There must be a reason for it. Something deep and karmic that he must have to struggle with in this life. His wretched, pygmy body was overwhelmed by his creativity. Poor Pete had to find a way to externalise his potential. That's why he was here. I'm sure he could not cope out there, where dog eats dog. He was at the bottom end of the food chain and he knew it.

Maybe I could help both of them? Yes, I was a canny Scots Greek. By helping them, I would gel quicker in the outer circle and get them organised as well.

'Pete, listen, I've got an idea. I can help you realise your ambitions, but you have got to work with me. You know what I want, don't you?' He looked at me with those soulful, black eyes, hesitated for a moment and sighed.

'Oh alright, I'll try to get my shit together, if you promise to help me.'

'I want you to talk to Steve too. It's all in our interests to improve standards around here. You get what you want and I get what I want. Is it a deal?'

'Yea, yea, it's a deal. I'll talk it over with Steve and get back to you,' he said and disappeared into the kitchen to prepare breakfast. 'I think DB is coming in for breakfast this morning. Sometimes he descends on us, just to break the patterns and monotony around here. We sit around and discuss his most recent astrology research. He gets it subjectively from some source. It's all new stuff, you know, it's channelled. The whole basis of esoteric astrology and the Claregate Method was structured in this way.'

I was fascinated and in awe of the astrology. I often wondered how it came into manifestation. As I understood it, the Claregate Method of astrological analysis was subjective and objective. Alice Bailey channelled the esoteric planetary rulerships years earlier. Her master DK, the Tibetan initiate, ascribed 12 planets to 12 signs, linking a single planet to a single sign. Orthodox astrology works with 10 planets, inferring Venus and Mercury have dual rulerships. But she said esoteric astrology could not be applied at a personality level; it could only be understood in relation to the soul. DB changed all that. His soul-centred astrology came from within, but it was strongly related to the personality and its field of activity.

'Hey Chris, you don't mind laying the table for me, do you? You'll have to get used to it, after all you'll be doing it occasionally.'

'No problem Pete, I've laid and served tables all my life. I've got no airs and graces.' I whizzed through the dining room in minutes, contemplating my position. I felt good; I had found Steve and Pete's buttons and I had a way of controlling them with tact and diplomacy. My Libra ascendant was always ready to compromise and harmonise. I was looking forward to DB's breakfast lecture. I was in a privileged position on the frontiers of spiritual insights. The teachings were being fed to us straight from the source. We were making history.

A blistering spark from the fire blasted a piece of ebony ember into my face. The flash brought back memories of a dream I had last night.

> *21st February 1983, 7.30am.*
>
> *Elena, wearing her sexy, transparent, violet top, an unknown male and I are in a car. Elena is driving, I am in the back and the unknown male is in the passenger seat. To my horror, with sardonic laughter, he starts fondling Elena's breast. I lunge over, trying to stop him, but he persists. Elena seems to be enjoying his sexual advances, laughing and encouraging him. I frantically climb over and punch him in the head. It has no effect; he fondles her again and again. Elena's taunting laughter swamps my mind as the car veers out of control and down a hill. Their sordid laughter flooded my consciousness before the car even comes to a halt. I hear a police siren in the distance. They arrest the delirious unknown male.*

I was livid with anger, confusion and frustration. The dream came with a vengeance, bringing back the aftermath of that nightmare I had in Brighton. Why was I having these recurring visions? What did they mean? Was my meeting with DB connected? Was the cruel bitch going to dump me? It all came seeping back; her sardonic laughter, her lover, the bloody murderous, stab in my chest. I was in despair, filled with jealousy and insecurity. A cloud of depression descended on me, swamping my aura with doubts, negativity and possession. I felt as if demons were dragging me deep into the bowels of hell. The dark denizens were devouring my flesh, fighting over my feeble, submitting soul.

> *It's the start of the breakdown; I can't understand it!*
> *It's the start of the breakdown; I can't understand it!*

The song kept playing and playing in my head as I sank deeper and deeper into oblivion. I managed to clamber upstairs, push the old dungeon door and crash into bed, scattering Max and waking *her*.

'What's the matter Christo? Why are you in bed again? I heard you get up and go downstairs.'

I pulled the dingy, old sheets and blankets over my head, turned my back on her and cried like a baby. I was cracking up. My whole world was crumbling all around me; I just wanted to die. DB's voice thundered in my head:

'All yours attachments will be torn from you. You will suffer; you will have to let go! Let go! Let go!'

Elena was trying to comfort me by now. I lashed out at her shouting.

'Let me go, let me go. You bitch, let me go!'

'Christo, what's happening to you. What happened downstairs?' she said, pulling at me.

'Fuck off, you bitch. Leave me alone, you fucking whore!' I hurled a load of obscenities at her until she got dressed and disappeared downstairs, distraught and sobbing. I felt as if I was possessed. I had triggered off a demonic, foul-mouthed entity that was rapidly consuming me like a hellish fire. As I sobbed uncontrollably, an excruciating pain pierced my chest. I crumpled up in a heap, breathless, my lungs bellowing and heart pounding.

'Elena, Elena, Elena, help, help, help!' I felt my life drain away. The pain shot in rivets and spasms all over my body. The door crashed open and Pete and Elena dashed in. She was hysterical; he was cool and calm.

'Elena, quick, call DB, the number is by the phone. Shout for Claire and Linda, I think he's having a heart attack, quick, quick!' The front door crashed open to DB's familiar call.

'I'm here. Does anyone want me?' In seconds he was pulling my shirt off, taking my pulse and comforting me.

'Open those damn windows; get some air in here quick. Elena, get the aspirin from my pocket, a glass of water and a wet cloth, now!' I had come round; my chest was throbbing with pain every time I took a breath of air.

'Well, it's not a heart attack, or angina, that's the good news. It looks like you've contracted pleurisy. You will have to stay in bed for a few days. There is no cure for it. You'll have to take antibiotics and painkillers. I'll get my doctor to come and see you.'

His diagnosis was correct. I was confined to bed. I missed his lecture and the next two weeks of community life. My psychological state had no quick fix though. I had spiritually haemorrhaged; the bout of pleurisy was the physical reaction to my fevered state. I was turning within; my body was spinning into a chrysalis. I felt I was being entombed. All I knew was the transformation had started. I was being reduced to a feeble mirror of my former self. It was what they all said would happen. I had to go with it, to the end.

CHAPTER 15

It was the worst possible time to be confined to bed. I was left alone for hours, grappling with incessant negative thoughts and dark feelings. My unconscious world was swamping me; vast forces I had no control over were consuming me. I felt like I was a small fishing boat, being swept along by awesome currents. Battered and beaten I was tossed around by a horrific, raging, cruel sea. I was at the mercy of the elements. I had no option but to go with the flow, praying for salvation and calm waters of serene tranquillity. I knew this was only the beginning. My poor ego was being ripped and ravaged. I had to cling on and endure the sadistic onslaught of unconscious forces I had unleashed. They were my energies, my *shadow* my *dweller on the threshold;* they were an accumulation of hundreds of years of fears, doubts, insecurities and negative actions. Pandora's box had flipped its lid, spewing out all the ills into the world. But some divine quality remained hidden... Hope! Hope! There was hope, shining with optimism and abundance. Her angelic visage sparkled as she showed the way to the still waters of the soul. She was my only salvation, but I had to weather the unforgiving, violent storm to access her protective and comforting rays. Thank God I had my diary and *He* was there for me. I was in the right environment too. They all understood what I was going through, they had already been there. Just imagine if I had to go through this out there. With the pressures of money, stress of work and trying to keep up with Jones's, it would have been unbearable. I'm sure I would have been committed to an asylum by now.

'He hears voices in his head. He talks with God. His spirit leaves his body and flies at night and he is emotionally unstable. He must be mad.'

Elena had been given a job as continuity girl on the film set. A major assault on Paracelsus had been planned. Famous British actors such as soap stars, Bill Roache - Ken Barlow of Coronation Street - and Ross Davidson of Eastenders, the heartthrob actor were given leading parts.

Stellios had arrived and had settled in with Rasta Steve. I needed to see him, I was desperate, I could not speak to Elena; I was in a mess. She wasn't to blame, poor thing, but I was still deeply insecure and unsure of her.

The old door creaked open, cobwebs tingled and fresh air rushed in. A searing bolt of promising light flashed into the room, animating the minute speckles of angel dust. Stellios familiar golden mop appeared, shining like the glorious dawn disk.

'Stellios, Stellios, Stellios!' I cried like a wimp, arms outstretched, heart throbbing and breath bellowing. I tried to move, but a jagged pain shot from my chest, thumping me downwards into my soggy, sweat-soaked bed. I curled up in a ball and sobbed my heart out.

'Stellios, I'm cracking up. I don't know what's happening to me. Look at me.' He looked like he'd seen a ghost. His eyes stared at my sorry, wretched frame huddled up on the bed.

'What's the matter Christo? Elena told me you were in a bad way. Pleurisy is painful, but you look awful.' He cradled me in his arms and wiped the tears streaming from my deep, sunken eyes. 'Don't worry Christo; you'll be all right. This process happens to everyone. I'm going through it myself, but thank God I am at the other end now. There is light at the end of the tunnel, I can assure you.' His words were comforting and compassionate. I could not face him. I was embarrassed; swamped with self-pity, reduced to a whimpering wreck. I was not even a whisper of that self-motivated, confident, strong man he knew in Brighton.

'It's a natural spiritualising process Christo, really. The transformation takes time; it consumes the old personality and transmutes it into a new shining instrument the soul can express itself through. It's like the myth of the Phoenix being reborn out of the ashes.'

'How long will I suffer this breakdown Stellios? It's killing me, look. I'm a nervous wreck, no good to anyone. I'm supposed to take control, manage the place. What will DB and the others think of me now? I'll be a laughing stock. Poor Elena, I've really mistreated her you know. It's all my fault. I dragged her here; I convinced her to come. My uncles have disowned me. I've lost my status, my money, my home, my family, my faith and above all my sanity.' I was delirious.

'You'll help me Stellios, won't you? You won't desert me will you?' I tugged at his jumper in desperation as the pain riveted through my body, sending me into spasms.

'It's okay, Christo, it's okay. I'll be here for you. Remember, we made a promise to each other. I want you to relax, rest and get some sleep. Start writing up your diary; use this time to turn within. I'll drop by with some books and let you know what's happening. I'm sure they will ask me to join them for inner circle meetings now that I've gained their trust. Don't worry; Elena understands what you are going through. She will support you.' He said cranked the old door ajar. 'See you later.'

He left me floundering, drowning in tears of anguish and self-pity. I had to climb out of this monstrous marsh, but somehow I knew I had to sink deeper before I could be redeemed. I was exhausted, wrenched in two, aching all over. I turned to my diary and scribbled.

> *22nd Feb. 1983. 1.30pm*
> *You know I am finding it extremely difficult to understand what's happening to me. I am lost in a sea of deep depression. I may not be able to reach you my father in heaven. Show me please what I am going through. Where am I on the path to self-discovery?*

I just managed to scrawl the last few words as my pen wavered on the page and my consciousness leaked out of my shattered body. I slid into a deep, soothing slumber until Elena awakened me. She was back from filming at Little Elephant. She bounded in, bouncing with energy and vitality. A jet of laser light from the open door seared my face. As I opened my eyes the lightning flash unzipped my memory, bringing back a dream I'd had during my sleep. Yes, yes, that dragon, I killed it with a zap of...

'Christo, Christo, you'll never believe who was on set today, you'll never believe it.'

God, here I was in the depths of despair, just barely holding my shit together and she's prancing around like a big kid.

Ross Davidson? You know, the heartthrob actor from Eastenders. He's so handsome. He speaks just like you and he's got the most beautiful blue eyes.' She was in an enchanted state, eyes gazing upwards, clutching her notes tightly against her bosom. 'Oh, he's so handsome and famous too,' she said again in a smitten, schoolgirl trance. 'He'll be acting with us for some time. He's landed a major part in the film. Isn't it great, rubbing shoulders with the rich and famous? Just wait until my sisters get to know about it. I'll have to get an autographed photo.' She stood there for minutes spewing out a load of gibberish and gushing with exuberance.

'Oh, how are you feeling now Christo? Have you taken your tablets? You look a lot better; your colour is coming back. It won't be long before you're bounding around like before.'

Bloody hell, I wish she would just shut her mouth, just for one second. I could not even get a thought in, never mind a word. I was still in between sleeping and waking consciousness. Propping my aching body up, I managed to engage in some conversation with my dear wife, who was almost orgasming with the prospect of another day filming.

'Did anyone ask how I was? DB, John, Barry?'

'Well, not exactly. They were too busy filming. We are up to our eyeballs. The continuity work is interesting. I'm on set all the time. I have to make sure their makeup is perfect, props are in the same place and all the electrics are not showing. I love it.' She was full of that leonine self-importance bullshit. Her head was in the clouds.

'Elena, I'm glad you are enjoying it. As long as you are happy, that's the important thing.' I propped up her ego even more. 'I need some rest, you don't mind leaving me do you?'

'No problem Christo, I'll see if Pete needs help, or I'll just read in the library.' She trotted off down stairs singing and dancing to a Greek love song. Nobody gave a shit whether I was alive or dead. They were all full of their own self-importance. They didn't give a toss, as long as their egos were being pumped up, that's all that mattered.

'My dream, yes my dream,' I shouted. I had to write it down. I knew it was important. It was a response to my question.

5.30pm Waking dream
I am part of a group wading into deep jungle swamps, hunting a dragon. We are housed in a makeshift wooden chalet on stilts in the centre of a lagoon. Menacing killer whales are circling around. Suddenly, out of the blue, a dragon appears, lashing out at a female companion. I must save her from the beast. She is upstairs screaming and panicking. I run up to a window and confront the dragon that has enchanted the girl and is about to devour her. I look around for a weapon to fight it off. I pick up a bedside lamp, pull off the bulb and switch it on. I thrust the lamp at the beast's jaws, electrocuting it. It mysteriously disappears into thin air and I save the girl. The others come up and congratulate me. Before I leave I collect a selection of silver pens, camera and clothes.

The whole experience was charged with energy, fear and challenge. But what did it mean, the dragon, the maiden, and the electric fire? What did it all mean? The Christian tale of Saint George and the dragon seeped out my tortured mind. Yes, maybe there is a connection. This dream was important. I needed a book of symbols, myths and dream analysis. As I lay there brooding on the significance of the dream, the door creaked open. It was Stellios with a pile of books for me.

'Hi Christo. Here are the books I promised you. I'm sure they will help you understand where you are at and give you some answers.' He was my shining light. I was so pleased I did not lose his friendship and trust.

'Christo, I'm to attend an inner circle meeting tomorrow morning. I'll be shunted off to LE in one of the beat up Claregate limos. It's exciting, but I'll have to keep my wits about me. Don't tell anyone I visit you. They may get to know about it and become suspicious.'

'Stellios, I've had this dream. I think it's really important.'

Thud, thud! 'Hello, are you awake Christo?'

'Quick Stellios, hide behind the drapes.' He scuffled towards them while I crept slowly to the door. It was Linda and Claire.

'Hi there, how are you feeling? God you've had the lot thrown at you, all at the same time. Don't worry about the place. We can manage it until you are well. Do you want supper in bed?'

I hadn't eaten much in days. The homely aroma of roast chicken and fresh vegetables oozed from the floorboards.

'That would be nice. Thanks for dropping by to see me.'

'Don't tell anyone we've come. We are not supposed to get emotionally involved. It's part of the dis-identification programme we are meant to follow. Anyway, it looks like you'll be back to your normal self in no time. Bye for now. I'll get Elena to bring you a plate at supper.' I thanked them; the door creaked closed and Stellios gasped a sigh of relief.

'I don't trust any of them. They all scurry back and report anything they find out to the inner circle. That Linda especially, she's a weird one. One minute she's gushing all over you and the next she's ready to claw your eyes out,' Stellios crept from behind the drapes. 'See you tomorrow. Meanwhile, get some rest.'

I stretched over to the pile of books and picked up the top one. It was a paperback titled Man and his Symbols by Carl Jung. I flicked it open at random to a page. Wao! I was in shock! The page depicted Kitchener in his famous *Your Country Needs You* stance. It was a montage of a World War One call-to-arms poster: infantry, a military cemetery and silhouettes of soldiers on a march. This was all too much. Was it a co-incidence or a way my *Daemon* was encouraging me to fight my way through this depressing time? What ever it was, it worked. Patriotic passion overflowed; songs of victory echoed in my ears, lifting my heavy soul out of the quagmire of despair. The opposite page was very interesting:

*The ego, nevertheless, is in conflict with the shadow, in what Dr. Jung once called **"the battle of deliverance"**. In the struggle of man to achieve consciousness, this conflict is expressed by the contest between the archetypal hero and the cosmic powers of evil, personified by dragons and other sea monsters.*

It concluded overleaf:

The battle between the hero and the dragon is the more active form, showing more clearly the archetypal theme of the ego's triumph over regressive trends. For most, the dark or negative side of the personality remains unconscious. The hero, on the contrary, must realise that the shadow exists and that he can draw strength from it. He must come to terms with its destructive powers if he is to become sufficiently terrible to overcome the dragon – i.e., before the ego can triumph, it must master and assimilate the shadow.

Bloody hell. The dream was so revealing. I could identify with it. The swamp in the jungle was a reflection of the state of my mind. The killer whales were swimming in the lagoon: dark, unconscious elements of the shadow, lurking in the depths, waiting to devour me. The makeshift structure represented the state of my conscious ego, battered and weather beaten, but still erect. The dragon was the dweller/shadow, with all its ferocity and venom, waiting to devour the girl. What did she represent? Why was she upstairs? Why was the dragon attacking her? The next page had the answers:

*It was a still shot of a locomotive almost crushing a damsel who is saved by a hero. It states, Heroes often battle with dragons to rescue **"damsels in distress"** (who symbolise the anima).*

An extract on the following page concluded:

One of the most important aspects of the myth of the typical hero was his capacity to save or protect beautiful women from terrible danger. This is one way in which myths or dreams refer to the 'anima', the feminine element of the male psyche.

In my dream the *anima* was under threat. She inhabits the upper floor of the structure. She is in an elevated position. The dragon is just about to strike her; she is mesmerised by its presence. I despatch the beast using the ingenuity of the intellect and divine energy, electricity. I electrocute it with a lamp without a light bulb. The dragon and the girl must be linked in some way. After all, the dragon disintegrates in front of her. The others congratulate me and before I leave, I pick up silver pens, a camera and clothes. These items are a mystery; perhaps they are prizes attained for dispatching the entity. Yes, clothes, a different personality and the camera; they capture images of reality and the silver pens represent authority, prizes for achievement.

It looked like I was on the right track. I had my first battle with dark, unconscious elements in my psyche. A shift was taking place. I was fighting back. I could attain the highest levels. I had won the battle, but the war was just beginning. I was on the frontiers of my inner life. I needed to be equipped for the onslaught. Carl Jung's research furnished me with knowledge that was imperative for my survival. I had Assagioli's books as well as DB's. My training had begun. I needed to familiarise myself with my psychological combat arms. I was a probationary disciple in the 'English Ashram'; I was on the front line; I was adamant I would not fall at the first charge. I would earn my spurs.

Steve's voice echoed in my ears. 'You've got to earn your spurs, you've got to earn your spurs.'

> *'It's the start of the breakdown,*
> *It's the start of the breakdown,*
> *I just can't understand it,*
> *I just can't understand it.'*

The lyrics blared in my head. The song was seeping through from the player, deep in the kitchen below. The psychosynthesis process was in full swing. My breakdown had begun.

CHAPTER 16

'There we are my darling, just what the doctor ordered, roast chicken, fresh veg and potatoes. That should get you back to your former glory in no time.' She plonked the tray in my lap, and before disappearing, she chirped 'you don't mind if I eat downstairs, they are discussing today's shoot and I don't want to miss anything?'

She didn't give a shit. I was beginning to suspect something was not quite right. She was acting strange, but I could not cope with the ramifications of it: not just yet. The roast dinner looked scrummy. Pete, for all his failings, was a master chef. I could not have done better myself.

I wonder how he is? I thought. I hadn't seen him in days, not that I wanted him to see me in this decrepit state. He was more together than I was at this stage. I flicked open *In the Steps of the Master*, one of DB's inspirational books.

'Oh my God, oh my God!' I shouted. I was confronted with a full-page colour print of *The Phoenix in Stained Glass and Wrought Iron*. Bloody hell. The opposite page was titled:

Breakdown of old personality and transfer to a new personality.

What was previously a mild interest in 'things esoteric' now becomes an all-absorbing fascination and obsession.

That's exactly what happened to me in Brighton. I was amazed and intrigued.

There are personality changes. In a supreme act of sacrifice, the individual crosses the Rubicon and makes the irrevocable decision to give everything he has, i.e., his integrated personality in its totality, to express the soul's purpose.

I almost choked. I fought for a few seconds before clearing my throat. I was reduced to tears as my emotional body haemorrhaged uncontrollably.

He begins to erode his old attachments, undermines his previous affiliations and codes of conduct. He orientates himself to universal laws rather than man-made ones and begins to transfer his energies towards a higher point of consciousness.

My whole body shuddered with the rush of nervous energy and I was flooded with meaning and understanding. My head was buzzing; *His* high-pitched laser resonated in my eardrums, sending me into ecstasy.

I'm not going mad. I'm not going mad, after all. It's part of my rebirth. It's part of my rebirth.' I shouted the words out loud, arms raised and tears of joy streaming from my bright, glassy eyes. Below that, a paragraph titled *Psychosynthesis* followed.

Psychosynthesis

Helped by the disciplines of discipleship, including meditation, breath control, study of the Ancient Wisdom, the commencement of a spiritual diary, etc., the new personality begins to emerge on its higher level of consciousness and its psychic elements are synthesised to become a soul-infused, rounded-out personality, the ideal instrument of the Master, a double-edged sword in the hand of King Arthur.

With my spirit rejuvenated and my body filled with light, I read the last chapter.

The Phoenix of legendary fame rises from the fire and ashes of its death (as a self-orientated personality) and soars towards the Sun (the Solar Angel within us). It depicts something of the glory of this process symbolised by Scorpio and the Eagle of the Fixed Cross in Astrology.

I sensed a welling up from within. My God it was all connected: the breakdown, psychosynthesis, the rebirth and even the Phoenix, a myth related to Scorpio.

'Humpty Dumpty sat on the wall,
Humpty Dumpty had a great fall.'

It played over and over again in my head. I'm sure it was **Him** teasing me with little titbits of meaning. Yes, I was Humpty Dumpty, all in pieces, my ego shattered, but I would get all my bits back together again and even more. I finished my supper and wandered slowly up to the toilet. I bumped into Pete on the way down.

'Thanks for the chicken dinner Pete, you'll have to give me the recipe.'

'No problem Chris, You okay now?'

'Almost. If I could just get rid of this constant pain in my lungs, I'd be alright.'

'Have you tried the breathing exercises? They are the preliminary techniques leading to meditation.'

'Meditation? Breathing exercises? Pete, I can hardly take in a couple of breaths without passing out.'

'Have you had a chance to talk to Steve?'

'Well, I've been busy. He's working down at LE. It's like ships passing in the night. I'll see him tomorrow before breakfast. Hey, you'll never guess what happened a couple of days ago. Dick and Steve got into a scuffle about the rickety, old teapot. It was like The Mad Hatters Tea Party, in Alice in Wonderland. They tugged to and fro, one holding the spout, the other the handle, with the little pot screaming in the middle. You ought to have heard the language. Then it exploded into bits, poor thing. They went flying into the kitchen dresser and almost smashed all the side plates. It was hilarious. I'll have to write it into one of my short stories.'

'I bet it was hilarious. I'd love to have been there. What a spectacle it must have been.'

Pete chuckled aloud as I crawled back into bed to think about his advice. Yes, I ought to familiarise myself with the techniques at least. Maybe I could practice some preliminary exercises. I groped around under the bed for the pile of books Stellios had left me. I pulled out two handbooks. *Super consciousness through Mediation* and *The Opening of the Third Eye*. Well, that was my next task, to instigate a meditation action plan. It was one of the disciplines needed in order to reach the 5th kingdom, the realm of the soul. I flicked through the former from the back and opened at Chapter 11, Preliminary Measures for Meditation. I read the four main stages, which were expounded in detail.

I had to start my meditation schedule as soon as I was better. I knew it was important. I had already set up my diary, started recording and analysing my dreams. I was studying the occult classics and I was here, attempting my service work to humanity. I needed to get my shit together fast. My body still ached, my outer and inner life was in chaos; my wife was acting weirder by the minute.

'Hi Christo. Did you enjoy you dinner, wasn't it good? I could live here forever if our meals were like this each night. Roast beef, roast lamb, roast chicken, pudding and custard to follow. It was better than eating out each night.' She babbled on and on incessantly, whilst I flicked through the books.

'Oh, I see you've got DB's handbook on Meditation. Are you going to start soon? You'll need your own space in the room for that, won't you?'

I was still fuming and churning within. She should have stayed with me. She deserted me; they are more important than me. She is up to something; I sensed it.

'Well, the cat got your tongue?' Oh, poor little Christo's wallowing in a pool of self-pity. What's the matter? Does it hurt? Oh, never mind, you can stay in bed forever, you might even root there and mutate into something worthwhile.'

'What do you know about it? Just piss off and leave me alone. All you think about nowadays is your fucking continuity job and rubbing shoulders with the glitzy-glam world of so-called actors. Your head is so far up your arse, you talk shit all the time.'

I buckled up in extreme pain as I lunged at her. I had lost the plot; I had been reduced to an emotional cripple. I had no control over my anger. It spewed out in volleys of verbal vomit. She slammed the door on me as I hurled another grenade of vile abuse at her. I didn't know where it was all coming from, this unbridled, degrading, unconscious expression. Then I heard a tingling voice in my inner ear,

'When you tread the path of return, all that is good and all that is evil is thrust to the surface.'

I had to let the unconscious ooze from me. It was sheer, unadulterated anger, passion and venom. I could not identify with this destructive power; it was not me. I was cultured, placid, and diplomatic and always thinking of others; I was in control of my energies. But not any more. I melted into my depression, feeling sorry for my obnoxious behaviour towards Elena. I crumbled up, sobbing violently, and clutched my diary, my only saviour. *The Tears For Fears* lyrics blasted in my head.

'Shout, shout, let it all out, these are the things we can do without!'

Within minutes I slid into a deep, soul soothing, slumber. All my anger had slowly subsided. I felt the sweet flutter of the inner worlds beckon me into the realms of dreams. Colours swished and swayed, sounds daintily danced across waves to a divine melody. An ethereal, angelic presence, gossamer gowned, wrapped around her Diva torso, flowing in the dream breeze. She gently soothed my hand and led me through a rose-white gate. Paths were strewn with a myriad of delicate, pastel fauna; their divine, sweet, aroma gently tickled my senses. The air was awash with a swarm of numinous, fairy presences, sweeping in and out, shining luminous light and buzzing like fireflies in the celestial sky. I was on the frontiers of Paradise...

'Creek... Thud!' My vision was shattered by the sound of the door. A cold, steely body swished the bedclothes back and crept in by my side. It was her. She clasped her hand around mine, from behind. Thinking I was sleeping she whispered, 'I'm really sorry Christo. It's so hard to know what you're going through. I do care, but I can't help you any more. You have to do it on your own.'

I knew from then on, I was alone. She had led me here for some reason. It would all be revealed soon enough; it was only a matter of time. Although she was beautiful, alluring and passionate, she was but a dim candle compared to my angelic encounter. She could never compete with my divine messenger, my inner bride to be and the mystical union.

CHAPTER 17

A few days swept in and out, like the rhythmic swishing of waves crashing against each other. They merged into a mish-mash of sleep and uncoordinated fragments of unconscious spew. Elena's fleeting daily and nightly visits were like ghostly apparitions in the vacuum of my existence.

I woke up one morning to a vivid dream. I was still in esolepsy, the state between sleeping and waking; a sort of twilight zone, where you are most receptive to inner impressions.

25th. Feb.1983. 7am, waking dream.
I decided to enter a horse in a race, but we had to give the organisers £3,000. I am on the horse riding bareback. The horse seems to me to be too fat to race. The race is over hurdles. I run desperately to find the organiser, who is in his cabin preparing himself for the race. I tell him the horse is not ready to run because he's carrying too much weight.

I perused the dream whilst still in the doldrums of sleep.
'What did it mean; the fat horse that I ride bareback? Why race over hurdles? Why was it not flat racing? The £3,000? I change my mind because I realise the horse is too heavy to win. The organiser in his cabin, who was he? I tell him the horse is not ready to run.

According to Jung, all dream elements are related to parts of the individual psyche. They are also grouped together by association; meaning symbols link up with symbols of similar meaning.

I could not make head or tail of it. I knew it had deep meaning and I needed to find a valid method of interpretation.

As I emerged from my slumber I felt the bed for Elena. She had got up early and had not disturbed me. I clambered upstairs and showered for the first time in days. Back in my room I was determined to start my meditation schedule. The early morning light shone brightly in my sacred space, animating it with Prana. You could almost see the minute, vitality globules chasing sunbeams and rainbows around the space. The ethers seemed highly charged; colour collided with light and incense waltzed around sound. I seated myself in preparation for my withdrawal.

I had practised my eye exercises the night before, so it was not a strain performing them now. I followed with 40 bellows breaths, ten to the front, ten to the left, ten to the right and the last ten to the front again. I did the 'anal lock', drawing my consciousness inside my body. I felt the blood pumping through my veins, my heart thump and my breathing slow down. It was a strange sensation, but it helped me withdraw my senses and melt into a serene state of mind. I sat there, my eyes turned upwards and inwards towards the brow centre. An indigo blue screen appeared in my mind's eye. It looked like the night sky, with minute flashes sparkling like stars. Spectrum colours slowly materialised, flowing around a central point and moving in kaleidoscopic fashion. I started to focus my attention on the point of light at the centre. Suddenly intense vibrations in my brow region jettisoned me towards the vortex. Thoughts, fears and anxieties started crowding in and in a flash I was unceremoniously dumped back to earth reality. I slowly regained consciousness and sat in a trance for some minutes, trying to rationalise my experience. It must have lasted minutes, but it seemed like hours. It was awesome; my first meditation attempt and it was euphoric. I had shot my consciousness towards the point of light, but I lacked the experience, courage and staying power to penetrate it. My lower mind, the undisciplined stallion, kicked in, sending me crashing back to reality. It was not what I expected, not at the first attempt at least. But it happened and I was privileged. I noted the event in my diary, hoping it would happen again.

I felt alive, full of vitality and energy. My illness was easing off and the breathing exercises had helped me regain my strength. I was adamant that I would rise from my convalescence and join the group tomorrow. I spied Assagioli's book *Psychosynthesis* on the floor. I hadn't had time to read it yet, but I flicked it open at random. It opened at a chapter headed

Self-Realisation and Psychological Disturbances.

Various manifestations of spiritual awakening bear a close relationship to some of the symptoms regarded as characteristic of psychoneuroses and borderline schizophrenic states. In some cases the stress and strain also produce physical symptoms, such as nervous tension, insomnia and various other troubles (digestive, circulatory, glandular).

That was it. Pleurisy was the start of my breakdown; it had contributed to the spiritual awakening. I felt relieved that my symptoms were a natural result in the process of self-realisation. I had more to experience; this was just the beginning, but it gave me great strength reading Assagioli's research and conclusions.

I pottered around the room, moving props and rearranging the technical apparatus. What a jungle it had become; coloured gels flapped around tripod spotlights like monstrous, exotic petals. Wires dangled from gadgets and frames, rooting themselves to terra firma. Silver gaffing tape, shades and old scripts littered the undergrowth. I half expected flamboyant, multi-coloured birds to flutter through this techno-wilderness.

I gathered up courage and ventured downstairs to the dining room. I heard a clatter of crockery coming from the kitchen and a female voice humming along to a classical score. A beautiful calmness saturated the space and I sat there mesmerised.

'Oh, hi Chris. I didn't realise anyone was here; half of the group are in the city, setting up for the International Mind Body and Spirit Festival at Olympia. All the others are set building. Fancy a cuppa? I've just brewed some.'

'Yes please Linda. That would be lovely.'

'It's great to see you up and about; you must be feeling better.'

'Well, I'm not a hundred per cent, but I just couldn't lie there stagnating any longer. I have, however, used my time to study. I've set up my diary and started meditating.'

'That's a good balanced start. All you need now is to throw yourself actively into your service work to humanity. There's so much to do and there are too many chiefs and not enough Indians.'

'Mm, yes, I know what you mean.' Was she insinuating I was another chief, I thought? Everything had double meaning in this place.

'Hasn't Elena blended in quickly? She's into filming in a big way, rubbing shoulders with all those gorgeous hunks. She loves it, it's a Leo thing, you know, all the show, attention and glamour,' she said, in a really sarcastic way.

What was she trying to say? If I read in between the lines, she was jealous of Elena. Of course she was; she was here, in the doghouse washing up and Elena was lapping up the limelight on the front line. But what was she scheming behind the scenes? What was she concealing? I sensed she had plans and she had the power to implement them. I had to be wary of her manipulating ways, but I wanted to show that I trusted her.

'Linda, I need to ask you something deep. It's being playing on my mind for sometime and I've had some vivid experiences.'

'Well, fire away, I'll try to help you if I can,' she said, bringing in the tea.

'I've had what I think is previous life recall in my dreams and during waking consciousness. They were really so traumatic and alive; they were just like real life.'

'Do you know who Thomas Wentworth was? I have the impression he lived during the reign of Charles the 1st.'

'Mmm, I'm not familiar with English history, but you could go to LE; DB's got a set of Encyclopaedia Britannica there. I'm sure you'll find what you need. Research the life thoroughly, and if you want confirmation, ask DB to submit it to the Nirmanakaya.'

'Nirmanakaya? What's a Nirmanakaya, a computer memory bank or something?'

'Well, not exactly, but you're not too far from the truth. Nirmanakaya is the Sanskrit word for 'Divine Rebel'. It is a light being of the highest order. The Nirmanakaya, having achieved adeptship on the Earth, decides to sacrifice its spiritual evolution by incarnating again to help humanity. This being of fire chooses to live through a number of highly evolved souls who serve The Divine Plan.

'A Nirmanakaya will sometimes select a physical body from the moment of its conception and progressively transform it with spiritual fire. The *Chosen One* that houses the consciousness of this great being becomes a Nirmanakaya in human form. DB's physical body is used by one of these beings. By virtue of its level of spiritual awareness and development, it can access the memory banks of all time, the Akashic records. All past, present and future lives are impressed in these memory banks - just like the collective unconscious of Carl Jung. Every ripple, breeze and crystal; every flower, bird and animal; every cataclysm, every action and reaction is never lost nor forgotten. An imprint of it stays forever; it's a record of the planet's evolution, through kingdom after kingdom, all eventually leading to perfection.'

I was in awe of Linda's exposition. They were all philosopher teachers. She was fired up; I could feel the energy and see it in her eyes.

I did not for one moment think that DB was so spiritually aware. He was almost a God. The group was privileged to have such a being living in their presence. I often wondered why they stayed, day after day, struggling with their unconscious and trying to maintain a positive outer personality. He knew their past lives, their karma and their potential. They must have had previous lives together and they must incarnate life after life, to serve the Will of God. I was beginning to believe I was one of them. I had lived with them, I had shared part of The Divine Plan; it was my destiny to be united with them, yet again. This time we had to hold the frontiers of the New Age open, for all Humanity.

'Linda, I recorded a waking dream I had this morning. I've tried to analyse it, but it does not make any sense. I know it's meaningful, because according to DB, the waking dream gives an answer to a question. Could you give me your opinion of its meaning?'

'Well, I'll try, but you must understand your personal symbols are related to your life circumstances. For example, the mother is a collective symbol of the emotions. In reality she can be nurturing, supportive and positive. On the other hand, she could be draining, possessive and negative. Your mother appearing in your dream would be positive or negative, depending on your personal relationship with her.'

'Mm, I'm beginning to understand Linda. It's not so cut and dried is it?'

'No, it's very complex indeed; Jung's research is the current, authoritative source on dream analysis, but DB has been able to map the unconscious using astrological symbolism. His approach is revolutionary. It links dream analysis with mythology, metaphysics and astrology. It is the basis of the Claregate Method. You've had your horoscope cast haven't you?'

'Yes, you did it for me, before my ray analysis.'

'Oh yes, I remember now. Do you know how to extract an aspect from it?'

'Mmm, I'm not quite sure. I've started studying the astrology. I know all the hieroglyphs.'

'Claire and I are starting a beginners' esoteric astrology class soon. You must attend it because the astrology is the most important key for the New Age.'

'Brilliant Linda, I'll look forward to it. I'm beginning to get my strength back, but I've still got a long way to go. Maybe my dream is symbolic of my position.'

I relayed the dream to Linda in graphic detail and emotion.

'Mmm, have you got your chart handy? There are groups of symbols in your dream that link to the same planets and signs.'

'Yes, it's upstairs in my diary. I'll just be a few seconds.'

'That's the best place for it. When it's open and you've propositioned your unconscious with a written question, your higher self will bathe you with meaning. It could come in a dream, a vision, or in a meditation. Do you use an arrow?'

'What? An arrow, what kind of arrow and where do I put it?'

'It's not in the books, but cut a small arrowhead shape out of card. Wrap it with silver foil and put a bit of blue tack on the back. Use it as a magnetic pointer under a question you've posited in your diary. It helps focus the energy and because of its metallic surround, it attracts an easier response from spirit. We're all bathed in magnetic fields; like attracts like.'

'I'll get my chart.'

They're all bonkers, I thought. A metallic arrow? A magnetic link with spirit? They were nuts.

'Here you are Linda, DB's scribbled some notes on the back of it when he did my rays. I can't decipher his doctor's scrawl, it's a mess.'

'Mmm, well it's nothing important; it's just some ray stuff. The horse with no saddle represents your need to harness your mind and personality. You need to put a saddle on it and direct it towards the path of self-realisation. It's too fat and heavy to jump over hurdles. You've got too many attachments; too many personality hooks holding you back. You change your mind because you realise you have no chance of winning and you'll loose £3,000. Maybe you've had second thoughts about coming here. It's hard and you don't want to commit yourself, but the £3,000 is a mystery. The organiser in his trailer getting ready for the race is a reflection of the higher self. You run to tell him the horse is not ready to run. It means you're not ready yet to let go; you've still got issues to sort out. The hurdles represent tests and trials you have to overcome before you can enter the race to the higher self.'

'Bloody hell Linda, It's exactly how I feel; it's uncanny, the depth of meaning and your interpretation was so clear. How do you do it?

'It's years of experience, and of course the astrology. In your chart, you must have the planet Earth in Taurus in the eighth house, or Saturn in Sagittarius in the second, with Scorpio on the cusp.'

Her beady, blue eyes lit up and a beaming smile shone from her bright face.

'There you are, just as I suspected. You've got both aspects in your chart. That's really weird.'

I was stunned. How could it be? My inner life was giving me direction through my astrology chart. It was brilliant. I was overwhelmed with enthusiasm.

'The Earth is not used in orthodox astrology as a planet with any effect. We attribute it to Sagittarius, which it rules. It points to our limitations and where we lack wholeness. It's where we have abused our energies in past lives. We need to understand it and integrate it in our present life before we can find our true spiritual direction. Your Earth in Taurus in the eighth house represents past life karma related to abuse of money and power. Saturn in Sagittarius in the second amplifies the same energy. Saturn highlights karmic responsibilities; Sagittarius in the second represents the use of money to support spiritual projects. It's all related to your dream.'

For Christ's sake, she knew my whole purpose! My karma, limitations and my potential were predicted from just two aspects in my chart and a dream. This astrology was a powerful tool; linked to the dream life, it was pure wisdom. I had to equip myself in the art of astrology and The Claregate Method. It was imperative if I was to survive here and fulfil my destiny.

'Linda, thanks a lot for the insight. I am overwhelmed by the simplicity of it. It's all connected isn't it?'

'Chris, I've got to go now; I've got some important typesetting to do for DB. He'll be on the blower soon; I can sense his vibrations.'

Dring, dring...Dring, dring.'See what I told you.'

I rummaged around the kitchen for some foil and card, made my arrow and disappeared upstairs, just like a wee boy with new toys to play with. These 'toys' were keys to unlocking ancient wisdom and my immortality. I needed to play with them carefully. I could not afford to abuse them again, not this time around.

CHAPTER 18

I hadn't seen Stellios in days; what was he up to? I wondered how his inner circle meeting went?

Crash, thud...thump! A volley of loud voices and laughter blasted in the lobby. Feet thundered upstairs, like cannon fire, as the boys trundled past. The old door murmured deliberately open. Stellios golden mop popped in, his face supporting a smile beaming from corner to corner.

'Hi Christo, I've bought you something from the Mind, Body and Spirit exhibition. It's nothing much but it's useful. We've been there all setting up our stand.' He opened his fist to reveal a shiny, bronze incense holder.

'Oh...Stellios you shouldn't have. That's really kind of you. I've just started to meditate, that's brilliant, just what I needed. What's this Mind Body and Spirit exhibition?'

'Christo, it's bloody marvellous! It's a gathering of prominent national and international spiritual groups, psychics, astrologers, everyone. It's an annual event we look forward to. We always have a stand there, selling books, tapes and giving out lecture programmes. We also do esoteric astrology readings there. It's fantastic and it lasts for ten days. It starts tomorrow; you ought to see all the weird and colourful faces; it's a sea of alternative thinking. Healers, yoga, Tai Chi, crystals, essential oils, new age music, meditation, the list is endless.' He was buzzing and full of enthusiasm.

'Maybe you could come along to help man the stand. Anyway, how are you? You look really good and almost back to normal.'

'Yes Stellios, I feel good, not yet a hundred per cent, but I'm getting there.'

'That's great.'

'Oh, I see you've been doing some research and analysing your dreams. Hey, who told you about the silver arrow trick?'

'Well, I had this vivid waking dream this morning. It was very powerful and so alive. I tried to analyse it, but I was getting nowhere. I pottered around and decided to go downstairs for a cuppa. Linda was there; we sat down; I needed to talk to someone about the previous life experiences I've had and my waking dream.'

'Christo, you didn't! Don't tell anyone, especially her. She'll use it against you; she's a scheming bitch. Anyway, what previous life experiences?'

'I'm not telling you, it's a secret,' I said in a serious tone.

'Hey, come on, I'm your friend remember; we go back.' His face dropped and his voice sulked.

'Only joking Stellios, you said never to share my experiences with anyone, didn't you?' We both chuckled aloud, throwing our arms around each other.

'Well, tell me, what previous life experiences?'

I relayed the visions I'd experienced to him in graphic detail, and the conversation I'd had with DB.

'Bloody hell Christo, I don't know what's happening to you. Somehow you are being primed for illumination. But it's so quick, too quick. I don't know why; it normally takes years of patient study, meditation and service work to release these types of experiences. Maybe you are needed now. There is no time for you to develop slowly. I don't know Christo, it's way out of my league.'

'Stellios, what should I do? Tell me? If you can't advise me, I'll go crazy.'

'Christo, open your heart to the divine: just go with the flow. Keep writing in your diary, meditate and record your dreams. It will all come together sooner or later.'

'Stellios I must tell you of my waking dream. It's really important I know it is.' I proceeded to tell him my dream. I felt his aura swoon when I mentioned the fear of loosing £3,000. It was as if he was swallowed up by a big black hole. He went quiet on me. With his face ashen, eyes dull and his heart heavy, he proceeded to spill the beans of his meeting with the hierarchy.

'Christo, I did not want to tell you, but they are desperate for more money. Filming costs a fortune; equipment, wages, post production, it all costs. That's why we're doing the exhibition. We've exchanged shares in the film for the stand. It's not cost a penny, but we need to make money. £3,000 to be exact.'

'Fuck sake Stellios, I don't understand it. My dream, the horse; my reluctance to race, the £3,000. What's happening to me? I'm cracking up, I really am. So they want me to give them £3,000, do they?'

'Not exactly, we are trying to raise the money by other means as well.'

I slumped onto my bed, crawled under the covers and bawled my eyes out.

'Stellios, just piss off and leave me alone. You weren't going to tell me, were you? You were going to butter me up with little gifts and tit-bits of knowledge, weren't you?'

'Christo, you've...'

'Don't interrupt me, you scheming little bastard. You're worse than the rest of them. Just fuck off, Stellios, and leave me in peace, go on.'

'Christo, I'm telling you the truth; it's not like that. I'm indebted to you, honest. We are in it together. What was I supposed to do? Think about it?'

'Stellios, just leave me and tell that bitch Elena to leave me alone too. You're all in it together, aren't you?'

He hung his face in shame and left the room, conscience-stricken, leaving me dangling on the fragile threads of my sanity.

Had Linda told me the truth? Was my karma to financially support spiritual projects? Or was it her ploy to get more money out of me? What if it was, though? I am in a position to help; they are struggling to stay afloat. But what about me? It's my money. What about my security? My future?

I was torn apart, dismembered and cut up into little pieces. What was I to do? Do I tell them all to bugger off, take my money and run? Fuck them all and the ancient wisdom. They were all a bunch of hypocrites. Money, money, money, that's all they were after. They were worse than all those materialists out there. At least they knew who their God was. But what about my visions and my dreams? There was something happening to me, something unique and extraordinary. My *daemon*, yes my *daemon*, where was he? Even *he* had deserted me. Was *he* in on the conspiracy too? I somehow had to let go, but I couldn't, not just yet. The horse dream came flooding back. Suddenly, echoing in the distance of my tortured mind, the sound of a melody tingled on my heartstrings.

> *Every breath you take*
> *Every move you make*
> *Every bond you break*
> *Every step you take*
> *I'll be watching you....*
> *I'll be watching you....*
> *I'll be watching you...you...you...*

Sting's haunting song mellowed my emotions and soothed my soul, and I melted into a deep, healing slumber.

I was awakened by *His* familiar calling tone. It came trailing clouds of glory, and I became aware that I was in his presence.

28th. Feb. 1983. 5.30pm, dream
I pass by a figure standing by a wall. Something attracts me to him. I sense his golden aura envelope me, sending out brilliant streams of love and light. It was **Him**, *my* **Daemon**. *I gazed into his deep, crystal clear, green eyes. They shone right through me, to my very core. He was wearing an exquisite, tall, golden headdress. His dark, curly, hair protruded from it in whorls, framing his beautiful, long, beaming visage. He looked like Christ, but different. The high-pitched laser sound zinged powerfully in my ears as a light, brighter than a thousand suns zapped my whole body. I was on fire; He touched me with his index finger on the sacred square inch, in the middle of my forehead, stemming the flow. It eased off into a feeling of total bliss, harmony and unity.*

He was still with me. He had revealed himself to me. It must be a sign. His energy; it filled me with fire and encouragement. I had to pull myself together; the Lord's work beckoned me. I decided to give all I had towards the group's work. They needed it; it was my karma to give it.

I was buzzing with anticipation. What next? I needed to get dressed and show my face downstairs. I quite fancied going to the Mind, Body and Spirit festival in the morning. I heard Elena's shrill in the hallway. She was back, full of beans. She stopped on the landing, chatting to someone for a few minutes, before pushing the creaky, old door.

'Hi Christo. Well, what a surprise, you're up and about.'

'Yes Elena, I am and I intend to take the bull by the horns.'

'What does that mean, take the bull by the horns?'

She looked at me with a puzzled expression. I had forgotten, she knew very little metaphoric language.

'It means I'm going to address certain issues which were causing me grief; I've made decisions about my future.'

'What decisions, tell me, what decisions?' She pleaded with me.

'You'll know soon enough,' I said, marching out of the room.

I saw Stellios on the stairway. He cowered as I approached him. My face was flushed, full of fire and I had a determined and focussed stare.

'Stellios, forgive me for my outburst, I'm sorry. I've given the matter some thought and you're right, you couldn't have handled it any differently. I appreciate your honesty; you could have hidden it from me, but you didn't.' He sighed with relief.

'No Christo, I should have told you right away. But you picked it up anyway, in your dream. I can't hide anything from you; you must be tuning into the group's collective consciousness.'

'What does that mean Stellios?'

'Well, you've earned your spurs. You have been accepted into the outer circle and I have no doubt, soon, you will be sitting deciding policy in the ranks of the inner circle. When you start picking up that sort of information from your dream life, you are ready. The previous life visions, your karmic ties with DB and your soul contact, confirm you are an accepted disciple now.'

We walked downstairs into the lounge; dinner was not until seven o'clock. We had time to chill out.

'Chris I've got something to tell you.'

'What is it Stellios, not another one of your confessions, is it?' He hung his head low, his tone of voice sagged.

'It's Pete. He's left, he's not coming back; he couldn't handle it any more. We all went to set up the stand at the festival. He took one look at the freedom of expression there and that was it. I doubt he'll make it out there; you know he has talent, his short stories were fantastic.'

'Stellios what a shame; He showed me his work, it was so inspirational, so spiritual, just what young kids need in this climate of delinquency. Under-age drink, drug taking, sex and broken homes are all ingredients of social, moral and spiritual depravity. What will he do? Where will he go? Does he have family?'

'Yes, his mum's still alive; she's a single parent. His father used to beat the shit out them. He was a chronic alcoholic and a heroin addict. God, Christo, we're lucky to be born into a Greek family. At least we had a solid foundation, moral and religious understanding. And we were taught respect.'

'Well, I hope he does well, I really hope so.'

'Steve is going to keep in touch with him. You know he's illustrated the book for him, don't you?'

'Yes Stellios, Steve's designs are brilliant. He's a talented illustrator.'

'Did you know he was a famous Victorian artist in a previous life?'

'Stellios, come on, you're pulling my leg.'

'He was Aubrey Beardsley, the cartoonist and illustrator. He worked closely with Oscar Wilde and illustrated Lord Tennyson's epic poem, 'Morte d'Arthur'.

I don't know much about him, Lord Tennyson or Oscar Wilde. I'll have to research it when I've got time.'

'Oh Chris, another thing. When someone opts out, you know, leaves; it's not talked about. No sentiment is ever shown, not openly at least. So don't mention it at the dinner table.'

'Talking of dinner. I'll have to start a cooking rota. We all need to share preparing breakfast, lunch and dinner now that Pete's gone.'

'I'm here. Does anyone want me?' DB's voice blasted. The dogs darted in, howling and barking with excitement, their claws tearing shards of wood out of the lounge door.

Ding, ding. Ding, ding!

Dinner was ready and the boys started appearing from all directions. It was a full house tonight. Two chairs remained vacant, Elena's and Pete's. The holes stood gaping, as if rotten teeth had been extracted from a set of gums. We all looked at each other, knowing that Pete had deserted camp. But where was Elena? Why did she not come down for dinner?

'Oh, Chris, is that you or am I seeing things?' DB said in a sarcastic tone, looking over his half-rims.

'Yes DB, it's me. Any chance of going to man the stand at the festival tomorrow?'

'Hey, you're well informed for a person who's been in bed for a fortnight.' He wanted a response; he was testing me to see if I was back to normal.

'DB, I have my spies out informing me of the activities. I've not missed a trick.' Stellios ducked his head slightly to hide his facial expression. Steve smirked, kicked him and Jeremy's rat shot out from his pocket onto the table. The dogs went wild; chairs flew, plates smashed and cutlery clashed against glass. The whole dinning room was in an uproar. DB sat there laughing at the chaos and pointing at me.

'Chris, you're certainly back on form. Where's the lovely Elena tonight? Is she exhausted? I worked her ragged. We had all the main actors on set today; it was so demanding.'

'She must be resting DB. She did look a wee bit jaded when she came in.'

'Nice meal Pete, where's the gravy?' DB shouted in the direction of the kitchen.

' Coming right away!' Claire shouted, as Linda magically appeared holding the gravy boat. It was his was of throwing down a gauntlet for debate. Silence loomed for a while. We all knew he had gone, even he did. What was he doing?

'He was a fucking loser anyway. Good riddance to the good-for-nothing, stuttering, dickhead.' It was Dick's voice, true to form. He never minced his words, ever.

'You fucking bastard Dick! All you ever think about is yourself and your poxy print works. I'll kill you, you fucking wanker.' Steve's towering body overshadowed Dick's impish frame. He was fuming with anger. I'd never seen him this way before. He had cracked. We had to restrain him; he was throwing blows into the air. They already had an axe to grind anyway, over that rickety old teapot. Dick just sat there grinning like a Cheshire cat. He knew he had found Steve's buttons and he was pushing them.

'Ha! And that book of his and your illustrations; they are all crap; all of it is crap. Just because he was Lewis Caroll and you were Aubrey Beardsley in a previous life it doesn't mean you're talented now. You all live in the fucking past, building castles in the air and being deluded by dreams of grandeur. It's what is in the here and now that counts: not what you were. The previous life thing is a load of bollocks anyway.'

'Right boys, that's enough now. Calm down, the party's over,' DB said in a sombre tone.

'Watch, I'll give him a fortnight. He'll be back, with his tail in between his legs, whimpering and licking ass; little fucking lap dog.'

'Now, Dick that's quite enough! We've had enough excitement for tonight, calm down!' DB shouted and thumped his fists on the table. Steve threw us off, sending us flying like skittles and stomped out. The table resumed as if nothing had happened. Silence ruled and tension seethed behind our placid personas.

'Chris, yes you can go with the boys tomorrow. Take Steve with you to cool down. Get him some healing and incense for meditation. I think he needs it.'

'Brilliant, I'll look forward to it DB.'

He promptly rose and left the table, without notice. The dogs followed their beloved master and the dining room door thudded closed behind them.

'Stellios, why didn't you tell me Pete was Lewis Caroll in a previous life?'

'Christo, I'll talk to you about it tomorrow. I'm off to calm Steve down. Goodnight.'

'See you tomorrow, Stellios, goodnight.' I raced upstairs to tell Elena about the night's events; she must have heard the fracas anyway. I creaked the door open. The light from the landing streaked into the dark, silent room, like a cinema torchlight.

'Elena, Elena! Are you sleeping?' There was no answer. I turned the light onto a bundle of clothes piled high on the bed. She had gone, disappeared, nowhere to be seen; I was in shock. Where could she have gone? It was my fault; I frightened her. Maybe she's gone to visit her aunt who lived in Finsbury Park? All types of scenarios flashed in my mind. Had she gone out? But with whom?

The girl's were cooking tonight; they were in the kitchen. I paced up and down for what seemed hours. It was my fault; I had driven her away with all that negative projection. I was a selfish bastard. She was a saint to put up with my feeble whimpering and foul language for so long. The door slowly creaked open... thank God. It was her.

'Where have you been? I've been worried sick about you. Are you all right?'

'I've been sitting in the garden pondering on things. There was a brilliant full moon and a crystal clear, starry sky. It was so peaceful, until I heard the racket inside. What was that all about? I saw Steve race past me. He was in a terrible state. Is he okay?'

'I'll tell you about it tomorrow. Guess where I'm going then?'

'Where?'

'The Mind, Body and Spirit festival, isn't it exciting?'

'That's great. I'm glad you are getting back to normal. I'd really had enough of your abuse and self-pity. I'm on set again tomorrow. We've got an early start and a heavy schedule. I won't wake you in the morning.'

'Okay Elena, I'm really sorry about my behaviour. I'll make it up to you, I promise.'

We cuddled up in bed for the first time in ages. Wounds subsided, cares melted away and peace reigned in our hearts, at least for now.

CHAPTER 19

Elena got up early; I sensed the void of her sweet, warm body as she left my side. I was embroiled in tense dreams at the time; my consciousness was colliding between two worlds. On waking, the euphoria I felt was still with me.

1st March 7.30am, waking dreams.

I am on a platform in an eerie, deserted, church. I am drawn to a massive painting by an overwhelming, magnetic energy. It's a painting of a robed, aristocrat, dressed in rich, deep colours and velvet, kingly textures. His domineering stance and steely stare from his beady, black eyes went right through me. As I focus on his pale and austere face, it dematerialises in front of me. It distorts into a succession of different visages. I am terrified and start running away. To my horror, the face blasts out of the painting, chasing me. I turn around and smash it with my fist. It shatters into a thousand shards and metamorphoses into my golden cross and chain.

I am in a deep, dark cave, searching for something. I discover a large, wooden chest. It's covered in cobwebs, dust and dirt. I start cleaning it and scrape away old paint. I hear two loud thumps and Stellios voice shouting my name.

'Christo, Christo, the Akashic records are in there; they are stone blocks which record all past, present and future lives.'

Before I could recall the remainder of the dream, Stellios popped his flaming mop around the door.

'Christo, I've been calling for you and knocking the hell out of the door. Are you awake?'

'Stellios, is that you? I've just heard your voice in a waking dream.'

'Christo, yes it's me. Get up, we're leaving in 30 minutes and we've got things to pack, come on.'

'Okay, I'll be down. I'm so excited, my first exposure to the Mind, Body and Spirit exhibition, it's just great.'

I jumped into the shower cubical and recalled my dreams as I scrubbed my face. They were so vivid and full of energy. I was being flooded with illumination. Two dreams linked together, with layers of meaning. God, that face dream and the cross and chain, what did all that mean? Out of the blue, I heard his calling vibrate in my ears. It thrust me into a vivid conscious experience.

> *8am, vivid conscious experience*
> *I was buzzing all over; pins and needles shot through my torso. My vision blanked; I was filled with light and catapulted into an inner space. I was shooting towards the centre of a multi-dimensional spiral. Waaoo! I penetrated the kaleidoscopic 'eye' and I found myself whizzing from life to life. The Great War, Victorian, Georgian, Hanoverian, French Revolution, Civil War, Renaissance Italy, Rome, Greece, Egypt and on, into infinity. The whole experience was like a merry-go-round. Every complete cycle merged into the next; I felt my consciousness smashing through a crystal sheet from chaos into earthly reality.*

My head was swimming as I came too, sprawled out, naked and shivering with fright, like a babe thrust out of its mothers' watery womb onto the floor.

Bloody hell, what was going on? Where was I? What is all this water? My consciousness swept back to reality, grounding me, as I clambered out of that space capsule. Dizzy and dazed, I waded downstairs, still in a state.

For Christ's' sake, what was happening? I couldn't comprehend it, couldn't control it; it was taking over my life. What am I going to do? How am I going to cope out here, in the real world? I've got responsibilities: a wife, people banking on my support.

'Christo, are you ready? We're leaving soon. We need to get going if we are to miss the M25 rush hour, come on.'

'Stellios, I'm coming, be with you in a tick.' Still wet, I threw on some clothes, squished into my socks and shoes, flicked my hair back and forth and dashed downstairs.

They were all sitting in the van waiting, Steve, Jeremy, Ron and Stellios. They had their Sunday best on, bless them. I'd never seen such a motley crew; ragged shirts, frayed collars, ripped jeans, holey cardies and threadbare jackets. But their angelic faces shone with a bright inner light. It did not matter what their outer garments looked like; they were not going to a fashion show. Their 'inner garments' were immaculate, pure and spiritual.

'Sorry I'm late guys, I blacked out in the shower.'

'Bloody hell Chris, are you sure you're okay? You must try to eat more. Do you take any vitamins?' Steve said, patting me on the back with one of his enormous, spatula hands.

'Thanks for the concern Steve. I think I'll be all right. The illness and inner stress has taken its toll, but I'm on the mend. Anyway, I wouldn't miss this for a million pounds.'

The doors slammed shut on the Claregate limo. It was a clapped out, beat up, light blue Ford Transit. Gerald kept it from falling apart. He was a mechanical genius. The whole 'fleet' was in ship-shape. They were all old rust buckets, but he got them through their MOT's. He was a miracle worker.

My mind cast back to Pete going 'awol' and his previous life as Lewis Caroll. Was he really Lewis Caroll? No, he couldn't have been, could he? I knew virtually nothing about him. All I knew was he had written *Alice in Wonderland* and *Through the Looking Glass*. Pete's short stories were inspired. His vision to help restore fantasy and imagination in children's minds and quality of life was honourable. Maybe he was? Maybe not? But Dick, the savage cynic stated he was.

'Listen guys, about Pete. Was he really Lewis Caroll in a previous life? And if he was, what the hell was he doing rustling up snacks in the Claregate kitchen?' There was a prolonged, spooky silence and I felt their auras internalise.

'Chris, do you know anything about the life of Lewis Caroll? His appearance, his personality, his failings, his gifts?' Ron huffed as he glanced back at me in the mirror.

'No not really, that's why I am intrigued.'

'Chris, I've seen a portrait of him and read a biography' Ron spouted. 'He's the spitting image of Pete. That dark, wavy mop, pale complexion, those deep, black, soulful eyes reflecting his tormented inner life. He even had a stutter, would you believe it. Lewis Caroll had a stutter. Pete, sure as dam it, inherited that and the rest.'

'But why was he at Claregate?' I asked.

'He and the rest of us belong to the English Ashram. We have been together, life-after-life, age-after-age: writers, poets, artists, philosophers, statesmen, kings and queens. The English Ashram is a focal point of planetary energy. It is a chakra in that august consciousness we call humanity. It is ensouled by a being called a Nirmanakaya, who overshadows DB.

'The ashrams' function is to draw towards it souls of the right calibre and spiritual standing, in order to enhance or maintain a quality needed for 'The Plan' of Great Britain. In the Dark Ages it was the Nirmanakaya Merlin and King Arthur who held the ashramic energies together. The crusading spirit of a Lionheart; A Chaucer who set the course of the English language. A Cromwell who established a parliamentary state. Poet laureates, writers and philosophers like Milton, Browning, Shakespeare, Bryon, Colleridge, Wordsworth, Wilde and Bacon. The dogged, bullish determination of a Churchill, winning in the face of insurmountable odds.

'We are all back now to usher in this New Age of Aquarius. Apart from ancient wisdom, the esoteric astrology is the most important teaching. It synthesises astrology, mythology, psychology and dream analysis. It's a vibrant, living, regenerating wisdom, which will carry us into the next millennium. It's immense; it's a new crusade. We need men of courage, commitment and honour, to battle against all odds, to maintain the energy flow to the ashram and help Britain be great again.'

Bloody hell, I did not for one minute realise the importance of it all. We were on the frontiers of a new age. We were the maintainers and saviours of the English ashram. They all nodded in appreciation of Ron's inspiring words and heavy sighs bellowed at the task ahead. We were on the front line; it was shit or bust. Our country needed us.

The battle cries of the ages echoed in my ears. Victory, defeat; life, death; praise and gloom. I saw the Union flag triumphantly fluttering to Land of Hope and Glory. We were the brave souls who soldiered on, to enhance the English ashram. I knew I was one of them called into battle, yet again.

We made good time on the motorway and in minutes we approached the Earls Court junction. Banners, signs and posters plastered all over the place led us to Olympia, the 'New Age Mecca'. Hoards of bodies lined up outside the venue, God what a sight. An array of rainbow colours clashed against a sea of demure black. Orange robes merged with whites. Drumbeats, bell tolls, chants and new age music bawled from ghetto blasters. What a weird bunch of humanity. They were certainly all different. Each one of them had a point and they were here to voice it.

We reversed the van into the loading bay and whacked the stuff onto a trolley, which we wheeled through row after row of stands. I gazed up towards the balcony to the 'readers' tables. Banner after banner meandered in a sea of sound, colour and incense; all were advertising amazing gifts; tarot, palmistry, clairvoyance, graphology, astrology, and runes. I felt my head lighten as I was overwhelmed by the awesome aura of the place. I held onto the trolley as it turned the corner to our stand. Two pixy-like frames clambering over computers greeted us as we approached.

'Hi boys, glad to see you. Oh who is this? Do we have a new recruit?' The elf said pointing to me.

'Dave this is Chris Kasparis. Chris, this is Dave and Jenny. They calculate the astrology charts for us,' Ron said, shaking their hands.

'Hi both, pleased to meet you. I didn't realise you would be here. So you calculate horoscopes then? I didn't know they were computed.'

'Well, we input the info and it churns out the data. Jenny draws up the chart and Ron interprets it,' said Dave, fiddling with the wires.

What a pair of weird souls. They looked like they'd been plucked out of a Tolkien book. They complimented each other perfectly though. Dave was pale, withdrawn, scrawny and dressed in black, with a matted, ponytail lashing his neck. Jenny was awash with multi-coloured robes and wore big, dangling earrings, a mop of dark, frizzy hair and the largest black, horn-rimmed specs. They dwarfed her pygmy face as she propped them up and screwed her eyes into a squint. I was sure I was in the company of hobgoblins and ragamuffins. I was the odd one out. I looked respectable, clean-shaven and approachable. I had to be if we were going to attract the attention of 'Joe Bloggs'. To tell you the truth, I was in utter shock and turmoil. I did not realise all this existed.

The new age and all its ramifications were like a Hydra with a hundred false heads to each true one. What was I doing in this Babylon? Had I made the right choice? I was a lost soul in this mega-mix of faith healers, weird cults, therapists, Indian yogis and hippies. Claregate seemed like a monastery compared to this lot. I had lived a sheltered life, brought up a Greek Orthodox, immersed in faith and respect. I had followed my family into a materialistic lifestyle, where money, status and marriage were important and I had end up here. I looked around at Stellios and the others; their faces were beaming and their eyes were glazed over. It seemed that their souls were possessed. They just stood there mesmerised by the whole arena.

New age music blared from a multitude of stands. An intermittent din and clash of cymbals harmonised with bells and drums. A mish-mash of tainted incense rose in the thick air, zigzagging and looping. Their pungent fragrances battled each other and rose like dragons breath.

'Oh my God, Oh my God!' I shouted and I clawed inside my open shirt searching for my cross. A devilish band of black, hooded scallywags, trunching in unison, swished towards our stand. With every step they made, a gash of crimson, satin lining flashed out before them. It looked like a sea of fresh, dripping blood against their black, dragging cloaks. As I glanced at the grotesque sight; I felt my stomach churning, then...whoosh, the leader unveiled himself... He had a pentagram etched in the middle of his pale, zombie-like cranium. His pure black hair was spiked up in devilish horns. Pentagram earrings hung from his lobes and his arms were a tapestry of ghoulish tattoos. He was drenched in pure ebony tunics. From under his black shroud he thrust a skull-encrusted, spindly staff at me. His beady, black, blood-shocked eyes rolled like a great white shark coming in for the kill. He stared right through me to my shivering soul. I fell into a momentary trance as he battled with my spirit. I grasped at my cross yet again, this time inwardly chanting The Lord's Prayer. I grappled with his satanic presence and he sensed the power of my faith. Suddenly, he blasted out an almighty, sardonic laugh, stuck out his long, snaky tongue, thumped his staff and stared at me with those soulless, hypnotic eyes. Swish... his black mantle shrouded my head and splintered my vision. I was buckled up on the floor by now, with my fist squeezing down hard on my cross, the chain almost strangling me.

'Chris, Chris! Are you all right? Chris, please say something.'

I came to, with Ron and Steve holding my feet in the air and Stellios sprinkling cold water on my face.

'Ron, Steve, Stellios, Is that you?' I grabbed at their clothing, trying to raise myself. My vision was still blurred and I was shivering all over.

'Did you see that? Did you see that?' I shouted, pointing frantically in the direction of the evil entourage.

'Stellios, get me the fuck out of here. This must be hell on Earth. This is no new age. There's no truth, beauty and goodness here. It's like Sodom and Gomorrah.'

'Christo, calm down, calm down. Sit here for a minute.'

'No, no, please get me out of here.'

'Alright, alright, let's go outside for a breath of fresh air.' He helped me stagger towards the door. I took one enormous breath of air and slowly came to my senses.

'Christo, it's my fault. I should have warned you about the Wiccans. They look so evil and devilish, but believe me, they are not black magicians, even if they look the part. They are pagans and they worship Earth gods and goddesses. They are harmless, really. He was the high priest. It's all a bit of drama; an act. They love dressing up. It breaks the monotony of their drab, outer lives. Some of them have respectable jobs, like accountants, solicitors and teachers; you'd be surprised.'

'Stellios, for fuck sake, they look like all the menacing figures in those satanic horror movies. I've had it; I want to go home. I've had enough of the new age. It's more like the old age of idol worship and ritual sacrifice. Where's the spirituality in that?'

'Christo, listen to me. The new age is like a fountain of life and energy. Old truths merge with new truths; it's like old wine in new bottles. Even the early Christians were persecuted for their revolutionary beliefs in the beginning. In this Age of Aquarius, the accent is on knowledge, universal understanding, tolerance and freedom of choice. Yes, some of the stands you'll find in here are a bit frightening, especially for a newcomer like you. You'll even find a couple of Christian stands in there. That's what it's all about, diversity, creativity, free will and free choice.

'It's a vast, multi-colourful, arena of wisdom and teaching. Yes, it's a minefield; you don't know what you're getting into. It could be for you, but if you don't try it, you won't find out. Some people drift all their lives, from this fad to that therapy, to this psychic to that medium, to this lecture and that workshop, never making any impact or gaining any understanding. We are lucky; we are part of an established philosophy that can be traced back to the birth of civilisation and beyond. We have a solid grounding and a sound foundation. We are also blessed with the presence of DB's direction. That's the difference between us and most of them in there.'

'Okay, okay, Stellios, just give me time to catch my breath. I'll take your word for it for now. Look at me, I've clutched my cross so hard in my fist my fingers have gone black and blue.'

'Seriously. Don't worry. I was the same when on my first visit. Chill out, have a leisurely walk around, ask questions, don't judge people by their appearance.'

'No chance, Stellios. Take me back to the stand. I'll just hide behind it for a while.'

'Don't be a big sissy Christo. Really, they are all harmless, most of them are like us.'

I was not convinced by Stellios' talk. But I waddled back in with my tail between my legs and settled down behind the stand.

CHAPTER 20

My dream this morning now made sense. The cross and chain were my saviour. I was in shock. The whole multi-sensory, multi-faceted exhibition experience had thrown me. That bloody witch and his horny visage had shattered my 'fluffy bunny' perception of the New Age forever. All the diversity was a maze, a labyrinth leading to a monstrous lair, where a beast consumes those who take the wrong path. Was I on the right path? My Christian roots still had a strong hold on me. Was my faith limiting my progress? Was it a crutch for me to balance my feeble frame upon? All these questions collided in my schizoid skull.

'Chris hand me a Psychology of Discipleship and In The Steps of the Masters. They're in that box under the table,' Stellios chirped as he chatted to a customer. He was beaming with enthusiasm; he had made a sale. Ron was busy interpreting a chart and Steve was showing someone a pile of posters.

I plucked up the courage and emerged from my protective pouch. I felt intimidated by the whole thing. I could not communicate because I did not know enough and my confidence was nil. How could I advise someone or sell anything? I sank into a sack of indecision and introversion. I was good for nothing, a failure. I just sat there, hopeless, while the others tried their best to sell. That £3,000 had to be raised somehow and I was not helping matters by just sitting there all taciturn.

The day passed quite quickly; the lads had done well. They were in high spirits as they closed the stand down. Dave and Jenny fiddled with their computers as we waved goodbye to them and set off for something to eat.

'We normally have a curry and a beer after a hard festival day; that's the reward for coming,' Ron said. He pushed open the door to be welcomed by a turbaned Pakistani giant. 'Table for five and five pints of beer please, we're gasping of thirst.'

We were seated quickly and a bowl of popadums and five jugs magically appeared out of the blue. We all dashed for our brew. I felt a bit uneasy, as I had not contributed much.

'Put that thing away Jeremy. If they see it on the table, it'll end up on the 'special of the day' menu tomorrow,' Steve blared as Rattie darted out, sniffing for food. We were in stitches. The rat scampered around the table, slaloming in and out of the cructs and cutlery.

'Fuck sake Jeremy, put it away; you'll get us chucked out or the health inspectors will close the place down,' whispered Ron and punched him on the shoulder.

'Yes, it's infested with rodents!'

'But Sab, it's a customers pet, honest Sab.'

'Come on. Try the other one; it's got bells on it. Do you think I was born yesterday?' Stellios joked mimicking the hypothetical conversation between the health inspector and the restaurant owner. The boys were in great spirits; the festival was a brilliant escape from the heaviness and seriousness of Claregate.

'Well Chris, what did you think of it all then? You were quite withdrawn,' Ron said probing inquisitively.

I hesitated for a while, brooding before I answered.

'Mmm, to tell you the truth, I was not prepared for it. I didn't realise the shock it would give me and seeing that horny witch and his ebony entourage capped it for me.'

'I noticed you were clutching your cross. Are you religious or something?' Jeremy butted in abruptly. 'You know it's an attachment, a crutch you need to get rid of,' he concluded.

'Listen, you might be right, but that little, horny devil scared the shit out of me. I know I have to deal with it; I've had it confirmed in a waking dream. It was....'

Stellios kicked me under the table and raised his eyebrows. I got the message.

'It was so revealing and so vivid. I'll have to work on its meaning. It's been great though. I'd like to come again. I promise I'll be more useful next time. I didn't realise we could drink alcohol and eat meat and still develop spiritually.'

'Yes, well it's okay really, and we swear a lot too, don't we lads?' Steve boasted with the recognition of the others. 'Vegetarianism does help attune the body to higher vibrations. But if working with all the disciplines is the gauge-stick, then swearing is just a way to get rid of unconscious shit that sometimes consumes us. It acts as a catharsis clearing the dross that surrounds the pearl of great price lost in the mud of matter,' Steve said in a philosophical tone.

'Celibacy is sometimes undertaken too, as a means of raising energies to the higher chakras. It's no easy feat, as you can imagine. It's another test on the road to adeptship,' Stellios added, as if he was an expert.

'It's all relative, if you were a person with very little sex drive and limited sexual experiences, it would be no great deal becoming celibate. On the other hand, a male heterosexual, testosterone blasting, slave to sex would benefit tremendously by controlling his sex drive and even becoming celibate,' Ron said nudging Steve and giving him the eye.

'The whole point is energy transfer. DB says only five chakras should be fully functioning in a disciple for any balanced development to take place: two below the diaphragm and three above. The root chakra always functions in all beings. That leaves either the solar plexus, the emotional chakra or the sacral, sex centre as the other. The choice is always up to the individual,' Jeremy said in between tucking into his Chicken Tikka.

'Mmm, that means fucking but with no emotional attachments, or emotional love with no sexual intimacy, doesn't it?' I deduced.

'You got it, but it's not forced upon us. We have free choice in the matter. After all we are human and we are not all going to be adepts, are we?' Jeremy said, chuckling and cheering to an encore around him.

'Let's get cracking, it's getting late and we've got another nine days to go,' Ron commanded as he settled the bill.

The roads were clear, that was one consolation. We tugged along in silence, each one of us in deep thought, meditation or sleeping. I needed to rid myself of my cross, my Christian crutch. It did not mean I was denying Christ's message, but I had to ultimately find the Christ within, that was true Christ consciousness. I faded into a reverie, brooding and pondering over dream images that faded into infinity.

The old van skidded and ground to a halt in the driveway. Ron sighed with relief as we all woke from our slumber.

'Guys, leave the stuff on for tomorrow. Get some rest, we'll be ready to go at eight o'clock sharp,' he shouted then disappeared into the main entrance.

'Fancy a nightcap Chris? I need to talk to you,' Stellios said in a secretive tone.

'Okay, I'm off to the toilet; I'm bursting. See you in a minute.'

Stellios had laid out the teacups and biscuits on the table. For all his OND in catering and hotel management, it was thrown willy-nilly, in a bundle. Not that it mattered; after all, we were not working in an Egon Ronay restaurant.

'You must stop telling everyone about your dreams and visions, Chris. They don't need to know. I understand you want to share your experiences with everyone; it's natural when you're beginning to tread the path, but it's a *glamour*.'

'*Glamour*? What does that mean Stellios? There's nothing glamorous about it, I can assure you. All the anguish, pain and the uncertainty. I'm on edge all the time.'

'Christo, people would kill for some of your experiences. Just keep quiet in future. Even I don't need to know. Do I ever confide in you about my dreams and things? Glamour in the spiritual sense is an umbrella expression for a number of things. It all boils down to boasting and self-importance. It is a major pitfall in spiritual development and bars aspirants to adeptship.

'Oh, I've made contact with my *daemon;* I've seen him in my dreams; I have OOBEs, I see auras, I have previous life recall.

I am. I have. It's all ego bullshit. The most important thing is humility. Remember, Christ entered Jerusalem on a donkey. Do you understand?'

'Yes Stellios, but I'll explode if I can't share it with someone.'

'That's what your diary's for; nobody has to know. It's between you and Him at the end of the day.'

I sagged as if I was an errant schoolboy being sent to the corner.

'*Silence is golden*' the ancients said. Digging for treasure was always undertaken in deadly silence. If there were any sounds you would be found out and the treasure would be lost forever. It's the same with wisdom. If it is leaked it is lost, it loses it's magic. Do you understand what I mean, Christo?'

I was very frustrated and angry, but I knew he was right.

'I'll try. Do you Steve never confide in each other? Bet you do, don't you?'

'Only if it is directly connected to him. I sometimes receive subjective information related to Steve. Of course, you can still exchange ideas, ask questions and debate with the group.'

'Okay, got your point; I'll bear it in mind in future. I'm really glad I can be honest with you Stellios. Thanks for all the support.'

It's all right; let's call it a day. Gosh, is that the time? Goodnight.'

'Yes goodnight; See you in the morning.'

I plodded upstairs and slowly squeaked the old door open to Elena's lovely, warm, sensuous body. I stole by her side and cuddled into her bosom. After all the chaos at the festival, it was so good to come back to her embrace. I slept soundly until the creek of the old door wakened me.

'Christo, are you up? We're setting off earlier, sorry to wake you.'

'Alright Stellios, shhh...don't wake Elena, she's still sleeping.'

The following few days passed so quickly. Elena and I were like ships in the night. We hardly spoke for days. She was busy and I was occupied with the festival. I had settled into the festival environment. The boys had broken me in. I was thrust into the cauldron and I could not escape. It was the last day, we had done really well: sold books, Ron did a number of charts, but it was still not enough to cover our filming expenses. I had already decided to give them the money, but I wanted to see an effort made on their part too. I was manning the stand on my own, thinking about the whole arena and what I was doing here. The boys had wandered off for a break when I was confronted by the organiser and her daughter.

'Hi there, I'm Gay Wilson and this is Katie. We are collecting a leaflet from all the stand holders. Katie and I are going to make a collage of the logos of this year's participating groups. We will frame it and it will be the main prize in a raffle. All the proceeds will be donated to cancer research. Come on give us your money and a leaflet.'

'No problem, How much is a strip?'

'Only £2, that's all. It's hardly going to break the bank, is it?'

'There we are, it's for a good cause, I doubt I'll win, I've never won anything in my life before.'

'Thanks Chris, Oh, say hello to John when you see him next.'

'Okay Gay, It was nice to meet you, bye Katie.'

I did my duty and contributed. The boys wandered back and persuaded me to venture out.

'Chris it's your last chance for another year. Make the most of it.'

I meandered round the stands. Some had jumped on the new age bandwagon and were selling all sorts of paraphernalia at extortionate prices. Yes, the materialists had infiltrated the ranks and were after a quick killing. Claregate was fighting for survival on the front line, begging and borrowing to say afloat, trying to do 'The Lord's work'. Others were lining their pockets with loot, taken from gullible, bleary-eyed public, who were after a quick fix with no effort. It was sickening to see, but some jewels shone out from the rabble. The National Federation of Spiritual Healers, The Brahma Kumaris meditation centres, the Hare Krishna Consciousness Society, the Theosophical Society, The Lucis Trust, Bailey's publishing house and a few more were gems in the crown of the exhibition.

I got back after buying Elena incense and a holder.

'What's this then Chris? Gay Wilson came round with it. She said you'd won it in the raffle. Congratulations. Look, it has all the exhibitor's logos on it. What a fantastic souvenir to take home.'

'Bloody hell, I've never won anything in my life before this. I am overwhelmed. Just wait until Elena sees it, she'll be thrilled to bits.'

'Come on guys. Lets break this stand down and get the hell out of here fast. The traffic back home will be horrendous if we get trapped in it,' Ron shouted, tearing off the drapes.

Within an hour we were on our way back to Claregate. We just missed rush hour and the M25 was not too congested. We were all knackered after long, hard days. I hadn't time to dream, never mind record any of them. My meditation schedule was up the spout, but I had a few moments at the exhibition each day. Anyway, it was a mega-meditation standing in that environment for days. I felt quite good about myself after that dreadful first day. That memory would never be erased; it's part of my personal consciousness now. It will be ingrained in my akashic records, it affected me deeply; it changed something inside of me for all eternity.

But what about the collage? Did it mean anything? Or was it a complete fluke that I won it. Imagine, out of over 500 stands, I won the thing. Was it symbolic? Maybe. I wasn't sure. It looked awesome though.

'We're home lads, thank God. Leave the stuff in the van; we can unload it in the morning. I'm absolutely shagged out, see you all tomorrow,' Ron said falling out of the van.

'Yes Ron, we deserve a lie-in tomorrow, don't you think?' Jeremy spouted as he crawled into the hall.

'Your lucky, I'll be down at LE giving DB a de-brief. You know what he's like.' Ron sighed and clambered upstairs.

I was buzzing with excitement; it was only 8.30. I could hear Linda and Claire talking as they washed up downstairs. I bounced to our room with my prize.

'Elena, Elena! Look what I won at the exhibition, and I've got you a little present too.'

The room was deserted. Her clothes were thrown all over the place. Her toiletries were in a bundle, as if she had got ready in a hurry. I wondered where she was; perhaps she was downstairs with the girls. I trundled down, my heart thudding in my chest and my emotions on overload.

'Hi girls. Is Elena with you? I thought I heard her voice in the back.'

'No Chris,' sneered Linda in a smug tone. 'She wasn't at dinner either. She was so excited. She did say she was going out, but I didn't catch where. It all happened too quickly. Isn't she upstairs getting ready for you?'

She knew where she was; the cow knew everything. I felt it deep in my bones. The bitch had something to do with it, I was sure.

I slammed the door, dashed upstairs and began rummaging around for clues.

Where the bloody hell was she? She should have left a note or something. Maybe it was on the bed, I thought, and I frantically flicked through a pile of her things. A black and white 'still shot' flipped from a file, sailed in slow motion and descended earthwards. I caught it in mid-air and flicked it over.

'Oh my God. Oh my God,' I shouted. My heart wrenched in two and my soul wailed in disbelief. It was one of our actors! The vile vision I had in Brighton came flooding back. He was the bastard shagging Elena. I could not believe it. It wasn't true. No it wasn't him; I was just imagining things. I was tired; it was a coincidence. Maybe she needed stills for continuity purposes, to record what he was wearing for particular scenes. Yes, that was it. I turned the picture over. It slipped out of my fingers onto the bed. I felt myself go cold all over. I fell straight into my collage. Shards of glass sprayed my face and the frame buckled under my body. His portrait stared me in the face as I lay there in a crumpled mess.

'What's the matter Christo? Oh my God. Are you all right?' It was Stellios. He'd been downstairs making a cuppa and heard the smash. He picked me up and brushed the splinters from my face.

'Those flying shards almost cut you to ribbons. Fuck sake Christo. What's up? Why did you smash the bloody thing?'

I was all choked up. I couldn't speak so I just pointed to the photo.

'That's Ross Davidson; one of our actors isn't it? The bitch! She hasn't, has she?' He said in disbelief. He turned the photo over. 'She has. The bitch has, hasn't she.' He read it out loud,

'To my dearest Elena, thanks for a lovely time, love Ross.'

'Stellios, I can't understand it. In the last few days we had got it together again. We had put the past behind us. I thought she had forgiven me.' I bolted upright, grasping a splintering shard in my fist and swiping the thin air, just narrowly missing Stellios.

'The bitch, the bitch, I'll kill her. I'll kill him. I'll kill them both.' I ripped open the ethers with razor-sharp swings like a maniac. 'I'm sure it was him,' I shouted, before I collapsed in a bundle with blood oozing from a gaping hand wound. 'I saw it all in that nightmare in Brighton. You know, the one I told you about. I'm going crazy Stellios. Why are they doing this to me? It's so cruel.'

'Christo, who's doing what? Who are they? I don't understand?'

The door creaked open to Claire and Linda's shocked faces.

'Oh my God! Linda quick get a large bandage and the first aid kit, quick; Chris has cut himself badly,' shouted Claire, brushing Stellios aside. Within minutes she showed her smarmy face around the door. I could see by the glint in her eyes that she had something to do with it. How sick that sardonic glare of revenge was.

'Oh Jesus Christ, Chris. What's happened? Did you accidentally fall on that collage you humped upstairs? Not to worry. We're both first-aiders. We'll have you patched up in no time,' she said, coming towards me.

'Fuck off, all of you. You knew what was happening and you didn't stop it,' I blasted.

'I don't know what you mean Chris. What are we supposed to know?' Claire cried in anguish.

'That bitch knew all about it. She set it up.' I thrust my bleeding hand at Linda before collapsing in agony. She shot out of the room in dramatic fashion.

'He's gone mad. He's gone quite mad, I'm sure of it. He can't cope with the changes. He's lost it, he's lost it,' she shouted and thundered downstairs.

'He's delirious, upset and tired; he doesn't know what he's saying,' Stellios shouted.

'Maybe he's lost too much blood? Quick let me see his hand,' Claire said, forcing open my clenched fist. 'Chris, you've got to let me have a look at it, please. You may have to go to hospital to get it stitched up.'

I submitted to her demands and eased my hand open.

'Mmm, it's not too wide, but it looks deep. I'll have to bathe it in iodine and bandage it for you.' She had me all patched up in no time. I looked like a Red Indian brave with all the iodine battle scars on my face and hands. I felt like shit. They brushed up the mess and Claire made me a cup of tea.

'I'll tell DB you tripped and cut yourself on some glass. He'll want to know what happened.'

'Thanks Claire, I'm really sorry for the outburst. I didn't mean what I said.'

'It's all right, Chris. Where's Elena? Has she gone out?'

She sensed my anger, despair and confusion and didn't bother to hang around for an answer. She knew I was not in a position to talk anyway.

'Stellios, stay with him for a while, just keep him company, he needs it,' she said winking in his direction as she dragged the old, prison door closed.

'Didn't you suspect something was going on, Christo? Didn't you get any signals?'

'I don't know Stellios. You know the state I've been in over the last few weeks. Come to think about it, she was gushing at the prospect of being on set with him. I didn't think anything of it at the time.'

'Are you sure it was him in your dream? You could be mistaken. Anyway, it was only a dream, wasn't it.'

'I don't know. I don't know what's real and what's an illusion anymore. All I know is she's gone, and I'm left with this death certificate.'

'Don't worry Chris, if it is meant to be, it's meant to be. You may have got it all wrong, you never know.'

'Fuck sake Stellios, are you taking the piss? Look you've seen the writing on the photo.'

To my dearest Elena, thanks for a lovely time, love Ross.'

'What does that suggest to you then? Oh, they had tea and biscuits and they were just holding hands under the table. Stellios grow up, she's shagging him; the bitch is shagging him, behind my back. I'll murder them Stellios; I will.'

'Calm down, calm down, Now's your chance to free yourself from her. Let her go; she's not worth it. Listen, he'll dump her soon enough, when another fancy woman comes along, you'll see.'

'Maybe you're right Stellios. That nightmare, DB's advice, the whole thing fits, but it's the stab in the back that hurts, that's the issue. I still love her, despite what's happened.'

'Chris, no you don't. She's an adulterous bitch. You just lust over her, it's natural, but you'll cope with it.'

'Stellios, do you think she'll come back tonight?'

'I don't know Christo. I reckon she'll stay away for a few days and let you cool off, that's what she'll do.'

'Mmm, you may be right Stellios. Listen, you don't mind staying here tonight. I'll kill her if she suddenly appears, I will.'

'Okay, Christo, but only if you promise you'll get some sleep, you don't hog the bed and you don't snore and fart.' The little shit made me laugh after all the drama I'd been through.

'I promise, Stellios. I promise.'

We settled down, said goodnight and in minutes we were sleeping.

CHAPTER 21

'Help! Help! Help! Stellios! Stellios!'
'Christo, bloody hell, what's the matter; you've scared the shit out of me. Stop thumping me; what is it?'

I was stuck in a horrific trance-like state, thrashing around on the bed like someone possessed.

'Christo, Christo, wake up. It's me Stellios. It's okay, wake up.'

I drifted out of that hellhole I was trapped in and into Stellios warm and reassuring embrace.

'Stellios, it was horrible. I was in Purgatory; I felt these groping hands clawing at my body and pulling me down, deeper into the bowels of hell.' I was shaking all over.

'Calm down, calm down, it's all right; you're safe now. You've just had a bad trip and you're in shock. Calm down, nobody's going to hurt you.'

I looked around and centred myself. Memories of last night came flooding back with a vengeance. I felt an excruciating pain in my hand, which earthed my reality.

'Stellios, it was horrendous. I thought I was going to die.'
'Tell me about it.'

'But, you said I should keep it to myself and write it in my diary, didn't you?'

'Listen, under the circumstances, it's better you share this one with me, don't you think?'

'Well, I don't remember anything much before the experience.

15th March, 7.30am. Dream/o.o.b.e.

I am in an inner dimension; I am completely conscious but I don't know where I am. Suddenly, I am being jerked around all over my abdomen, chest and throat. In utter shock I glanced at my body. Oh my God. All I could see were three or four pairs of grizzly hands clawing and gripping me. My heart was pounding. I felt a pair of hands squeezed tightly around my throat. I struggled and struggled to free myself, but their grip was getting tighter and tighter. I felt my life force slowly drain away; that's when I started shouting for you. My voice echoed all around, in slow deliberate sound. Nobody heard; nobody came; nobody cared. It was then I had a conscious realisation. I was in the astral world, this was not real; it was an illusion caused by the emotional anguish I was going through. I could only release myself by calming down and breathing deeply. In seconds I was sucked out of that terrifying space into reality.

'Didn't you hear me shouting for you? I bawled my heart out.'

'What? You were shouting for me? I didn't hear a thing. All I felt was you kicking and hitting out at me.'

'Ah, so I was using my astral voice to shout astral words in the astral world. Stellios, are you sure you didn't hear anything?'

'Christo I told you, I didn't hear a thing, believe me. You've had your first bad trip; it's understandable with the state you were in last night. When we are at a really low emotional ebb we can succumb to lower astral energies. They can catapult us into the lower astral world, our portion of it, if you understand what I mean.'

'No Stellios, tell me what are you getting at.'

'Well, we live in a whole sea of dimensions: the physical, emotional, mental and the higher spiritual. We constantly contribute to these worlds and they bombard us with energy via our own physical, emotional and mental bodies. That's what makes up our auras. We are responsible for our contribution to these dimensions, be it positive or negative.'

'Okay Stellios, but what's that got to do with me?'

'Christo, you always interrupt, you're so impatient. Well, what we don't realise is that we make all the difference. We contribute to the formation of our physical body by the way we treat it. Equally, we contribute to the formation of our emotional, mental and higher spiritual vehicles, by the nature of our energies. You were thrust into a segment of your lower astral world, which you created by your negative emotional state. Do you understand how it works now Christo?'

'What you're saying is, we are ultimately responsible for all our actions and reactions. We make tidal waves out of ripples; we make mountains out of mole hills.'

'You got it. The ancient wisdom is so natural and simple. It's all rhythmic. What you have also got to consider now is, if that is the case, we are responsible for fashioning humanity's reality; physically, emotionally, mentally and so on.'

'Bloody hell Stellios, Do you mean to say we are almost like God?'

'According to the Bible *He made us in his image*; therefore we are gods in the making. Our very essence, that spark of divine fire is a fragment of His form.

Having pervaded the entire universe with a fragment of myself I remain.

'Stellios I never really thought of it in that way. So our little, insignificant lives do really matter?'

'Christo, do you think *He* would squander souls willy-nilly? We are a divine expression of *Him*. *He* needs us just as much as we need *Him*. That's why reincarnation is so important.'

'What do you mean?'

'When a soul comes into its terrestrial cycle, its primary purpose is to gain further experience, fulfil its potential and balance the karma of its previous lives. On passing into its heavenly state, all its experiences are deposited in the cosmic bank, perfecting that august consciousness we call God.'

'Stellios, that's heretical. You'd be burnt at the stake in the past. I thought *He* was perfect, omnipresent and omnipotent.'

'*He* is Christo. *He* is our soul our spirit, perfect, but after each incarnation we add another design to it, perfecting it even more. That's why we have so many incarnations; you can't achieve perfection in one solitary life.'

Thus God dwells in us all,
From life's minute beginnings,
Up at last to Man - -the consummation
Of this scheme of being,
The completion of this sphere of life:
Whose attributes had here and there
Been scattered o'er the visible world
Before, asking to be combined, dim
Fragments meant to be united in some
Wondrous whole, imperfect qualities
Throughout creation, suggesting some
One creature yet to make,
Some point where all those scattered
Rays should meet convergent in the
Faculties of Man.

Master Browning's poem *Paracelsus* describes the process beautifully.'

'Stellios, that's way over my head. Let's get back to basics, my experience.'

'Okay, okay, you've.........'

The old door creaked and slowly yawned open to Steve's mutt, peering at me.

'Chris, have you seen Stellios? He never...Stellios, what the fuck are you doing in Chris's bed? You're not, are you?'

'Don't be daft Steve, you silly sod; no, I'm not gay. Chris cut his hand on glass from that collage. He was also in state, after that Wiccan experience.'

'Where's Elena then. Is she sleeping with Linda?'

'Don't ask, Steve, that's another story I don't want to get into, okay,' Stellios said glaring at me.

'Okay. Does anyone fancy a cuppa?'

'That will be brilliant, bring some biscuits up too; we may as well have a tea party,' Stellios shouted.

'Don't tell Steve anything; he doesn't need to know about Elena'

'Alright Stellios, but what about my OOBE?'

'Record it; it's a 'one off', hopefully. You've had all sorts of inter-dimensional experiences anyway, this is just another one of your repertoire.'

'Stellios, don't take the piss. I'm not a magician; I don't do tricks, they just happen, I have no control over them.'

'Oh yes you do, that's the meaning of the OOBE. You made it happen by your emotional state.'

'Mmm, you're right Stellios.'

'Stellios, help me man, I can't open the door with this bloody tray in my hands.'

The tray was swimming with tea, milk and sugar. What a mess. Never mind, it was the thought that counted.

'Thanks Steve, that's just the job, I'm parched,' I said, licking my lips.

'Steve, have you heard from Pete then? He's been gone for at least two weeks.'

'He hasn't left a message and we've been so busy. I'll give it a few days and I'll call him, if he doesn't call me. I don't want to encroach into his personal life.'

'I hope he's okay. You know how sensitive he is,' Stellios added.

'Steve, you were Aubrey Beardsey in a previous life, weren't you? How did you find out and how has it affected you?'

'Christo, that's not for you to know. It's Steve's business, it's personal, you're so pushy and forward,' Stellios said in disbelief.

'It's all right Stellios, it's no secret. The whole group know anyway. Well, it was all quite strange you know. As a child I had a deep interest in illustration and cartoons. I loved drawing caricatures of all the family. In my adolescence I got into a rough crowd and for kicks I used to spray all the walls with elaborate graffiti. I loved it; it was pure magic to steel out in the dead of night, like I was on a mission. My designs were inspired but they were not my ideas. I'd start with a plan then something took over and after a while I let it. Well, to cut it short, the long arm of the law caught up with me and I was punished. 200 hours of community work, which included scrubbing all my masterpieces off the walls around my neighbourhood. It was hard work and all my creativity went down the drain.

'I didn't even look like any of my family and I didn't think like them either. I thought that was odd. I asked my mum one-day why I looked so different from the rest of my siblings and do you know what she said? 'I don't know, Steve darling, perhaps we changed milkman or postman, I don't know'.'

He had us in stitches, rolling around on the bed.

'Then she said I must have taken from my father's side. Some uncle or someone was as tall as me and had similar facial characteristics. You see, I never knew my father; he left us when we were toddlers. My mother is short and plump; look at me.

'Eventually I developed an interest in romantic art, poetry and music. I loved Art Nouveau, Art Deco pieces, Pre-Raphaelite posters and paintings. Oscar Wilde, Mallory, Tennyson, The Arthurian quest. It was really inspiring stuff, but I had no idea why. I just went with it. I was searching for answers, got into drink, drugs and women, as you do, but that wasn't enough.

'Do you known what?' He said, interrupting the flow in a deeply secretive schoolboy-like voice. 'I just love big, bulbous women with massive tits. I love them. I didn't know why then, but now I do.'

We all fell off the bed, rolling around with laughter. It was great to have this camaraderie and the banter was soul healing. He was a fantastic storyteller.

'Something deep was stirring and it plagued me constantly. It gnawed at my very core. Eventually I came across a series of fantastic books by an author called Lobsang Rampa. The Third Eye was his most famous; you should read it. Then I started having strange dreams and visions.'

I burst into laughter as Stellios made a rude gesture with his hand.

'Not those kind of dreams, but I've had some saucy ones recently where I'm doing it with my *anima*. It's so real and my fantasies all come alive. Ooo, massive buttocks and boobs the size of space hoppers.'

He set us off again. God what a giggle we had.

'Hey, if we're not having it, at least we can talk about it and dream about it. Now I know why monks always had a smirk on their faces; they had multi-sensory, sexual experiences in their dreams, all the time.'

'You see, there is something positive about this celibacy malarkey,' Stellios added as he spluttered with laughter.

My God he was a comedian. We were acting like a bunch of adolescents sharing our first, fumbling sexual encounters. It was so refreshing and hilarious.

'Anyway boys, I kept getting flashbacks of a fantasy fairy palace with ornate furniture and opulent surroundings. They were interspersed with Victorian architecture, piers jutting out and transforming into gigantic phalluses shagging the ocean. It was all so bizarre: the swish of pebbles, deckchairs, caricatures, illustrations and posters. The gaudy images of sexual eccentricities and exaggerated human forms flooded back. It was a merry-go-round of fleeting images, laughter and massive, rouged whores in parlours and bars.

'No, don't start again, you two. I'm trying to be serious,' he exclaimed, pointing in our direction. It was so difficult to keep a straight face.

'During this time I came across one of DB's books and went to a few of his lectures. One particular night, I felt really restless. It was full moon; you know how the moon affects me, don't you Stellios?'

Stellios, nodded. 'Steve's a real moonchild. He's all Cancer. Sun sign, Moon sign and Ascendant. That's why he's so clumsy and he lives in his own, little world, with his sexual fantasies and fat, fairy women.'

'Ah, Stellios don't take the piss. Well, I was tossing and turning and suddenly I was sucked into another dimension. It was a sort of artist studio. I didn't know who I was. All I could see was a mass of black and white illustrations covering a whole wall. Papers were scattered all over the drab surroundings and an easel jutted out in front. This scrawny, knobbly hand protruding from a white starchy cuff with a gold link on it stretched out and started sketching an unfinished piece. Whoosh. He finished it off with a rapid stroke and signed it, *Aubrey Beardsley.*

'I felt him cough, splutter and wheeze as he crossed his chest with his feeble hands. I knew he was seriously ill; I could feel it in my bones. Cough, cough, cough, splutter and then, whoosh. I was thumped back into my body, fighting for air.'

'Bloody hell Steve, what a story; It was your imagination, right?'

'Chris, it wasn't my imagination; I can assure you. It was as real as us, here, now.'

'Well, what did you do?' I said, probing further.

'Initially I thought it might have been a dream, but it was so clear, so vivid; and that name *Aubrey Beardsley.* I felt him, his breath, his sight, his hand on the easel, his illness. It was as if I was him. I can't explain it any other way.'

'So what did you do then?' Stellios interrupted.

'Well, I remembered DB's handbooks on reincarnation and life after death. There were some relevant passages in them about previous life recall. Then a voice in my head shouted,

Encyclopaedia Britannica, Britannica

'Of course, I got up, got dressed and raced to the local library. Well you can imagine the shock I got.'

Beardsley, Aubrey (Vincent)
Born Aug. 21, 1872, Brighton, Sussex, England. Died Mar. 16, 1898, Menton, France. The leading English illustrator of the 1890s and after Oscar Wilde, the outstanding figure in the aestheticism movement.

Brighton? Oscar Wilde? A leading English illustrator? I thought in utter amazement and a rush of adrenaline pumped around my veins.

'The Brighton pavilion, the beach, the piers… Do you know he suffered from chronic TB and died at the age of 25? That's why I experienced the severe chest pains and coughing. It all came flooding back. I read the biography thoroughly. I didn't know how to explain my feelings. It was proof of my immortality. I had lived before. I could identify with his life so much. It was like I was swallowed by this massive, black hole; the womb of all mankind, where cyclically, I was yanked out, a babe, for each successive life.'

'Jesus Christ Steve, it must have felt so weird,' I said, in awe of his interpretation.

'But I was still not convinced. I had no photograph of him. I scurried around the shelves for a biography and there it was, staring at me. I could see its spine shining *Aubrey Beardsley* in bright, gold, calligraphy. I eased it out and flicked it open. There he was. It was me. Fucking hell, it was me, the spitting image of me! I was so taken aback I tripped and fell over an old biddy behind me. There she was, bloomers in the air, hair net all over the place, her purple/silver mop dangling in her face.'

'For God's sake Steve, come on. Don't get carried away with her, tell us what you saw,' I blasted with impatience.

'I could not believe it. There he was in a starchy Victorian suit, high collar and bow tie. He was tall, lean and scrawny with withdrawn facial features, strong Roman beak and the blackest, deepest, soulful eyes I'd ever come across. He looked straight through me from that portrait. It was alive, I'm sure it was alive. Stellios, Chris, it was me. No doubt about it at all, it was me.'

'So what did you do?' I enquired.

'I was still on top of the old biddy. She was screaming and hitting out at me. I was so spaced out, I didn't know what had happened.'

'Come on Steve.'

'No seriously, I was out of it completely. I staggered to a table and slouched down on a chair. I spent all day in there. He illustrated Sir Thomas Mallory's *Morte D'Arthur*. He was appointed art editor and illustrator of *The Yellow Book* and a number of other quarterly publications. His illustrations for Oscar Wilde's play *Salome* won him widespread notoriety. Do you know what he loved drawing?'

'I can give an educated guess Steve,' Stellios said, with his eyes rolling and a beaming smile conspiring to take over his face.

'Highly erotic caricatures of big, bulbous, sensuous women and men with overtly exaggerated balls, bums and willies. They all bordered on morbid eroticism and pornography. I couldn't believe it.'

'That's where you get your fetishes from Steve. All the way back from there. It's unbelievable what we carry over to each life, isn't it,' I said, laughing in utter disbelief.

'Well it's all true. DB's confirmed it for me. I'm 1,000 per cent convinced. It's given me a tremendous amount of confidence ever since. I've drawn on those inner strength's whilst creating my illustrations for Pete's book.'

'Brilliant Steve, So you mean to say that once you have a confirmed previous life, you can access the qualities of that life and bring them into the present?' I retorted.

'Yes, Christo, that's how it works. But, you also bring with you negative patterns too, such as illness, habits and bad karma. All lives have lessons attached as well as gifts,' Stellios added.

'Wao, I can't wait for confirmation of one of my previous lives. I'm going down to LE today to research Encyclopaedia Britannica. I was...'

Stellios kicked me and raised his brows. 'Glamour. Glamour. Glamour.'

I felt like a little schoolboy being sent to the corner for misbehaving.

'All right, I get the message Stellios. You're just no fun any more, you boring little fart. Listen, I've got a lot to think about. Stellios knows what's happened. I'd appreciate some time on my own.'

'Okay Chris, I can imagine, good luck. We'll leave you in peace. Come on Stellios, let's get going,' he said.

'Steve, thanks for the insight, I really do appreciate it. Oh Stellios, come here, I've got something to tell you. It almost slipped my mind. Bye Steve, see you at dinner. Stellios, I've decided to donate £3,000 to the filming.'

'Oh, Christo, you're a saint, you really are.'

'Listen, I want you to break the news to DB again. Get all the credit, like before, and keep in there. I want to know all that's going on okay.'

'I'll tell him tonight after dinner. Are you going to be all right? What are you going to do about Elena?'

'Stellios, I need time to work it out. I'm still hurting deeply. I don't know.'

He left me with my thoughts. As I lay down, the whole sordid affair flashed by me again and again. I needed rest. I was still exhausted from the mammoth exertion of energy I expended at the exhibition.

CHAPTER 22

I was so physically and emotionally exhausted I slept all day and even missed dinner. I hadn't one single thought or vision about the tense dilemma I was in. That laugh we had and the deep slumber had refreshed my spirit, but I had major decisions to make. The old door creaked open.

'Hi, Christo, you awake? I passed your room just after the bell for dinner, but I couldn't hear any movement. I gathered you'd sleep right through.'

'Thanks for not disturbing me Stellios. I was knackered after all that yesterday. Steve made me laugh, thank God. It was a wonderful break from the shit I'm in.'

'DB, John and Barry were elated when I told them I'd convinced you to donate £3,000. Your plan is working a treat. I've been invited to sit in at meetings now. They think I can be a sort of go-between, you know, an ambassador or something.'

'That's brilliant Stellios. Did he ask about me?'

'Yes, well Claire told him about your accident and Ron debriefed him about the festival.'

'You didn't mention Elena, did you?'

'No Chris, but filming has been suspended for now, due to lack of money. Elena won't be needed for a while. Maybe she has gone to her aunts after all.'

'Stellios, get real. She's fucked off with him. He's had his wicked way with her and I'll have to deal with it.'

'Okay, I'm just trying to keep all your options open.'

'Stellios, if she had gone to her aunts she would have left a message with someone or phoned by now. Instead, I get an autographed, publicity shot of him.

To my dearest Elena.

God, the whole thing is making me sick.'

'Christo, maybe she's not totally to blame. You know how she stood by you, through the breakdown. All the abuse you've thrown at her. She's bound to have sought solace somewhere else.'

'Why are you sticking up for her? Why are you defending her? She's the adulterous bitch. She fucked off, leaving me here to suffer.'

'Christo, have you ever stopped to think what she's been going through? Her insecurities, her negative thoughts, her *Dweller* issues? You brought her here, a gorgeous girl, full of life, bounding with sensuality, from a secure, well off, materialistic life, to this. Come on Christo, you're too blinkered.'

'Stellios, we knew the challenges; we knew it was going to be hard. We came here to find our spiritual purpose, not to get laid.'

'Maybe so, but it might be your karma to go through this experience. You never know, you could have been an adulterous bastard in a previous life and now you've got to pay the consequences. What goes around comes around Christo.'

'Stellios, what if all you're saying is a load of crap. To many normal people out there, it is a load of crap. Karma to them is an airy-fairy, Eastern philosophy based on the premise that there is rebirth. To that lot, the blame lies with them, not theoretical, idealistic clap-trap.'

'Listen, it's your choice at the end of the day. It's your karma. Perhaps you've got to let her go, to release yourself and delve deeply into spirituality. Maybe you've got to centre your love in your heart instead of in your balls and solar plexus. You know unconditional love, true heart love, is a soul quality.'

'Stellios, don't lecture me, that's all you seem to do. What do you know about love and sexuality? Bet you're still a fucking virgin, aren't you? Who are you to talk.'

He glared at me, his eyes sunk into his sorry face and he plodded slowly out.

'You may be right, but I'm only trying to help you see different perspectives.'

I was fuming with anger, frustration and resentment. I was completely confused: karma, unconditional love, attachments, the pain and suffering. My head was swimming in a monstrous sea of inconsistencies and contradictions. Logic battled with spirituality for the crown of consciousness. I was battered, ripped to shreds, my compass shattered. I floated along precariously, on a vicious tide that lead to a sheer, soul-destroying cliff and a watery death. I had no hope, no dry land, and no rock of Gibraltar ahead. I had lost that; even Stellios had deserted me. Completely consumed in self-pity, I reached for my trusted diary for solace.

9.30pm
I am torn apart and I have nowhere to turn to. Major challenges loom. I need your direction, my Father in heaven.
What's my karmic link with Elena and should I free myself from her?

I extracted the Saturn aspect from my chart, which relates to long-standing karma and also my Sun/Mercury aspect, which relates to short-term karma and relationships. I put my arrow under it and placed my chart on the opposite page. I just managed the last letters as my eyelids fluttered and my vision blanked.

I had been sleeping for hours, then suddenly, a melody echoed from the depths of my unconscious mind.

I have stood here before inside the
pouring rain,
With the world turning circles running
round my brain,
I guess I'm always hoping that you'll
end this reign,
But it's my destiny to be the king of
pain.

King of pain
King of pain
King of pain
I'll always be the king of pain.'

It was one of The Police's greatest hits. It played in my head until I was immersed into a series of dreams, with the song still blaring in the ethers.

> *16th Mar. 6.15am*
>
> *A ragged, weather-beaten, old man, struggling through a desert landscape. He's gasping for water and food. His scrawny hand is outstretched and he's on his knees, crying out 'It's a cancer; it's like a cancer eating at my soul!*
>
> *Elena leads me into a cave, where we have to cross an area of mud and quicksand. She takes me by the hand, but I see a massive snake wallowing in the sand. It spies us and before we know it, we are up to our necks in quicksand. The snake lashes and unwinds towards us; she panics and tries to pull me under. I fight and fight to stay afloat, grabbing and clawing. The snake coils its body gently around my throat and pulls me to safety, leaving Elena to drown. I feel this great sense of freedom as the snake releases me.*

Another dream tagged onto it.

> *I am riding a motorbike. A car, driven by an old man and Elena follow me. I come to a busy crossroads and I am caught in the middle. Cars are coming from all directions; I accelerate and leave them behind. I stop and Elena gets out of the car and straddles the motorbike with me. I am worried the bike won't be able to take the strain. I rev up and push off only to find the wheels buckle and the suspension cracks. I say, Elena you're too heavy to carry, you'll have to go back to the car. She is crying uncontrollably saying 'I know I'm a burden; you'll have to go without me. The car speeds off into the distance, leaving me at a glorious, golden sand, beachfront.*

I was in shock at the dreams. They were so vivid. The three images all linked to my questions. According to Jung's method of dream analysis, a series of dreams is always more meaningful and easier to analyse. The elements had to be grouped together. Elena, the old man and the vehicles, were all aspects of myself. But what about the Cancer, the quicksand and the snake around my neck? There was a definite feeling of constriction, abandonment and letting go. I needed time to work it all out and to link the astrology to it. That would be the ultimate key.

I brooded on the content as I pottered around. I spied my crumpled collage. The frame was in pieces but there was no damage to the actual collage. I was sure it was symbolic of something deep and meaningful. My mind flitted from one thought to another. 'Yes, that's it!' I shouted. 'My dreams, I know what they mean. I know what they mean.'

All the elements were aspects of my psyche. The emaciated old man being ravaged by a cancer represented the need to nourish myself and attain wisdom. I am alienated, isolated and neglected. The cancer is soul destroying; it's the situation with Elena and is a constant reminder of things which hold me back from achieving my quest for knowledge.

The cave represents the womb, the fertile unconscious. Elena leads me inside. She is a symbol of my *anima*, the inner partner. The quicksand is a quagmire of negative emotions. We are up to our necks in it. She wants to pull me deeper into it when she sees the snake.

According to Jung, the *anima* can take on a dark, destructive form, limiting the transformation process. Elena becomes a negative *anima* figure, intending to swamp me. The snake pulls me out by the throat. It's an astrological symbol of Scorpio. The higher aspect of it means rebirth, but it also links with sexuality. It grabs me gently around the throat. I have to transmute sexual energy into higher creative power, through the sacral centre and towards the throat. It was so clear, I shouted in elation.

The last image suggested I had to tread the path on my own: I'm on a motorbike; I can't carry Elena. I try but she's too much of a burden. She joins the 'rat-race' back in the car. I feel free and liberated by the seaside. I am ready to dive deeper into the unconscious. I have no limitations.

Her karma was to lead me to the cave, the womb of all life and wisdom. Through our relationship she teaches me detachment and forces me to transmute my energies. My karma is to release myself from bondage, deal with my emotional attachments, transmute sexual energy and nourish the soul. I felt confident of the analysis, but I still needed to work on the astrological associations. I was amazed at the feedback I got from my questions. It was really working. I didn't understand the mechanics of it, but something was feeding me with information. It was phenomenal. What a tool.

I felt so guilty about what I said to Stellios. He'll never forgive me and he shouldn't. I was an animal, an insensitive bastard. He's my only hope in this minefield of experience and I've blown it again, I thought.

Dring-dring, dring-dring, dring-dring. The phone was having a ringing fit.

God, who could be ringing at this early hour? It must be important or a wrong number, I thought, to the echo of a barrage of feet from above. They marched past the room and into the office. In seconds I heard Stellios' voice speaking Greek in the background. My door thudded and I heard footsteps stomp outside.

'Christo, can I come in? It's urgent. It's a call from Elena.'

'Tell her to fuck off, I don't want to speak to her.' There were a few moments of uneasy silence and then he sheepishly popped his head around the door.

'Christo, before you shout, please listen to me, she's...'

'Why should I listen to you or her? She's a filthy whore.'

'Please, Christo. I know how you feel, but you've got it all wrong. She's at her aunt's house.'

'What? You're so naive sometimes Stellios. She's told you a load of bollocks and you believed her.'

'Christo, please talk to her. I told her what you found. I hope you didn't mind.'

'Well, what did she say then?'

'Talk to her yourself, Christo, please. It may all be a misunderstanding.'

'Misunderstanding my arse. Oh, alright then, tell her to put the phone down and call back in 10 minutes.' He scurried out like a frightened rat to relay my message and then bolted back.

'What did she tell you Stellios? And cut the bullshit.'

'She said that she told Linda she was going to see her aunt. She'd had a nervous breakdown and she needed help.'

'Well, that may explain the fast getaway. But why didn't that bitch Linda tell me the truth? She's a scheming cow. What's she up to Stellios? Is she trying to frame Elena?'

'Christo, I told you before, don't trust her and certainly don't confide in her.'

'What about that signed photo then? I suppose she denied having it. That's the incriminating evidence, the nail in her coffin. Stellios, she's history. I want her out of my fucking life.'

'Calm down, She was so shocked when I told her about it. Of course she denied anything to do with it.'

'That's a load of bollocks, Stellios. If it's not hers, then who planted it in her things for me to find? Who could be so devious and cruel? Who's got it in for me? That bitch Linda must be behind it.'

'Why do you think that?'

'Stellios, it's obvious, isn't it? Elena's in the limelight, lapping up praise from DB. She's replaced Linda hasn't she?'

'Yes, but she's no real threat to her. Linda is DB's secretary. He needs her around him all the time. There's the typesetting; she runs the correspondence course and she's one of our best tutors. What's she got to worry about?'

'I don't know. I can't think of anyone else who has a motive to do such a thing. The only alternative is that Elena is shagging around and she's trying to set up Linda. I don't know Stellios, I really don't know. The whole thing's a soap opera, a fucking nightmare. What am I going to say to her? Tell me'

'Well, I think she's telling the truth. Listen to her, give her a chance.'

The phone started to ring in the hall.

'It must be for you Christo. I'll get it, you throw some clothes on.' He dashed out and answered the call while I put on my jeans.

What do I do? I was so angry. I was seething with resentment and in a jealous rage. Was she innocent? Was she playing the victim or was she a plotting whore? I was very confused. I eased the office door open and Stellios handed me the phone. He lingered around like a bad smell but I waved him away.

'Yes. What the fuck's happening?'

'Christo, you've got to believe me. I'm not having an affair with him. I'm being set up, framed. I don't know anything about a photo.'

'Come on, you don't expect me to believe you, do you? I remember you almost having an orgasm with the thought of being on set with him. I also heard you that night saying, *I'm really sorry, but I can't help you anymore, you have to do it on your own.*'

'You thought I was sleeping, didn't you? Anyway, who would have the balls and the motive to creep in and hide a signed photo of Ross Davidson in your personal belongings? Fuck sake, I'm not that green.'

'It's the truth Christo. On my mother's life, I'm not sleeping with him.'

'I even saw you both at it; in a dream I had in Brighton. I had a flashback of it when I entered the Claregate hall for the first time.'

'So you trust your dreams and visions more than me? You're really screwed up aren't you?'

'Don't take the piss. I know something's happened, I can feel it.'

'I'd been talking to him on set, everyone has. I told him about the call from my aunt and he offered to drive me to Finsbury Park. That's...'

'Oh, so you admit to it now? What the fuck is he doing, driving you to Finsbury Park? Don't I drive? Couldn't you wait for me? Oh, I suppose I'm not good enough any more? You make me sick, you whore. Don't come back showing your face around here. Just piss off and leave me alone.'

'Listen Christo, I'm really sorry. It's not what you think. He only gave me a lift, honest.'

'Don't fucking lie as well. That's even worse.'

'If you want me to stay away for a while, I will. I'll be at my aunt's. She needs me around for now.'

'Good fucking riddance, you bitch.'

I slammed the old phone down so hard it shattered into pieces. My broken heart crashed against my rib cage. I sprang up, pacing the floorboards in frustration and anger, then I heard Stellios voice squeak behind the door.

'Christo, what's happened? Did you forgive her?'

'Stellios, I wasn't born yesterday. I can smell a rat. Something's happened and I intend to get to the root of it.'

'So, is she coming back?'

'No, I told her to stay away.'

'Don't you think you're being a bit harsh on...?'

'Stellios, I've told you, don't lecture me. Anyway, it's none of your business, is it?'

'Sorry Christo, I promise not to interfere ever again. I'm only trying to help.'

'Stellios, listen. I'm really fucked up at the moment. You know what I've gone through. I'm sorry about my behaviour. I've been projecting all my shit at you.'

'Christo, believe me, I understand. Just give us a shout if you need to talk. Okay? What are you going to do tomorrow?'

'I'm going down to LE to research that Kitchener and Wentworth life.'

'Oh, before I forget, Claire and Linda are taking an astrology class tomorrow night. Are you up for it?'

'Bloody magic; I'm having all these vivid dreams and I need to learn how to relate them to my chart. I'll see you later Stellios.'

He left me with the aftermath of my hellish situation. She'll have to come back and pick up her toiletries and clothes, I thought. How will I cope seeing her again? I still felt for her deeply; you can't sweep seven years of emotion under the carpet in one foul swoop, can you?

I plodded back to my solitary confinement in a sunken mood, dragging my sagging, devastated aura behind me. I needed to rest and think.

CHAPTER 23

Within minutes, I slid into esolepsy after dozing off. My physical body was exhausted but my mind and other faculties were alert. They were the classic criteria for vivid, lucid dreaming. I had a series of dream images through the night, which I recollected and noted in the morning.

17th March, 8.30am. Dreams

I am using a scouring pad to scrub a filthy bath. There is a little water in it, which is stagnant and infested with cigarette butts and other debris. A young attractive girl is helping me clean it.

Margaret Thatcher is sitting alone at a family party. Everybody is ignoring her. I get up and ask if I can get her something. She's really glad I've recognised her and made an effort to serve her. She's been drinking whisky in a small glass. I try to find another glass for her, but all the ones I look at are filthy.

I am holding a book and walking precariously along a narrow ledge, which is cluttered with books, grocery sets and ornaments. I see people falling off the ledge, down into an abyss. I hold on and slowly move along, but I drop my book. I need to go back to find it. I rummage around all sorts of items left scattered on the ledge. They are all in new boxes. I can't find my book, but I pick up two small boxes of expensive, rare porcelain.

My memory had become clearer ever since I started to record my dreams. This was the desired effect and would ultimately aid further recall. I recorded my visions and left them for analysis later on in the evening. I needed to get down to LE in the next available car. I also needed to transfer £3,000 to Claregate's account.

I jumped into some clothes and trundled downstairs to the dining room. It was deserted, no Linda or Claire. I suppose they were keeping a low profile. Bet the boys were having breakfast in bed, I thought, and dashed into the hallway.

'I'm here. Does anyone want me?' It was DB; his capped head shot out from the cranked door. He had just arrived back from his daily cafe breakfast.

'Hi DB. Can I catch a lift down to LE with you? I want to research the encyclopaedias. I also want to donate the money that I promised Stellios.'

'Chris, yes, jump in the back with the dogs; Barry and John are in there. I'll be out in a minute. I need to see Linda for some corrections to the Paracelsus script.'

I plodded outside and jumped into the inner circles' limo to a welcome from the lapdog lieutenants and the Alsatians.

'Chris, thanks yet again for the donation. It will go towards the next filming schedule. It's been so demanding and costly lately. Well, we won't need Ross for a while; he's the main expense. He might be back for some re-shoots later, if we need him.'

I could feel my blood boil. My face raged red and adrenalin shot through my veins like snake venom at the mention of his name. There was an awkward silence for a few seconds. I sensed they knew something. The sickening conspiracy deepened.

DB marched out with a pile of scripts in his hands.

'Come on Barry, put your foot down, we've got an inner circle meeting. You know I hate being late.'

'Where's Elena Chris? She wasn't at dinner last night,' DB said.

The others glanced nervously at me. They knew where she was all right; it stuck out like dogs' bollocks.

'She got a call from her aunt. She's had a nervous breakdown and she can't cope. Elena may be away for a while. I hope you don't mind.'

'Filming has been suspended for now. We need to plan another phase and that will take weeks. I'm sure we'll manage without her, won't we lads?'

The nodding dogs responded as we sped down the meandering road to LE.

'Little Boy, Little Boy, Charlie, Charlie, Charlie,' DB shouted at the cats as we approached the cottage. 'Watch out Barry! Snags! Get out of the fucking way! That cat will be the death of me one day.' DB blasted.

The car screeched to a halt; the burning scent of rubber and grinding iron seeped through the vents into the cabin. The dogs were all over me, yelping for their walkies and desperate to get out of the car.

'Let them go Chris; they're dying for a piss. Go on my lions; go piss, go piss,' he shouted as they darted out.

'Come in Chris. Now you're back to some semblance of normality, I'd like a word before we have our meeting.'

'Stellios, Lance get us a cuppa and I don't want to be disturbed for a while.'

Stellios ducked his head around the door and winked as DB turned his head towards me.

'Chris. Thank you for the donation. What I'll do is give you shares in the film project. At least when it's sold you'll get your money back. It's an offer we've decided on, to raise further funds.'

The door slid open to Lance's balding eagle head. He was carrying the tray of refreshments.

'Leave us now; I'll call you when Chris and I are finished. Tell the others to stand down for a while.'

'So, you've come down to research the Thomas Wentworth life? Yes, he was one of your previous lives. He was a great soul, loyal and committed, right to the end.'

I just seized up all over. My life force blasted out of my torso. My aura felt like an empty, eggshell with the yolk sucked out. How did he know? I never told him. Perhaps that plotting bitch Linda spilled the beans, I thought. Before I could respond, he interjected.

'No, the plotting bitch Linda did not tell me. I knew from your experience the first time you came to LE. Don't you know I have access to the collective consciousness of the ashram and the akashic records? Nothing goes unnoticed, not even your bust up with Elena.'

'Is there anything you don't know?' I asked in complete shock.

'Chris, you must understand. We all have access to the akashic records to some degree or other. It takes time, discipline, dedication and mastership to access them fully. That's only for the highest degree initiates. If you devote yourself to The Plan, then through your efforts, you will be led to the doors of the records. You've got what it takes, but you'll have to let her go. I told you weeks ago, but you were adamant I was talking crap and only wanted to manipulate you.'

I was utterly speechless and in awe of his powers.

'Oh, you don't have to apologise for lying to me either. That's understandable. Get rid of her. She's a nice girl, but not for this type of life.'

I was a nervous, stuttering wreck. I could not respond to his piercing monologue. My armour was defenceless against his razor-sharp mind. He zipped me open like a can of beans. I had neither protection nor any return fire.

'Think about it Chris, You've got a wonderful future here. The wisdom teachings are yours to unfold, but you cannot serve two masters. The choice is yours,' he said, and he shouted for Stellios to call the inner circle together.

'By the way, you were right about Kitchener too. He was a loyal servant of Britain. So bold, so focussed, but he lacked man management skills. That's one for you to put right, this time around.'

He dismissed me to the library and beckoned his lieutenants in for the inner circle meeting. Before I left he called after me.

'Ask Lance to show you where Britannica is and tell him to have tea, biscuits and *dogs* ready at 11 o'clock.'

'Okay DB and thanks for the confirmations.' I was blown to bits. My aura was like a malignant tumour mushrooming out of control. My mind tried desperately to contain it. I now knew what Steve had felt when he had a life confirmed. It was an awesome experience; one that I would never forget.

'Hi Chris. What are you doing down here? Oh, what happened to your hand? Fancy a cup of tea?'

Lance was all questions, but I was walking about like a soulless zombie.

'Huh, oh hi Lance. What did you say?'

'God you're as spaced out as me. I never thought it was contagious, look at you.'

'Come in, Mike and Dick are having a cuppa with me.'

'Hi Chris. Mike's the name. I've not really met you properly, but I have seen you at dinner,' he said, in a heavy, cockney accent. I was taken aback by his appearance. He had a small, whippet-like frame, jet black, greased, floppy hair, dark skin and the most deep-brown, penetrating, philosophical eyes I'd ever seen. He didn't look English at all. He looked Italian or Greek.

'You know me well enough.' Dick spouted, cutting Mike up.

'How did you get on at Mind Body and Spirit? Isn't it a brilliant arena? I love it,' Mike said, glowing with light.

'Oh, that monstrous pile of cow dung. It's a haven for all the fluffy bunnies who love burrowing into that sort of shit. They're all fucked up.'

'Fuck off Dick,' Lance blasted. 'Why don't you keep that foul toilet of a mouth shut for a change. It stinks of shit every time you open it.' The words caught him totally by surprise and his mouth dropped open as he fumed.

'I've go no time for all this spiritual masturbation,' Dick shouted in disgust. 'I've got a print works to run.' He disappeared in a huff, muttering and mumbling, 'fluffy fucking bunnies, there's not a practical brain amongst them'.

Dick was at his eloquent best, but Lawrence surpassed him this time. Dick was so full of himself. He was anathema to all spirituality. I was beginning to wonder what he was doing here. We were all falling around, laughing our heads off at Lance's obvious embarrassment. It was just the tonic to ground me after that session with DB.

'What happened to your hand Chris?' Mike enquired.

'Well, I cut it on the glass of a collage I won at MBS.'

'Oh yes, that was lucky. What type of collage was it?' Lance said.

'It was a compilation of the logos of all the participants of the exhibition. I've never won anything in my life before. I was so surprised and over the moon. But I fell over it and a shard stuck in my hand.'

'Oh, that's a shame,' Lance sympathised. Mike was deep in thought.

'You know it's synchronicity. There's a cryptic message in it.'

'Synchronicity. What does that mean? I said, screwing up my face.

'Synchronicity is a revolutionary theory Carl Jung first recognised. It stems from *synchronism*, the Greek word meaning coincidence. Synchronicity therefore means the simultaneous occurrence of a certain psychic state with one or more external events that appear as meaningful parallels to the momentary subjective state.'

My tired mind tried to wrestle with his psychological exposition. I hadn't a hope in hell, not after my ordeal with DB.

'Mike, could you explain it to me in layman's terms, I'm not quite with it.'

'Listen, something happened to me a couple of days ago. I was walking along brooding upon a girl I met a few months ago. She really made an impact on me. The only problem was, she was already attached to someone. I liked her and she really liked me, but she could not finish her existing relationship. We agreed to put it on hold for a while until she sorted herself out. Well I kept in touch, phoning her on occasions, but it seemed to drag on and on. Anyway, that day, whilst I was thinking of her, head down, I started to whistle the song, *Oh Joanna*, her name, then I just happened to glance at a soggy, old card on the pavement. I looked closely at it and do you know what it said?'

'No Mike, go on, tell us what it said,' Lance added excitedly.

'My soul mate.'

'Bloody hell, Mike, that's really spooky. Surely it was a coincidence?' remarked Lance.

'No it wasn't. It was synchronous. It's quite simple really. My thoughts triggered off the song and the glance at the card gave me the answer to my question. We tend to look inwardly for answers to our dilemmas, but nature provides us with constant external clues, if only we were aware of them.'

It made common sense to me. I often wondered if things happened by chance or if they are all meant to happen. It's like being in the right place at the right time.

'Chris, Mike loves symbolism, mythology and psychology; it's his forte. He's so deep, he even looses me,' Lance added in awe.

'But how does that relate to the collage I won? I don't understand.'

'What were you thinking about when you bought the raffle tickets? Can you remember?'

'Yes clearly, I was wondering what I was doing at the exhibition with all those freaks, hobgoblins and air heads.'

'Exactly, you got your answer placed in your hands. The collage is a synthesis of international new age groups. Your long term purpose is to synthesise new age philosophies under one united umbrella of unconditional, universal wisdom.'

Lance and I were dumbstruck by his interpretation.

'You mean to say I could be responsible for unifying new age ideas? You must be wrong Mike; I was terrified out there. I clung to my cross and spouted The Lords Prayer when the Wiccan high priest confronted me. I almost shit myself.'

'Chris, you've got the potential to work with groups. It could be hosting your own exhibitions or workshops, or even publishing a magazine linking new age philosophies together.'

'Mike, I can't string two sentences together, never mind publish a magazine. You must be off your rocker.'

'Listen, I'm indicating your potential gifts. Have you had a horoscope cast? It will all be in there, I'm sure.'

'Yes, Linda cast it for me. Actually, I'm attending an astrology class tonight that Claire and Linda are hosting.'

'Great, look at where Aquarius is in your chart. Also find Jupiter's placement and what's in your 11th house. They all link to new age groups, publications, festivals, communication and gifts. Locate Sagittarius, the Earth and your ninth house. They relate to your spiritual path, journalism and direction.'

'Mike. Jesus fucking Christ, I'm waiting for you to finish off making this printing plate. Enough wanking with those toss pots, I've go work to do.' Dick blared like a foghorn.

'Got to go lads, or he'll make my life a misery. That'll fire him up for ages. I can hear him now, cursing and swearing like a trooper. Fucking wankers and losers; bloody new age bollocks; their brains are all full of spiritual shit. He'll go on and on with his verbal diarrhoea. You know how neurotic he is.' Mike sauntered out with his tea splashing all over the lino.

'Lance, could you show me where the Britannica's are kept?'

'Sure. You researching a previous life then?' His face lit up and his eyes gleamed with delight.

'Well, sort off, but I'm not sure,' I said, heeding Stellios advice.

'There you are, have a good read. If you need me I'll be in here washing up and preparing elevenses.

I decided to have a walk outside to clear my head before I immersed myself. The air was fresh and the sun's sweet rays sprayed the beds with gold dust. Spring flowers flashed their multi-coloured eyelashes at me. Wearing their best frocks and alluring scents, they jostled in the morning sun for my attention, like an array of beautiful girls out walking in the countryside. I closed my eyes and mellowed in natures' bosom, but thoughts of Elena came flooding back, like black clouds full of impending gloom and doom.

What was I going to do? I felt trapped in the situation. My energies were stagnating and I felt strangulated. I opened my eyes to a little, cracked flowerpot that had been thrown to one side. A little plant struggled desperately to survive. Its roots had broken the bottom of the pot. It had outgrown it and needed re-potting.

Suddenly, with a flash of intuition, I had a synchronistic revelation. I was that little plant, struggling to grow in a tiny pot. My roots were crammed so tight I was cracking up. My life force was thwarted and my creativity restricted. I needed space to bloom into perfection and fulfil my true potential. I pulled the crushed plant out of its cramped coffin, re-potted it in a larger pot and flooded it with water and love. I felt an instantaneous release within me, a rush of energy as light saturated my heavy soul. I knew what I had to do. I had to release myself from Elena and my dungeon of depression.

I remembered Stellios wise words; learn to love unconditionally, from the heart. I heard His calling zinging in my head. A melody echoed in my ears and my soul fluttered like the wings of a dove, soaring high, free to roam unrestricted to the heavens above.

> *If you love somebody*
> *If you love someone,*
> *If you love somebody*
> *If you love someone,*
> *Set them free, set them free*
> *Set them free, set them free.*
>
> *If you want to keep something*
> *Precious,*
> *Don't lock it up and throw away the*
> *Key,*
> *If you want to hold onto your*
> *Possessions, don't even think about*
> **Me.**
>
> *Free, free, set them free*
> *Free free, set them free*
> *Free free set them free!*

It was The Police's hit song, *'If You Love Someone Set Them Free'*. My *Daemon* knew from the start what I had to do. I had to release myself from my stifling relationship. I had to transmute sexual, emotional and possessive love to pure detached heart love. I took my plant with me back to the library. I felt totally renewed, knowing my destiny and I welcomed the change.

CHAPTER 24

The library felt like a crypt housing ancient memories of my immortality. I located the relevant volumes and I propped them up in front of me. They looked like the twin colossus of Memnon guarding the gateway of the famous funereal temple at Thebes. They were a symbol of the pharaoh Amenhoteps' immortality. The encyclopaedias were my pillars of immortality, supporting the Parthenon of my soul.

I decided to peer into the Wentworth life first. I flicked open the book to the page in anticipation of what I might find. To my disappointment it read,

Sir Wentworth Thomas, see Strafford, Thomas Wentworth, 1st earl, Baron of Raby.

I was impatient and frustrated by now and I thumped the heavy tome down on the table. I plucked out another book and flicked to the relevant page only to find it dog-eared. I thought that was strange. Who else would want to know about his life? I was intrigued and suspicious of the whole thing. As I opened it, that damp, musty smell of old books hit the back of my throat. I was speechless and gasped in utter disbelief. My consciousness caved into a vast, black, titanic chasm. Dazed and disoriented, I looked again. There he was, in a full frontal, head and shoulders shot, painted by Sir Anthony Van Dyck, 1636. He was dressed in black, battle armour. A flouncy royalist collar graced his elegant breastplate. Thick, dark hair sat nobly on a high forehead. His penetrating eyes focused like lasers and seared my soul. He sported a turned up moustache and a small, goatee beard, which partially detracted from his grave, forbidding expression and pale, sombre complexion.

I was still in shock. I could feel his presence stirring deep inside of me. I could see the physical resemblance. It was me, sure enough. It was uncanny. A rush of adrenaline blasted through me as the full force of his life exploded into my consciousness. It was as if I had opened up a seething, festering wound, which had lain dormant for years - 500 to be exact. I couldn't take it all in, the courtroom drama and the beheading swept back to me, swamping my feeble frame. The pain, the anguish, the conspiracy and the betrayal mingled with the whimpering voices of his wife and children and the jeers and shouts of the mob.

> *'Black Tom is no more!*
> *Black Tom is no more!'*

I slowly centred myself, took in a few deep breaths and read the biography. Every now and then the hairs on the back of my neck tingled and rose and I was flushed from head to toe.

He was born an Aries on the 13th April 1593 in London, and died on the 12th May 1641, on London's Tower Hill. He was the principal advisor to King Charles the 1st, who made him Lord President of the North before he became Baron Raby and Lord Lieutenant of Ireland. He was Lieutenant General of the Kings' forces at war with Scotland and he was eventually created Earl of Strafford, a Knight of the Royal Order of the Garter.

His star faded however, and he was impeached and tried for treason against the crown; a charge brought on by a conspiring mob of English, Scottish and Irish nobles. Yet, he skilfully defended himself and it looked as though he would be acquitted. However, the treacherous Lord Pym introduced a *bill of attainder*, an antiquated law that was a summary condemnation to death by a special act of parliament. The Commons passed it by a large majority and the Lords, intimidated and coerced by popular rioting, passed it too. The King had to sign the bill, reneging on his promise to save him. By his hand he sent his trusted friend and loyal adviser to the block.

He was betrayed by his king, condemned by a conspiracy and beheaded. Yet, even on the scaffold he professed allegiance to the Crown, to his country, its laws and religion. He forgave the king for his betrayal; his last, poignant words before meeting his executor were;

'I am at the door going out and my next step must be from time to eternity; to clear myself to you all, I do solemnly profess before God, I am not guilty of that great crime laid to my charge; nor have I ever had the least inclination or intention to damnify or prejudice the King, the state, the laws or religion of this Kingdom, but with my best endeavours to serve all and to support all.

Tears poured uncontrollably down my cheeks. My heart and soul wrenched in two, I shouted, and thumped my fist in disgust at the injustice perpetrated on this most noble and loyal servant. The mob needed a scapegoat and he consented to be *the lamb to the slaughter* in order to protect his king and appease the mob.

Deep down I knew his motives were honourable. I felt his deep pain, leaving his young family, wife and friends in the lecherous hands of his enemies. I sensed those last words, as he laid his head on the block.

'That stock must be my pillow; here must I rest from my labours; no thoughts of envy, no dreams of treason, jealousies of foes, cares for the King, the state or myself shall interrupt this sleep...

I was deeply wounded and thrust into that dark, unconscious pocket of terror and despair. I had inherited his actions, his wounds, his dreams and nightmares. I needed to heal this rancid rift and reconcile the injustices perpetrated on the great Earl of Strafford. I realised that was a price of past life knowledge.

I had to get outside for some fresh air. The expression, those eyes, that stern moustache. I always had a moustache. Even as a lad growing up, the 'bum fluff' never left my upper lip. The bell rang for elevenses.

'DB, tea's outside today. It's such a gorgeous day,' Lance shouted, bobbing up and down in his trademark waddle. 'Chris, you don't mind bringing the 'dogs' out? They are in the kitchen.'

'Okay Lance, no problem.' I turned to find them but they were nowhere to be seen.

'Oh, give the others another shout too, Chris. I don't think they heard me the first time.'

I sauntered along and knocked on the office door before entering. They were all sitting there, in deep contemplation. The whole aura of the room was as quiet and sombre as a morgue. Pale, hollow faces dripped deep emotions as DB beckoned me in.

'Come in Chris, we've had some bad news. It's Pete, he's O.d.'

A steely silence slid through the room as their auras swamped each other. They tried to control their anguish, but it oozed out and swamped me too.

'I don't understand? Why? What happened?' I lamented.

Stellios, his face ashen spoke: 'His mother called Steve. She was in a hell of a state. He'd been feeling isolated, lonely and frustrated. His family never really understood him. He could not relate to anyone out there. He had left us; the only real help and understanding he ever had. But he could not come back. Guilt, anguish, hope, despair, confusion elation, the stutter and the seeds of genius; they all conspired against him. It was a deadly Molotov cocktail begging for an explosive spark. She found him in his bedroom; face down. He'd choked on his own vomit listening to his favourite track over and over on a continuous loop. He always listened to The Hurting; he loved Tears For Fears.

'I'm on my own
Could you release my load
Could you see my pain
Could you please explain
The Hurting.

'She said the room stank of booze, dope and incense. There was an empty bottle of vodka on the bed and a pile of poppers all over the floor.'

He was dead. Twenty-one years old. Suicide. Another young soul wasted before the prime of his life. What a crying shame, but he was gone. Passed into spirit, released from his torment. But what would happen to his soul now? I had heard DB say suicides came back rapidly into incarnation. I wondered if that would be true for Pete.

Everyone shuffled outside into the beautiful, mid-morning sunshine. There was no real conversation. It was quiet apart from the dogs playing in the shade and the cranky cats tumbling around in the flowerbeds. A delicate, pristine white butterfly, fluttered from flower to flower before soaring skywards into infinity. It was him. His soul. His spirit. Pete had released himself. He was basking in the light of the solar deity.

> *A butterfly rested upon a flower,*
> *Gay was he and light as a flake,*
> *And there he met a caterpillar,*
> *Sobbing as though his heart*
> *would break;*
> *It hurt the happy butterfly*
> *To see a caterpillar cry.*
>
> *Said he, 'whatever is the matter?*
> *And may I help in any way?'*
> *'I've lost my brother,' wept the other,*
> *He's been unwell for many a day;*
> *Now I discover, sad to tell,*
> *He's only a dead and empty shell.'*
>
> *Unhappy grub, be done with weeping,*
> *Your sickly brother is not dead;*
> *His body's stronger and no longer*
> *Crawls like a worm, but flies instead.*
> *He dances through the sunny hours*
> *And drinks sweet nectar from*
> *the flowers.'*

G.Eustace Owen's poem The Butterfly danced gaily into my consciousness. I was bathed in serene peace. I knew Pete had shuffled from his chrysalis. He was an angel in spirit. *Psyche*, the Greek word for butterfly is the same word for soul. They knew the cycle of birth, death and rebirth. They had inherited the ancient wisdom from initiate high priests of Egypt.

One by one, they all filtered away into the house. Stellios sat quietly, as if in prayer, under an old oak. I tiptoed over and placed my hand on his shoulder. He opened his soulful eyes. I felt his pain, but he also knew Pete was free to roam the realms of spirit. He would be one again with all his characters in Wonderland. I could see him now, at the Mad Hatter's side, supping tea, laughing his head off and talking unrestricted, ten to the dozen, to Alice, his anima, and his dream bride.

'How's the research going Christo?'

'Oh the research, Oh yes, that. It's going great Stellios. I'd almost forgotten all about it. Do you think he'll be back, you know, in another body? Will it be soon?'

'Well, that's what DB says. In suicides, the personality abruptly terminates the incarnation by its own freewill. The life lessons have not been learnt; past life karma has not been balanced. He will have to come back again soon. Unfortunately, the next personality will have to endure the same restrictions and even more.'

'Do you mean to say, it will inherit Pete's stutter?'

'Yes, and possibly another more severe disability.'

'How much more severe?'

'As he opted out and because he must have had constant emotional and mental crisis, the personality could come back with a Down's Syndrome disorder or something similar.'

'Stellios, surely not as severe as that?'

'Well, the way I understand it, a Down's Syndrome case needs a life or two of rest from the pressures of the rat-race. The soul chooses the condition to heal, harmonise and balance the mental and emotional bodies, which the previous personality could not cope with in a past life.'

'Do you mean to say all Down's Syndrome cases were suicides in past lives, then?'

'Not at all, but some, possibly. If we come into the world with a block or disability then we have to overcome it positively, with understanding, courage and acceptance. If we don't deal with it, then more severe karmic lessons will come back to haunt us in the next incarnation.'

'I understand. What about people who are born normal, but through an accident they are forced to spend the remainder of their lives in a wheelchair?'

'It's the same Christo. They have to overcome their disability and get on with life in the best possible way. If they resent the position they are in, or make other people suffer because of their disability, they'll come back with more to cope with.'

'Stellios, you know, out there, that would not be acceptable; it's heresy. They'd have you strung up for that.'

'Chris that's not my law, it's cosmic law; *'what ever ye shall sow shall ye reap'*. We don't realise it's not just our physical actions which are bound by karmic law; our feelings and especially our thoughts are too. It's all in the mind. Our attitudes are so important.'

'Well, let's hope he has a little rest in between.'

'Christo, it's in the lap of the gods now. We can only pray they are kind to him.'

'Stellios, we're waiting,' John shouted in his all American louder hailer. 'Come on, we've got policy to decide. Stop faffing around.'

'Got to go Christo. We'll talk later, okay.'

'Okay. See you.'

I was left with the aftermath of elevenses. Lance had disappeared, leaving me to gather the cups together and toddle off to the kitchen.

'What are you doing Lance?' He was sitting down stuffing his face with jam doughnuts. He had about two or three in his mouth. He almost choked. I had taken him by surprise. After a few seconds and a couple of gulps of tea he cleared his throat.

'Chris, shh. Don't disturb them.'

'What the hell are you doing?'

'Well, I don't like the 'dogs' going to waste, so each morning, after eleven's I stuff my face with them. I can't help it. I've got a wicked sweet tooth.'

'Ah, so those were the dogs you asked me to get from the kitchen.'

'What did you think they were, Poodles or Jack Russell's?' He had me in stitches. 'Look at me', he said, patting his little bump. 'I've put on a stone since coming here. I really must stop eating them or I'll end up looking like Friar Tuck.' What a character he was. Even Pete's suicide didn't seem to affect him, or at least he didn't show it.

'Can I have a dog before you scoff them all?'

'Sure, take two, that'll save me a pound or two. I'll have to go on a diet tomorrow. Or maybe I'll start next week,' he said laughing.

'I'm off for another session in the library,' I said, picking up the doughnuts.

'I'll let you get to it then Chris. Oooo, the previous life thing gives me a real buzz.' I could tell he was expecting a reply but I left him spying the remainder of the dogs. Lance stood there, perched like a vulture swaying from side to side, in indecision. I turned around slyly, woof... he scoffed the lot, licking his lips and pruning his feathers.

'Lance bring another pot of tea in. Where are those dogs I bought this morning?' I left him gorged up in panic as I sauntered towards the library, gathering my thoughts as I went.

I wonder how Steve's taken the news? They were really close. My thoughts were interrupted when I bumped into Dick carrying a load of metal printing plates.

'Fuck sake, didn't you see me coming?' he shouted as the whole lot sprang into the air. 'Oh no, don't tell me, we've inherited another airhead.'

'Oops, sorry Dick, I was in deep thought. I didn't see you.'

'We get rid of one stuttering dumb wit and he's replaced with another. What's DB doing, he must be mad.'

I'd had enough of him by now. I felt my Scorpionic anger rip and rage through me.

'Who the fuck do you think you are, you cockney cunt?' I pinned him up against the wall with my fist around his scrawny throat and my head forced against his nose. 'Do you know what a Glaswegian kiss is?'

'Fuck off, ya 'greasy bubble'. You're full of shit. Leave me alone.' I tossed him onto the pile of plates on the floor. 'Ah my lips! You've burst my lips, ya nutter!'

'You're lucky I didn't break your nose. You've been a fucking pain in the arse ever since I met you. No wonder Pete O.D'd with you on his tits all the time. Keep your crap to yourself from now on, you fucking little wanker,' I blasted and kicked the plates all over him.

'All right, all right, I've had enough. I pushed you too far. I didn't expect you to physically retaliate. Nobody ever has in the past.' He paused for a moment and a look of recognition crossed his face. 'What did you say about Pete? You mean he's topped himself? What happened? Who told you?'

I could see his persona had mellowed and he felt genuine remorse. He was gutted when I told him the gruesome details.

'God, that's so sad, I liked him, really I did. We used to talk, you know, in the mornings. He would confide in me a lot. I knew he was finding it tough in here, but out there, he knew he had no chance. He was a romantic, a deeply troubled soul. He suffered badly as a child you know. I didn't mean what I said about his work. It was brilliant, a true spiritual insight into his unique creativity.'

'Dick, I don't understand, why are you so antagonistic towards everyone?'

'Chris, this is a tough place to live in and survive. You've felt the energies. It sorts the men out from the boys. I may come across as a belligerent bastard, but that's my protection. It's my facade and it works for me. I'm a first ray soul, with a fourth ray personality. It's fucking hell to cope with.'

'Oh, so you know about esoteric psychology then? I thought you weren't spiritual.'

'Chris, I've printed all DB's books. I know them inside out and back to front. The astrology and the rays fascinate me. I'm a Sagittarius sun and Scorpio ascendant. Yes, I swear a lot and cause aggro, but I'm a sort of catalyst of energy in the group. I poke and prod until I get a response. When all hell is let loose and energies have been released, there is always calm. That's how the fourth ray operates: harmony and growth through conflict.'

'How do you cope with your first ray soul? It must be a bugger to express.'

'All I can say is that it flogs me on and on. It's a fire within me: a burning, wilful force, which drives me to more effort. It never lets me rest. Coupled with my frustrated fourth ray personality, it spews out, causing conflict, antagonism and battles; I can't help it.'

'Isn't it recommended to change the personality to the second ray? Its harmonising love-wisdom energies love the focus and willpower of the first ray soul.'

'Well yes Chris; that's easier said than done. I find it really difficult to be diplomatic. I can't stand 'faffing around'. I don't suffer fools gladly nor do I use the heart much. I'm trying to though, I really am.'

'I think it's all to do with integration. I've heard DB say the clenched fist and the open palm are an analogy of the integrated personality. The clenched fist is the strength and iron will of the first ray, and the open palm is the second ray - love wisely applied and wisdom lovingly administered. They complement each other beautifully.'

'Well, I'm all clenched fist at the moment. There are mountains of work to be done and I'm dithering here with you. Mike, fuck sake, give us a hand. All you do is talk, talk and guzzle tea all day.'

He trundled off like an old locomotive, belching balloons of hot air, nostrils flaring and hooter blasting.

CHAPTER 25

Dick had a heart after all. His stern exterior and defiant stance were his protection. Deep down he embraced spirituality, but on his own terms. I had a funny feeling he knew more than he showed. His Scorpio ascendant plunged him into vast, raging, psychological rivers. Those heroic Herculean qualities, embedded deep in the cave of his psyche, were in constant conflict with his *Dweller/Shadow*. He had to battle with that awesome entity to free his tormented soul from the clutches of the material world. He wanted money, power and fame. He wanted independence, but at what expense? Was he going to sell his soul? Who could know? The battle waged on inside him and we had to suffer all his negative projections.

I settled my mind to research the Kitchener life. Fragments and flashbacks had plagued me for months. There had to be a reason behind it and hopefully I was going to find out. I had primed myself by the reaction I felt researching the Strafford life. Surely it could not be any different. All I knew was that he was a public icon, a symbol of victory and courage for Britain in World War 1. Now, sadly, his identity is plastered on a whole range of souvenirs being bartered around by market traders in Carnaby Street. How his stern and focused stance is banded around to line the pockets of hawkers; it was sick. It was a degradation of his name and mission. Something passionate stirred within me. I felt deeply betrayed by their actions. He gave his life serving the nation; it was so derogatory and down right unfair to degrade his honour in this way.

I flicked to the page and opened it to his proud, stern, moustachioed face and that focussed stare. The print showed him in his mature years, wearing a military jacket with lashings of braiding and an array of glittering decorations. Immediately I noticed the similarities we shared. A heavy set, powerful jaw line, a regal nose and hooded eyelids housed alert, steely blue eyes. His brows flanked each side of his face, marching like lines of proud soldiers on parade. He also sported a middle parting, like me, intensifying his austere persona.

Tingling rushed through my body, setting off *His* calling siren. I was thrust into a pocket of previous life memory. There was dust and clouds everywhere. I was charging around in the dense heat of battle; my horse buckled, kicking violently, almost ejecting me from my saddle.

Bang! Bang! My head was catapulted backwards as I was shot in the face. A severe, numbing pain zapped my lower jaw. Suddenly my consciousness was tossed and turned inside out by violent, rampant torrents. I was in a whirlpool of raw energy, being tugged here and bullied there. I frantically rasped for air, hands outstretched as a raging, icy, sea consumed me. Darkness reigned and I felt the life force leak from me and merge with the great ocean of life. I came round on the floor with the encyclopaedias spread in a bundle on top of me. I was shivering and shaking all over; a cold sweat swamped me.

'Fucking hell! What was that all about?' I shouted, as I lay there in disbelief. Where did this awesome response from the unconscious come from? I felt him, his energy, his proud stance, his gallant lead, and the smell of his sweat-soaked, khaki uniform. The foul stench of death swept in and out, like an endless tide, ripping crying souls from their destitute, shattered frames. The torrents, raging storms and that icy seabed; what was that all about? I was terrified, I felt like I was drowning.

I steadied myself and started to read the biography.

Kitchener (of Khartoum and of Broome), Herbert, 1st Earl, *also called Baron Kitchener of Khartoum and of the Vaal and Aspal. Born June 24th, near Listowel, County Kerry, Ireland. Died June 5th, 1916 at sea off the Orkney Islands.*

'That was it!' I shouted and was flushed from head to toe. I felt his life leak out of him in those, dark, icy-cold northern waters. I experienced the anguish in his soul. He was not ready to die, at least not this way.

'He was lost at sea. He was lost at sea!' I belched. A wave of nostalgia swept through me. I felt the nation's deep mourning; crowds caught in a frenzied cauldron of despair, lamented the loss of their most favourite son and War Lord. Flags fluttered at half-mast and headliners leaked out the sad message.

Lord Kitchener lost at sea! Hampshire torpedoed! Kitchener dead!

I centred myself and read further.

British Field Marshal, imperial administrator, conqueror of the Sudan, commander in chief during the Boer war, secretary of state for war at the beginning of World War 1. At that time he organised armies on a scale unprecedented in British history and became a symbol of the national will to victory.

I was humbled and confused. My mind still in tatters, I tried to reconcile the vast gulf, which had torn me apart. I continued to read in disbelief, shocks stirring the very fabric of my soul.

He served in the Royal Engineers, Chatham, learning field fortification, surveying, estimating and building.

Bloody hell, he even settled in Cyprus, surveying the island and producing an accurate map that scholars and archaeologists could use. It all came flooding back. I had worked for the Larnaca County Council. My duties were surveying land for construction of new refugee settlements. Kitchener had put a paper together recommending that the island was ideal for colonisation. He stated it was a sound policy to base a garrison on it, to protect British interests in the eastern Mediterranean. I tingled all over as I mulled the consequences around my tender mind.

'So, we are thrust back life after life, to places we lived before,' I shouted out loud, in disbelief. Strafford was Lord President of Ireland and Kitchener was born there. I was born a Greek Cypriot and lived in Cyprus for four years. Kitchener spent at least four years there, before taking a post as a captain in the Anglo-Egyptian army. The synchronicities were uncanny, but it may all be coincidental; I really didn't know. How could I be him? I could identify with his energy and personality.

He became commander-in-chief of the Egyptian army and Governor-General of the Sudan. He was wounded in the face by a stray Dervish bullet as he charged to cover a hasty retreat. The bullet shattered his jaw, but it was not a serious injury.

'The loud bangs; yes that was it,' I shouted. The blasting sound, the horse bucking, the pain, the stench of battle. I had rein acted the whole thing. The traumatic events were sown up in a hidden pocket of my unconscious mind. They ripped through the lining, trailing threads back to memories of past actions.

He orchestrated Britain's victory over the Boer's in South Africa, becoming Viscount Kitchener. He was sent to India as commander-in-chief, but was frustrated by fierce opposition from Viceroy Curzon. He left India and accepted proconsulship of Egypt.

In June 1914, he received an earldom and reluctantly accepted an appointment to the cabinet as secretary of state for war and was promoted to field marshal.

*He is remembered most for his unprecedented recruitment of soldiers, '**Kitchener's armies**', planning of strategy and mobilisation of industry. He disliked teamwork and delegation of responsibility, thereby handicapping his term in the cabinet. Due to this, he was released from his duties but refused to quit.*

His career was ended suddenly, by drowning, when the cruiser 'Hampshire', bearing him on a mission to Russia, was sunk by a German mine or torpedo.

Both lives made an awesome impact on me. There were immense lessons to be gleaned from circumstances initiated in the past. After all, they were important pieces in an intricate cosmic jigsaw, which I was part off. I was the end result of their trials, their failures and their successes. My thirst had been quenched for now, but I needed to delve deeper into their lives to fashion out my purpose this time around. The library door creaked open to Lance's quizzing expression.

'Chris, a car's going back in 30 minutes, if you are ready to go. If not you can hitch a lift with DB when he comes in for dinner.'

'Thanks Lance, How did you get round the 'dogs' issue then?'

'Easy, I told them Wolf and Poppet scoffed them off the table, outside in the courtyard. You ought to have seen the expressions on their faces when DB scolded them. If they could speak, I'd be in the doghouse, not them. Nobody knew any better, but I was almost sick for my sins.'

'Chris, it's a call for you, it's urgent,' John said guiltily. He knew who it was from, I could see it in his conscience-stricken eyes.

'Hello Christo, it's me. I need to collect some of my stuff later. My cousin is giving me a lift. Is that okay?'

I was momentarily dazed; the previous life research was still vivid in my mind. To earth myself to this reality was difficult. My relationship seemed quite insignificant compared to the last few hours here. I had not given it much thought, what with Pete's OD and the evidence of my immortality. I paused and hesitated momentarily.

'Well, I suppose it's okay. When will you be arriving?'

'You're not mad? I expected you to tear my head off. What's going on?'

'Elena, when will you be coming? I'm just a bit spaced out. I've had a few insights and revelations.'

'Oh, okay, about 8.30, is that okay?'

'Yes, see you then. Bye.'

I gathered my thoughts and still a little bewildered, I bumped into Lance. He was carrying a box of paper from the print works. He almost dropped it on my toes.

'Bloody hell Chris, what's up with you? You look quite pale. Is everything all right?'

'Sorry Lance, I'm all over the place. I can't seem to focus. Too much past life research has put my mind into reverse.'

'I'm going back now, do you want to come with me?'

'No Lance, I'll go back with DB. I need to talk to him about something.'

'No problem, you'll be in the back with the dogs. Mike normally drives DB down.'

I wandered out behind the cottage to a beautiful, secluded, verdant oasis. A pathway etched out of the deciduous brush meandered to a gentle running brook. A series of old, oak trees and stumps formed a mystic circle in the long, wild grass. The sun's golden rays speckled the green velvet cloth. As I sat there, a sweet breeze flounced in on the ethers, wafting puffs of violet and tantalising sprays of primrose. The chatter of birds played an encore in nature's symphony. I was one with them. My heart beat like a rhythmic drum and my lungs bellowed in tune with the breeze rustling around the leafy undergrowth. I felt my feet root deep into the bowels of the earth. My hands stretched skywards twisting like boughs and my hair frizzed into fronds. I was part of the 'Anima Mundi', one with all nature. I shut my eyelids and merged with the elements. My soul sang, my spirit rejoiced and my emotions danced daintily to the sound of the clear, purifying stream. I had found true centre, my destiny and myself. I had let go all the trappings of the material world. I was free. No secure home, no binding partner, no money, no religious prejudices and no family dharma. I was stripped bare of my possessions and as I sat there naked of worldly goods, I breathed the lives of all my ancestors, terrestrial and spiritual.

'Chris. If you want to see DB, he's ready for you now,' Lance's foghorn blasted, interrupting my meditation.

'I'll be there in a minute.' I shook off my green mantle and squelched back up the well-trodden path to the open door of the cottage.

'Come in Chris. I see you've discovered my secret garden. Isn't it refreshing?'

'It's heaven on earth DB. I just lost myself in it. The colours, the textures, the melodies, they were magic.'

'What do you want to talk to me about?'

'I've decided to release myself from Elena. I had a few realisations today. My meditation in the grove sparked off my rebirth. I feel free and liberated. My soul strings sang an ancient melody, bewitching me back to memories of my immortality. **Only Everything.** I understand what it truly means now.'

'I knew you would come through, Chris. The choice was yours. It was your free will to release yourself. I was quite concerned about her relationship with him. Actors are all the same, all full of shit and glamour. But I don't want her fucking up my filming schedule with her 'squirting ovaries' gushing all over the place. I hope she's not coming back.'

'She's coming tonight to collect her things. I'll tell her of my decision.'

'Chris, don't get trapped in her beguiling aura. She'll plunge her hooks deeper in you, given half a chance. Tell her straight; tell her to take it all away tonight.'

'DB, she's got nowhere to go, I have...'

'Listen, she'll find someone to shack up with. She may even be moving in with him. Do you really believe she's gone to her aunt's?'

'I'm not sure. But I don't want to kick her out on the streets. We've been together...'

'Jesus fucking Christ man, don't get all soppy. Do you think she thought twice about you when she was fucking him? Come on Chris grow up. Take those rosy-coloured specks off.'

'DB, I'll do it my way. Okay?'

'No, you'll do it my way. I want her off the premises tonight. If not, you can piss off with her, tied to her apron strings.'

I felt anger rage through my veins and my blood boiled. All my first ray energies rumbled like a volcano about to blow its top. I slowly and deliberately rose from my seated position. My fists rained down on the table as I blasted my attack.

'I said, I will do it my way. I will not be bullied nor blackmailed by you or any of your lapdog lieutenants. Oh, and by the way, I think I'll put a hold on that donation I was going to give you. I might even fuck off out of here, leaving you all wallowing in your own shit.' I walked out, head held high and pride bolstered. John and Barry were in shock. Stellios and Lance muttered amongst themselves in utter amazement.

'Did you hear that! Nobody had the balls to stand up to DB before like that, not even Dick,' skulked Lance from the kitchen.

I had scored a victory for the outer circle. I had my first run in with DB. My sense of justice and fair play exploded through my being. It was not me standing there; it was a collective embodiment of all my lives, in the fight for liberty and equality. I would always stand my ground against the oppressor, whoever they may be. I had earned my spurs. My mettle had been tested; I had the strength and power. Perhaps that was his way of goading it out of me. It was successful anyway and I had made an impact on the group. I had made my stand and I had reinforced my position in the outer circle's hierarchy.

I caught a lift back with the boys. Silence reigned until we cleared the dirt track to the main road, then an almighty cheer rang through the mob. I was truly one of the boys now. I had stood up to DB and established my intent, but I had triggered off the seeds of civil war in the community. We all had to choose sides. It was tough on Stellios; he had been given special privileges. I needed him more than ever to pry into their business. He had to be seen to be part of the inner circle, even if he was, deep down, one of us. The clapped out, old van ground to a halt in the Claregate grounds.

'Anyone for a pint lads?' I shouted. We need to celebrate the occasion, don't we?'

'Yes guys, I'll get Steve and Jeremy too. I'm sure they'll want to hear the gossip,' Stellios cheered.

'It will be good to get him out of that caravan tonight. We don't want him wallowing in self-pity and guilt over Pete's suicide,' I added.

'Hey, why don't we boycott dinner tonight? That would be a brilliant act of defiance, wouldn't it?' Lance said, waiving his fist in the air.

'Fantastic idea! I'd love to see their faces as they enter the half-derelict, dining room. Can you imagine the atmosphere?

'*Oh, Linda, Claire, where are the boys tonight? Didn't you ring the bell?*'

'*Yes, DB, we did, but it's like a morgue out there. There's nobody in the TV room, nor the library.*'

I would love to be a fly on the wall in there tonight, just to see their empty expressions,' said Stellios.

'Come on guys, we've got some serious strategy to discuss. We need to take advantage of this situation. It's time to re-negotiate our rights. I've got to get back at 8.30, to sort my situation out with Elena.'

Steve and Jeremy appeared from their dens, buzzing with excitement, and we all piled into the van and sped down to the local pub.

CHAPTER 26

The mood in the pub wavered from elation to depression. We all paid homage to Pete, our spiritual brother. Steve was particularly affected, but he mellowed after I told him my vision of the butterfly. We all understood he was free and we rejoiced in his release from his mortal prison. The matter of my confrontation with DB boosted the conversation. They had waited for years for someone to come along to challenge the inner circle's dominance. It looked like I was destined to be the one to lead them against their undemocratic ruler.

'Well guys, you don't have to get involved with this battle. After all, it's my challenge, not yours. I am not going to back down.'

There was a moment of silence: faces blanked and body language buckled. I felt their auras haemorrhage.

'I'm off to the loo. Have a think about it and when I come back, we'll talk.'

'Oh, I'm bursting too, I'll come along with you Chris,' Stellios blurted, holding his willy. He never could hold his drink; his wee bladder was crying to be vacated.

'Stellios, are you with me on this one? It's important I have your support. You know I've taken your advice and decided to split from Elena.'

'Christo, you don't have to ask me. I am indebted to you. I think you're doing the right thing with her. What made you decide? You were in utter turmoil the last time we spoke.'

'Stellios, I had an illuminating revelation as I sat down in DB's grassy retreat. All my anguish dissipated into images of freedom, release and liberation. It was so euphoric, no words can describe the elation I experienced.'

'Christo, she's a good girl, but at the end of the day, she's beautiful and so sensual. She needs a man to love her and provide all her home comforts. I'm glad you've calmed down and you've decided to end it amicably. She'll find it hard in the beginning, but I'm sure she'll realise it's for the best. Anyway, you're still going to be friends aren't you?'

'Of course I am. I forgive her; I was equally to blame. If I had treated her better, confided in her, understood her, maybe things would have been different.'

'Christo, she's not the sort of woman to live in this type of community. All the guys had the hots for her and the girls, especially Linda, were jealous of her. Can you imagine the projections she had to endure as well as your negativity blasting at her.'

'Okay, okay; don't rub it in. You knew what I was going through. I feel guilty as it is. I don't need you to regurgitate the whole thing to me. Come on Stellios, stop playing with yourself, put that wee winkle away, it's time for the reckoning to begin.'

I had him chuckling as we left. The local lads in the loo frowned at us as we walked away hand in hand. You ought to have seen their faces; they were all built like brick shit houses with beer guts down to their knees. They hadn't seen their willies in years, never mind play with them.

'I want you to keep your ears and eyes open. You're one of us, but they rate you in their ranks.'

'I'll do my best Christo, but they're not stupid. I know their tactics well.'

'All right guys, are you with us? Stellios is supporting me. You know I set him up with special privileges, don't you?'

'What do you mean Chris?' Steve questioned.

'Well, I positioned him in the inner circle's ranks. He got the praise for enticing me here. They were also impressed when he persuaded me to give donations towards the work.'

'You mean to say he did all that? I didn't know he was a scheming little mole,' Jeremy blurted.

'Boys, come on, do you think he could get leverage over me? I played it that way to get him into their ranks.'

'Bloody hell, Chris, you're canny. I thought you were so green when you first came here,' Lance croaked.

'So you've given donations. How much? That's really honourable of you. We don't have two pennies to rub together, but we've contributed in other ways,' Steve added.

'Guys, I'd give my right arm for the work. I know how important it is to externalise the teachings. It just so happens I've got savings and I wanted to put them to good use. I now realise part of my karma is to financially support spiritual projects.'

'You must be mad,' Jeremy shouted. 'I would never give my life savings away if I had any. I'd invest it all in bonds and stocks.' He was in awe of my commitment. He was a schizophrenic astrological mix, sun Taurus with Gemini rising. He loved money and possessions, but needed space and freedom.

'Listen, all or nothing, shit or bust. It's taken me months of deep soul searching, personal crisis and breakdown to realise my path. I've even decided to separate from Elena.'

They were in shock, confused and gaping at me in disbelief. They couldn't comprehend me. I had it all, money, security, position, the glamour girl wife on my arm, a brilliant career ahead of me and I'd sacrificed it all for the path.

'You've let it all go for a vision, a whim and a dream, which could lead to nowhere Chris. You must be mad or inspired,' Lance shouted in adulation.

'Lance, I've tasted something deep inside. It's like a drug. I'm hooked, I'm obsessed, I want more. I'm prepared to sacrifice my attachments to drink the divine ambrosia of the gods.'

'Chris, that's so inspiring. Look at us; we had very little to lose coming here. Most of us couldn't survive in the rat race anyway. Don't get me wrong, we're all very creative, we have gifts and talents, but we're too sensitive for the materialistic life out there. It would have consumed us and we'd have ended up like poor Pete,' Lance conceded.

'What's it to be then? Are we in this together or not?'

'Chris, we're with you,' Steve cheered. 'But we don't want the work to suffer. We know how hard it is to maintain Claregate and materialise projects. We all respect DB and his devotion to the path. We even understand the need for the inner circle, but we've been treated like scum for years and it's going to stop.' We all crashed our mugs together.

'Drink up lads, the next round is on the way. I'll have to leave you; Elena's coming to collect her stuff.'

'Okay Christo, good luck with her.'

'Thanks Stellios, I'll need it.'

I walked back on foot, my thoughts charged with enthusiasm. I had managed to unite them, received their trust and won their loyalty. I had to meet DB and his lapdog lieutenants head on. Deep down, we were all in the same boat, fighting on the same side, but there had to be mutual respect and communication. The battle was not with them; the war was with the materialists.

I sauntered into the driveway where an unfamiliar car with its boot gaping open hogged the front porch. The main door was ajar and I could hear voices on the landing. It was her; she'd come early. I trotted upstairs and pushed the croaky old door open.

'So you got here early. I didn't expect you to be here so soon,' I said, slashing the atmosphere.

'You know my cousin Andreas, don't you?' She snapped. She looked so stunning and sensuous as usual. Her ruby red lips pouted like an aroused labia. Her hypnotic, green eyes gleamed like emeralds and they seared my soul. I felt a surge of passion gorge my groin. God, she was gorgeous. I ached for her warm bosom; my heart pounded in my cold cage as testosterone raged around my body, sending me wild. Her alluring puffs of perfume wafted towards me, like ghostly fingers groping me in the ethers. She knew how to get me going all right. I felt her enticing hold tighten and her web of seduction swamp me as I struggled to free myself from her beguiling grip.

'Andreas, can I have a few minutes of privacy please? We need to talk.'

'No problem Christo, I'll pop out and have a fag.'

He clumped out taking some of her stuff with him. There was an awkward silence as our auras weaved around each other. What was it to be? Should I throw my arms around her? That's what she was angling for, I was sure. It was so easy to melt into her aura and embrace her voluptuous body again. My emotions wanted to ravage her, but hang on a minute! She fucked off with him. She put me through hell and back. She's an adulterous, scheming bitch, a Mata Hari waiting to seduce me again.

'Christo, I'm really so sorry, please forgive me. I've realised I really love you. I was confused. I felt unloved and unwanted. You treated me like shit. What was I supposed to do?' She said, slithering towards me.

'Elena, I've thought long and hard over our relationship. It's my fault as much as yours, but I don't think it's going to work.'

'Oh Christo. Please, please, give me another chance. I promise to make it up to you, I promise,' she shouted in a fit of deep despair, as she lounged towards me.

'No! I really mean it. There is no chance of us getting back together, no way,' I said pushing her aside.

'You're all fucked up anyway,' she hissed. 'Look at you. You look awful. You've lost your self-respect and you're so gullible. Baker's brainwashed you. You're a loser with distorted dreams of grandeur. Go on; throw it all away, you sucker. To think I even thought of coming back to you; I must have been mad.'

I was not going to be drawn into her cesspool of negativity.

'Elena, I'm no good for you. I dragged you here and degraded you. You're not cut out for this place. Your place is out there, in amongst the glitzy glam world of money and power.'

'Christo, don't throw it all away. We can try again, it's not too late,' she said clawing towards me.

'Elena, no, I can't. I just can't. I hated you. I cursed you. You ripped my heart in two. I wanted to kill you; I was possessed. My anger and jealousy were rampant. But, I've had a few revelations since then. I've been illuminated; I have no fear, no anger nor resentment anymore.'

She was momentarily stunned by my rebuke. Her chest heaved and her eyes cleared up.

'Right, it's your decision. It's finished, is it? Seven years flushed down the drain?'

The door edged open just at the right time, revealing Andreas curly dark mop of hair.

'Oops sorry; I'll just disappear again, I thought you'd finished.' Andreas apologised, feeling embarrassed by our embrace.

'Yes, we *are* finished. I'll just collect some more of my things and we'll be off,' said Elena in a stern and resolute way.

'Okay I'll wait for you downstairs.'

'Elena, you'll be okay at your aunt's, won't you?'

'Sure, I'll be fine for the moment. I need to be with her; she needs constant support. I'll decide what I need to do in the future. I might go back to Cyprus for a while; mum's been really worried about us. I suppose I'll have to spill the beans, won't I?' She sneered sarcastically.

'Don't follow me down. I'm likely to burst into tears again. I'm sure Linda will be pleased about my departure, but I'll miss Claire. She was so sweet and understanding.' She weaved downstairs, sobbing quietly as she disappeared out of the door and into the dense, moody night.

Thank God it was over. I felt a warm glow charge my heart as a loud fracas blasted in the hallway. The lads were back. Linda's head peeped out of her room, throwing daggers at them as they plonked themselves down in the lounge.

'I'm fucking famished. Fancy some doorstop cheese sandwiches guys?' Steve hollered at the top of his voice.

'Keep the bloody noise down you lot, or I'll tell DB in the morning. Anyway, where were you?' Linda croaked.

'Piss off and give us a break. Tell DB; we don't care. Things are going to change around here really soon,' Jeremy triumphantly blasted.

She turned in disgust and violently thudded her bedroom door shut.

I creaked the old door open and met Stellios on the stairs; he needed to piss again.

'How did it go?' he asked.

'Brilliant, it's really worked out for the better. Did you talk to the lads?'

'Yes. We're all for it; the boys are on a high.'

'Okay, give me 10 minutes and we'll have it out in the lounge.'

I needed time to think my strategy. I wanted to unite them, but I also needed them to buck up their image and ideas. I was adamant to start a series of reforms. I wanted to instigate a teaching program too. Filming had consumed all the wisdom teachings. There were no workshops nor lectures or classes.

I wandered down to the lounge where the lads were ripping into large doorstops and guzzling tea. They were in no mood to talk; they were all pissed as farts. We had a good laugh; their spirits were buzzing and the camaraderie was excellent. I had a lot to think about. I left them to it and withdrew to the solitude of my empty room. I was exhausted, but I managed a few lines in my diary before swooning into a deep slumber.

> *27th March, 10.30pm*
>
> *Major conflict with DB. Civil rights being challenged. I adamantly held my stand. Got the boys behind me. We will fight for our rights.*
>
> *Free to follow the path now. Elena and I have split. Very emotional, but for the best. Still wanted her, my passions were on fire, but I resisted the temptation. Need your loving support and encouragement.*

CHAPTER 27

'Oh my God; fuck off and leave me alone!' I shouted, punching the air and trembling all over, as I emerged from a violent, waking dream.

> *28th March 6.30am, waking dream*
>
> *I'm in a castle under siege; my troops are battling to keep the enemy out. We are outnumbered; they start catapulting great hooks onto the battlements and start climbing up. We are taken by surprise; the castle doors crunch open; a multitude of marauding soldiers pour in. We surrender after putting up a brave fight. They kick, punch and goad us, while their officers look on laughing. Linda is one of them. They ransack the place, taking us all prisoners. Shackled and chained, we are marched into a cell. A massive guard grabs me in a stranglehold, gags me and is threatening to beat me up.*

It was so real and so full of emotion. My heart pounded as I tried to ground myself. A monstrous sound echoed in the hall drowning me.

'Right, everybody up, now! Come on you shower of bastards; get downstairs now, all of you,' Dick shouted. 'Kick the lazy slobs out of the caravan!'

Heavy footsteps thundered all around. Shouts, screams and cries blasted all over the place. The old door crashed open off its hinges.

'Get the fuck up now. DB wants you downstairs in the lounge immediately!' Dick rasped in a savage, revengeful attack.

All bloody hell was let loose and it was only 6.45am. In a daze and still groggy from the dream, I jumped into my clothes and straggled downstairs. Doors banged, windows smashed and shouts bellowed as we were herded in the hallway. They had taken us by surprise. John, Barry, Dick and Mike stood there, smirking and jeering at us as we were frogmarched towards the lounge.

'I'll fucking kill you, ya Cockney bastard. You pushed Pete too far; you forced him to OD' blasted Steve and he took a swing at Dick, narrowly missing his face.

'Listen; don't try to pin his death on me. I had nothing to do with it. You were his friends; you should have encouraged him to stay. It's on your heads, not mine.'

We pinned Steve to the wall as Dick retreated, nursing his bruised ego. DB was propped up on his throne, cap off and his shoulders arched like a wrestler.

'So you want to play war games do you?' He pointed the finger at me. 'The element of surprise is the most effective form of attack, don't you think? I will not tolerate insurrection at Claregate. You do as you're told or you can all piss off out of here!'

'We are neither animals nor slaves,' I blasted in retaliation. 'Look at us, being herded in here at the crack of dawn. We are human beings. We are only exercising our rights, by democratic protest. You can't dictate to us.'

'Who the hell do you think you are? Oh, I see you've been appointed leader of this bunch of losers, have you? You were still holding onto your wife's underskirt, the last time I saw you. Suddenly you've grown balls!' Pointing at John he shouted, 'right, get the upstairs room cleared of his shit; he's moving into the caravan immediately.'

'Stellios, you little conspirator; you're coming down to LE with me. Get your crap out of the caravan, now! Jeremy, I've called the health inspectors in today. I told them the place is infested with rats. You've got 24 hours to get that rodent of yours off the premises!' He continued his rant. 'Steve, you've got some hard labour. I want you to come down to LE too. I need the drains cleared; there's shit belching out all over the place. It bloody stinks.

'As for you Lance, blame my dogs for eating the doughnuts? I want you to clear their hut out. It sinks of shit and piss. I want them smelling of roses. Do you hear me? He thundered on like a sergeant major, thumping his fists on the table.

'Divide and rule. Divide and rule!' He shouted and stormed off, raving. 'If you don't like it, you can all fuck off. All of you.' He thumped the doors behind him as he left.

We all stood there in silence, bleary-eyed and dazed. They were still half cut from the night before. The lapdog lieutenants marched us out sneering and goading us as the mass evacuation started. The doors crashed open. It was him again, clumping in those big, hob-nailed shoes of his.

'I want to see you in here, on your own, Kasparis, now!' The lounge door thumped behind me and I was ordered in for another grilling.

'Don't underestimate me, Chris. I'm too old in the tooth for this faction malarkey. I can't stand disobedience in the ranks. I'll grind any conspiracy into the dirt. Do you understand me?'

'DB, you'll never get any respect by using those methods. It just doesn't work. I know you have to whip them into shape and they're a lazy bunch of layabouts, but they have rights.'

'Rights! Rights! They do as they're told. That's their rights. The work is the focus here and if it suffers, then they suffer. Do you get my point?'

'I know you're chastising me for having stood up to you, but they did you no harm. I put them up to boycotting dinner. It was my fault totally.' An awkward silence swept the room as he contemplated his next move.

'Mmm, Chris, this is a lesson for you. If you ever want to lead a group, you can't show any weakness. You need to be wilful, direct and sometimes dictatorial. They'll walk all over you otherwise. That's how a first ray personality operates. I'm going to discipline you as well as move you into the caravan. I'm going to send you out fly-leafing the future lectures on your own. It's hard work, splashing around in the cold with freezing paste all over your hands. You'll have to dodge policemen and council workers. I'm also sending you out on the front line. You'll be manning the festivals for me, all of them. Oh yes, I'm holding you responsible for organising your loser's brigade. I want them whipped into line. Is that understood?'

He was trying to alienate me and test my character. He wanted to humiliate me and break me. I'd never been on the streets before, like some political activist dobbing blatant propaganda all over the place. The festival circuit? Mmm, I reckoned I could handle that, but I needed to build up my esoteric knowledge. Getting the boys into shape? Well that was my plan after all.

'Okay, I accept the challenge, but I want some concessions out of you.' He stared at me with those big, brown, bull's eyes.

'Mmm, well it depends what they are. Go on, blurt them out then.'

'I want more group communication between the inner circle and us. The boys want the right to discuss policy too. They are always kept in the dark.'

'I keep them in the dark to protect them. You don't know how we survive. If I involved them in the financial affairs, they would shit themselves. We have to endure heavy burdens to keep all this afloat.'

'I understand, but surely other issues can be debated. What about new projects, existing tasks, and the general direction of the work? I think it's helpful for them to be aware of these issues. It would promote more group unity.'

'I'll think about it, but you'll need to plan it and mediate for me. I don't want them to know the inner circle's methods and secrets; that's not for the uninitiated. Anyway, most of them are quite content plodding along, without any real responsibilities.'

'I also want an effort made for ongoing classes and lectures. With all this filming we are not receiving any wisdom teachings. That's one of the reasons why we're here, isn't it?'

'Is there anything else before I kick you out? I need to keep up my facade in front of them.'

'Yes one more thing. We want some beer money every week. I think I could work miracles with them. It will keep their moral up if we had a good bevy once a week.'

'I don't want any alcoholics in here. It's bad enough having a few odd balls around. If it gets out of hand, I'll hold you personally responsible.'

'That's settled then. Oh, before I forget, I've spoken to Elena. She's moved out.'

'That's good news. You both need to find your own paths. Yours is going to be harsher and more demanding now. You could not have managed the energies with her around. Is that it?'

'Yes, DB, that's it. You can start ranting and raving again. God, you're such a bullshiter, aren't you?'

'Don't share any of this conversation with anyone. It's between you and me, okay?' He blasted the door open and stormed out in a thunderous rage, cursing and swearing like a trooper. 'I want sweeping changes around here, or you'll all be out on your arses. You hear me?'

He booted the door open and left the place in utter turmoil. I walked out, head hanging as I brushed past Linda. She was beaming with pride; her plotting visage had the writing all over it. She had alerted DB. She was his trusted spy. I had to be very wary of her from now on.

I went upstairs to pack my belongings. Somehow, the move felt right. As I gathered my books, my dream came flooding back. It was so precognitive; it was unbelievable. My unconscious mind was warning me of impending doom. Even Linda's symbolic role was clear; she stitched me up. But what about the gagging in the dream? What did that mean? Yes, that's it. DB bid me to secrecy regarding our conversation.

I passed Stellios in the hallway. He was loading up the van with his stuff. He was still in shock and his face was ashen. I winked at him, beckoning him to the lounge.

'It's done. I negotiated a deal for us, but I've got to suffer the consequences. It's Baker's way of getting his pound of flesh. Tell the boys to meet me later to discuss the terms.'

'All right, Chris, see you later. By the way, Steve's a messy bugger; he smells like a warthog, farts like a camel and snores like a pig in shit.'

223

'Oh, thanks very much for the welcome party Stellios; that's all I need now, to be living in a zoo.'

It didn't take me long to settle in. My half of the caravan was sparse and cold, with an old bed slung in the corner. The walls were dripping with condensation and the carpet stank of damp. I had a cracked window that was sealed with Selotape. My only source of heat was a rusty, old, Calor gas fire. What a climb down from the decadence of The Brighton Lanes. I lay on my bed contemplating my next plan of action. I was clear about my role now. I had won my leadership in the outer circle and I had gained a personal understanding with DB. I had resolved the conflict with Elena and I was free to delve deeper into the esoteric wisdom of the ages.

I decided to take a trip down to Barnet Library. Stellios said it had a brilliant biography section. I wanted to research the Strafford life in greater detail. I packed my rucksack and in an hour I was there. I located the biography section and scanned the ordered shelves.

'There it is,' I shouted and the whole library conspired against me. It was right at the bottom, tucked away behind a large tome. **Thomas Wentworth, First Earl of Strafford 1593-1641, a revaluation.** The author's name was CV Wedgwood. I slid it off the shelf and it fell to the floor, where it opened to a black and white photo of a painting. Three children, two girls and a young lad dressed in fine gowns and clothes graced the page. On the bottom, the title read, *Nan, Arabella, and Will.* My gaze centred on the lad's face. My heart thundered in my ribcage, a cold sweat swept over me and the hairs on my neck propped upright.

'It can't be. No, it can't be. Oh my God, it is. It's him,' I shouted. The lad was the spitting image of my brother George. I could not believe my eyes. It was him; the black, curved brows, dark puffy eyes, dimpled chin and full cheeks. Even his curly hair was similar. I could not take it all in. I had to sit down. Who were the people in the picture? Were they his children? I flicked through the plate index. There it was: Will, Nan and Arabella Wentworth, Strafford's children by his second wife. Painting by Van Dyke. Blood rushed around my face, my heart pounded in my ears and my head felt as if it was going explode.

'It can't be true. It just can't be,' I murmured under my breath. I wished Stellios were here. He would know if it were possible that my brother George was my son in a previous life. I took a closer look at the cover photo. There he stood, the great Earl of Strafford, proud and valiant, in a three-quarter pose. He was draped in his black armour; one hand lay on the hilt of his sword and the other was outstretched, as if he was offering it to someone.

'Look at his hands, look at his hands,' I said inwardly. They were identical to mine. I sat there, stunned and disoriented. How could it be? Do we really come back again with similar physical characteristics?

My mind was haemorrhaging. Too many synchronicities had short-circuited it. I shut the book, closed my eyes and rested for a few minutes. Maybe I was hallucinating or imagining the whole thing. I didn't know what was real or unreal anymore. I was overwhelmed and so excited. I clocked out the book, jumped on the bus and ran back to Claregate.

CHAPTER 28

'Stellios! Steve! Is anyone here?' I shouted ecstatically, as I thundered into the hall.

'What's all the racket? Who's down there? You've disturbed my meditation.' It was Linda, the bitch from hell, poking her lecherous head out of her room.

'Sorry. Have you seen Steve or Stellios? I need to speak with them urgently.'

'No, I bloody haven't. You should be more respectful next time. Don't come barging in shouting your head off, it's so selfish and downright rude.'

She was in a foul mood. I felt the full force of her venomous attack in my solar plexus. She made my stomach churn and almost brought tears to my eyes. I stormed into the kitchen for a quick brew. She trundled down pushing past me.

'I thought you learnt your lesson, or do you want me to report you to DB again?'

'Listen Linda, I've got no quarrel with you. I should have, because of the way you treated Elena.'

'What do you mean? I didn't do anything to her. She started flirting with him; she ran off with him. She's the bitch, not me,' she blasted.

'You knew all about it and you didn't even think of stopping it, or telling me. You probably encouraged it, to kick-start her ejection from the group. She was taking all the limelight away from

226

you. Wasn't she? She was a threat to your position. You were jealous, so engineered it. Didn't you?'

'You must be mad. You've lost it completely this time. How dare you accuse me of conspiring to set up adultery? You're bloody nuts.'

'Anyway, it's all over between us now. We decided to split.'

'Oh, that's too bad Chris, obviously she couldn't handle the energies,' she said in a sarcastic tone. She was giving me the come on. That's what she wanted all along, my body. God, what a scheming bitch; I could not believe it.

'I'm taking an astrology class tonight. DB told me to get you all up to scratch, for next year's Mind, Body and Spirit exhibition,' she blurted in a coy sort of way.

'That's brilliant Linda. I'm really looking forward to it.'

'Bring your chart with you and any dreams you've had. I'll illustrate it in the class. It will give you an insight into the Claregate method.'

'That will be really helpful. I've had a series of dreams recently. I know they're connected to my chart, but I never posted an astrological aspect or question. The dreams just flowed in on waking.'

'What's that you're carrying? Been to the library? Are you researching the Strafford life?'

'If you want to know, yes, that's exactly what I'm doing. You know about it already, don't you?'

'What are you trying to say? I'm not interested in any of your miserable past lives. I've got no reason to research it. It's got nothing to do with me.'

She stormed out in a huff, leaving me with the biography in my hands. I grabbed a cuppa and disappeared to my new residence. I tugged at the door, prizing it off its hinges.

'Easy tiger easy, it needs a little gentle persuasion. It doesn't respond to man handling,' a voice from inside echoed. Steve's gangly frame blotted out the doorway as he slid the door back on.

'See, it's like a woman. Just a little gentle persuasion, less of the man handling and you'll get into her knickers.'

'Bloody hell Steve; is that all you think about? You're a randy old sod. What are you doing here? I thought you had to get down to LE, ASAP.'

'Well, I'll do it tomorrow. There's always tomorrow.'

'DB will be furious. He'll kick you out, he will.'

'Ha, ha! Chris, you don't get it, do you?'

'Get what?'

'DB always springs something like this on us. It gives him an opportunity to off load some of his shit. It's all a big act, but it kind of gets us going again.'

Steve he had me going. I thought all those threats of expulsions were for real.

'It isn't the first time and it certainly won't be the last, believe me. He gives us a good kick up the backside every now and then. He's so childish sometimes.'

'So you don't take him seriously then?'

'Yes, of course we do, but we don't swallow any of his bullshit. I remember one time he came charging into Claregate ranting and raving. He frogmarched us all into the hall and shat all over us. Do you know what it was all about? Fucking cucumber sandwiches!'

'What? Cucumber sandwiches; what about them?'

'Lance apparently sliced the cucumber too thick and didn't peel or salt it. He went berserk shouting, 'can't you get anything right, you lot. *You're all to blame, how many times have I got to tell you, I want my cucumber peeled, salted and sliced almost transparent. You haven't got a fucking clue about real English afternoon tea*' It was hilarious and ridiculous. Do you know what happened next?'

'I can't imagine. Go on, tell me.'

'Andrew, a Canadian lad, had had enough. He turned around in defiance and walked away shouting, '*we don't have to take this bollocks from you*'. Baker went ape shit. He chased him all the way up the stairs and into the attic. The poor kid had to jump out of the skylight to escape.'

'I'd love to have seen that.'

'Well that's life around here; never a dull moment. What's that book you've got tucked under your arm?'

'It's a biography of a previous life of mine.'

'Oo, that sounds juicy. Who were you then? Come on, spill the beans.'

'Stellios advised me not to tell anyone. He said it was sacred to me and I'd lose the essence of it if I shared it.'

'Come on, what a load of bollocks. You know one of my lives.'

'All right, I need your advice on something.'

'Great, come on, show me.'

I lay the book on the bed and his eyes sparkled just as if he'd uncovered hidden treasure.

'Thomas Wentworth, Earl of Strafford, 1493-1541,' he said and added 'that's pre English Civil War isn't it? It's the reign of Charles the 1st, if I'm not mistaken.'

'Yes, that's right, how did you know? Have you a life around the same period?'

'No, but I know someone who has. That's what happens when a past life is uncovered. There are always karmic connections in the group.'

'You mean to say they are here, living in the group now? That's bloody ridiculous. How can it be?'

'Listen, Chris, that's how it works. You've been here long enough to figure out who your friends are and whom you feel uncomfortable with. We are all linked by past life karma. Some positively and some negatively. We are thrust back into a cauldron of activity, to balance out our misgivings and resolve our debts.'

'That explains a lot about my feelings towards Barry, John and DB. Oh, there's also my conflict with Linda and Dick. Claire's really sweet; I get good vibes from her. Then there's you lot too. We get on well, don't we?'

'It's fascinating isn't it? We are reliving all our past actions in the here and now. So many dimensions crammed into this one. It's awesome.'

'No wonder some of us go off the rails. Imagine having to cope with the thought of a previous life as a famous writer and not being able to string two words together in this one.'

'That's what happens in many cases. Poor Pete was a classic one. He had the creativity, but he couldn't quite deal with his karmic limitations. The sheer frustration killed him. It's so sad. Sometimes I think it's better not to know. There's a hell of a lot of responsibility on your shoulders when you access a previous life. It could consume you or prompt you to try and recreate the creative source hidden within. That's why the soul is sometimes called *The Hidden Splendour*.'

'Steve, look at this, it's extraordinary,' I shouted, flicking to the plate of his children.

'The lad Will, Strafford's son, is the spitting image of my younger brother George. The resemblance is so uncanny. Could he have been my son in a previous life?'

'We are all connected. *No man is an island unto himself.* Families incarnate together. Some were sons in a past life and now they are fathers or brothers. Some were daughters and now they are mothers or aunts. We are thrust back together life after life, to work out karma. It's a very complex issue, but it is possible that your brother was your son in 1426. I know it sounds absurd and many out there would make you a laughing stock, but it's true. It's a spiritual reality.'

'So why are all our recent past lives famous people then? Surely to God we've had lives as laymen and normal householders.'

'Yes, that's true. We've all had to develop, life after life, from labourer to landowner, to baron, to lord, to kings or queens. The fact is, in this cycle of incarnations, we are all spiritually inspired. We have won the right to serve the Lord in his work, by our past efforts. This is the final run-in of lives for us. The last frontiers of service work is to serve the land and then ultimately the spiritual path.'

'That explains it. DB asked me during my ray analysis what I thought my purpose was. Do you know what I said?'

'No, tell me?'

'To serve and to lead the way to a spiritual reality.'

'Well, there you have it Chris. You are here to serve the land at its highest level, the spiritual. You are here to prepare it for the new dawn, the dawning of The New Age of Aquarius. It's the light workers' responsibility to prepare the population for this major transition period. That's our ultimate purpose, to externalise the teachings to the masses. Evidence of past lives is the kingpin to the philosophy of rebirth and karmic law.'

'Steve, the task is awesome. I really respect DB's immense contribution and personal sacrifice to the work, even with all his personality hang-ups and crap.'

'It's the commitment to the path and service to humanity which is paramount. It's the indwelling soul's energies that are the gauge-stick of greatness, not the rough, raging, undisciplined personality. You ought to read how Blavatsky treated her disciples. She was vile all the time. But she brought through the wisdom of the ages via a group of master beings. She is the matriarch of Theosophy and one of the wisest souls on the planet.'

'We should thank our lucky stars we got DB then. At least he shows humanity and understanding sometimes.'

'Hey, Stellios said you were able to win some concessions for us. That's smashing. How did you manage to swing it?'

'It wasn't easy. I've got to endure some personal penances for it, but I'm sure it will all be worth it, in the long run. I'll tell you all later, I need a rest now. Oh, by the way, Linda's is starting an astrology class tonight. That's one of the concessions I prized out of him.'

'Brilliant. We've had to work on our own with no instruction for ages. I'll really look forward to it. Oh, I heard Barry say another lad is joining us next week. His name is Roy. He's a Brummy.'

'Well, the more the better; He's coming just at the right time. The reforms should be up and running by then. Talk to you later Steve, I'm shattered.'

I lay on the soggy bed, with the mid-afternoon sun beating down on the metal box. It creaked and croaked as it expanded and contracted. The clatter of birds trotting all over it tickled my senses. Condensation globules slalomed down the window. Their zigzag patterns unzipped the lining of my unconscious. Sunbeams glanced here and there, shafting searing bolts of light on my face as I slid into a soothing slumber thinking of Elena. Had I made the right choice? Was I an idealistic scatterbrain? God, I'm going to miss her warm body, her sweet breath in my ears, her perfume and her sunny smile. But I had made my decision. My transformation was almost complete now, but I had to spread my wings and sound my own note. I missed the bell for dinner, even though it was only 7.30pm.

I straggled to the house. The girls were clearing the kitchen and Stellios was preparing the lounge for the astrology lecture.

'Hi Chris, we've saved a plate of food for you. It's warming in the oven.'

'Thanks Claire, that's thoughtful of you.'

'I'm sorry to hear you've split with Elena. I suppose she found it difficult to fit in. She wasn't exactly cut out for community life.'

'It's okay Claire, we'll both get over it.'

Linda cowered in the background, frantically wiping down the cupboards in a neurotic frenzy. Her face was so red with frustration I thought she was going to explode.

'I'll go and prepare our notes for the lecture Claire,' Linda said. 'See you later.' As she marched past she glanced daggers at me, and my stomach churned with every dig. She knew how to wound someone. All that Piscean solar plexus shit made her vomit astral crap at anyone she disliked. I somehow had to find a way to protect myself from her emotional excrement in the future.

'Chris, how old are you?' Claire probed inquisitively.

'I'm 25. Why?'

'Mmm that's why you've gone through such a major change so quickly.'

'I don't understand. Is my age that important?'

'You're a Scorpio, aren't you?'

'Yes, but what's that got to do with it?'

'About a year ago, Saturn moved into Scorpio. It spends about two and a half years in each sign. Therefore it started affecting your life last year. Scorpio rules sudden stressful changes, illumination, esoteric arts and rebirth. Saturn rules major upheavals, uprooting, loss and breakdown.'

'So what does that mean in layman's terms?'

'Well, during this cycle that started from last year, you went through a major u-turn. Suddenly and unexpectedly you were introduced to the esoteric. The material life lessened it grip around you when you embraced spiritual realities and mind-boggling experiences. You changed your lifestyle completely, gave up all your old associations and found yourself on the doorstep of an esoteric school. You went through a major personality breakdown, experienced strange phenomena and come down with a severe, painful ailment. You are a victim of adultery and you split from your partner. But in doing so you find freedom and now you are spiritually liberated. With no attachments, you soar the inner worlds as a phoenix reborn out of its ashes. Does that make any sense to you?'

I was dumbstruck. Her interpretation read like an open book.

'What an explanation Claire! I'm just overwhelmed at your accuracy. Your interpretation is unbelievable. Is it all astrological?'

'Timing is the important element though. It also depends if your sun sign is positively aspected or negatively aspected with other planets. A negative Mars can cause severe pain and anguish, even death. Uranus rules volatile change, rebellion and anarchy. Pluto rules escapism, drugs and alcohol. Your sun must be benignly placed.'

'I don't know Claire, it's all so new to me, but I'm really enthusiastic about learning. I can't wait to get into it.'

'Give Stellios your chart to write on the blackboard. Linda and I will use it to illustrate the Claregate method of interpretation. It should give you some pointers to your gifts and limitations.'

'Great. When is it going to start?'

'At 8 o'clock sharp, in the lounge.'

'I've just enough time to eat. I'll get my chart and notebook and see you soon.'

I charged to the caravan, collected my things and in minutes I was seated at the front. Stellios and Steve were tacking up notepaper on an easel. There was a massive chart wheel painted on a long, blackboard, ready to house my chart.

'Chris, give me your chart. Linda wants me to draw it up on the board for her.'

'All right Stellios, here you are. DB's written all over it in his doctors scrawl.'

'Mmm, Libra ascendant, Mars and Moon in Pisces; four planets in Scorpio, oh, you've got intercepted signs too.'

He continued to babble on whilst he drew up my chart. The girls waltzed in and the lads trailed in behind them in dribs and drabs.

'Right guys, settle down,' Linda said in a commanding voice. Tonight we're going to use Chris's chart to illustrate the basis of the astrology. He's had dreams, which we'll try to link to his horoscope. So, who can tell me what Libra ascendant means?'

'Politics, parliament, legal matters, justice, balance and relationships.'

'That's correct, Stellios, but please let someone else contribute too,' Claire called.

'Someone who holds the balance of power, a negotiator or counsellor,' Linda interjected.

'In esoteric terms, what does the ascendant always indicate?' Claire probed.

'The soul's purpose and how it can be expressed.'

'That's right Steve. Libra is Roman karma, a possible past life in the Roman Senate, perhaps a politician, general, ambassador or advisor. There are also links with writing as Libra rules books.'

'Maybe a political philosopher?' Claire chirped.

'Uranus rules Libra in esoteric astrology. But where is it placed and how will it affect the ascendant?'

'Linda, it's in Leo,' said Lance. 'But retrograde and intercepted in the 10th house. The interception suggests a great gift, but also a limitation, which blocks the gift from materialising. Uranus rules projected power; Leo rules authority, control, the throne and therefore kings and queens.'

'Brilliant Lance, is there anything else you can tell me guys?'

'Libra rules lecturing and Uranus is in the career sector. That means a unique gift for projecting the spoken and written word. The soul's purpose is linked to self-expression and the career, isn't it?'

'Excellent Jeremy! Uranus is retrograde, meaning its qualities are turned inwardly. Uranus also rules weirdness, cranks and wacky ideas. Uranians always dress to shock. Punks are typical Uranians. Look at their dress code, their persona and their rebellious views. Is Chris a punk? Of course not, but he may well be weird inside. Chris, are you cranky inside?'

'I suppose so, with all my spiritual experiences and visions.'

'Look at him. He's so conventional on the outside, but a wacko on the inside.'

Claire had us rolling around in stitches. It was true, I was quite starchy outwardly, but my inner life was so vibrant and colourful. The interpretation was interesting so far.

'What's the next most important observation guys? What's in the first house?'

'Neptune's in Scorpio and it challenges his Uranus,' said Lance.

'That's good,' Linda relied encouragingly. 'But what does it indicate?'

'Deviousness, deception, vagueness, forgetfulness and misunderstandings.'

'Yes Stellios, but lets have some positives too. What about intuition, memory of past lives through dreams and visions, imagination, an appreciation of mythology and the psychic arts? But there are blocks and challenges, aren't there? Where are they and how can they be overcome?'

'Aloofness, isolation, blindness and careless in understanding situations. An unwillingness to delegate and an obsession for control.'

'Excellent Jeremy, You've been reading up. Yes, we're getting a good feel of the chart. What about relationships? After all, Libra rules relationships.'

I shuffled awkwardly in my chair now. I could feel myself becoming agitated.

'Looking at relationships through rosy coloured spectacles,' Steve put in. 'Naivety and blindness. Confusion, having the wool pulled over one's eyes.'

Linda smiled. 'But what about being deceived and lied to? That's Neptune, isn't it? What about the partner having clandestine relationships? His Venus is in Libra in the 12th, the house of secrecy. Yes, it's all there.'

The bitch stuck the boot in. There was an awkward silence and the boys glanced nervously at each other. I just melted away in my seat. I was so embarrassed and shocked. She had all my dirty washing all on the line. Poor Claire didn't know where to put her face.

'Lets move on now guys. Chris has got some dreams he'd like to share with us. Let's see if we can relate them back to his chart.'

I relayed my dreams to them and they took notes.

'We'll have a little break now and when we come back, let's all share our interpretations. Back here in 15 minutes,' Claire concluded.

That was it. Linda had thrown the gauntlet in my face. She was ready to drag my reputation through the gutter. Revenge was so sweet for her. She was in total control and she was intent in destroying me. The boys made a beeline to the kitchen. I followed behind with my head hung low. She sneered at me as I headed towards the gaping door to the darkness of the hall and my soul. As the void consumed me, I knew the worst was to come.

CHAPTER 29

I disappeared to the loo to think about my tactics. She was goading me for a response. I needed to detach myself emotionally and centre myself mentally. That way she would not stand a chance of provoking me. I could hear the boys in the kitchen raiding the pantry. I sauntered in seemingly unscathed by her blatant attacks.

'Chris, I didn't think it was a good idea to give her your chart to work with. She's crucifying you. I told you not to trust her.' Stellios harped.

'Stellios, I don't mind really. As long as she's not bull-shiting me; is she talking a load of crap?'

'No, it's all astrologically correct.'

'Then I don't have a problem with it. I'll get my own back. What goes around comes around.'

'She'll rip you apart Chris. She's got her talons out. I can see it coming.'

'Steve, don't worry. I'm not emotionally polarised. I'm not going to let her get to me. I know how to handle her energies.'

'I would have ripped her head off if she was doing that to me, I really would,' Jeremy retorted.

We filtered in after sharing our views. I needed to show restraint and calmness. I knew she was going to go for the jugular.

'All right now, settle down,' said Claire. 'We know the astrology works on a subjective level. Yes, when we tread the path of enlightenment, our unconscious throws up clues related to our challenges, as well as to our gifts. It highlights our blocks and encourages us to more effort. By creating a dialogue with the unconscious we are bathed with energy and meaning. How do we do this, guys?'

'We link dream symbols to astrological planets and signs. It's called *parsing*,' answered Steve.

'That's right. Through DB's research he's been able to establish a link between the dream life and a personal horoscope. *Parsing* is writing a glyph over a dream symbol that astrologically relates to it. For example, the bath in Chris's dream relates to Jupiter and the 11th house, as they both link to vessels that contain and pour out. It constitutes a major part of the Claregare Method. He has recognised that outer relationships stimulate inner responses and vice versa.'

'Let's now have a look at the series of dreams Chris had around the 17th of March. I've written them up on the board for easy reference. Chris can you remember the events leading up to that date?' Linda probed with menace in her eyes.

'Yes, I was in turmoil, confused and frustrated. My relationship with Elena was hellish. I was torn up. I found out she was fucking one of our actors and I was devastated.'

They all turned round in awe of my honesty and starkness. Even Linda was shocked and Claire went bright red.

'Yes, well, thanks for your graphic account Chris. Okay it's important to know the external circumstances, as the unconscious tries to adapt and adjust to them. Before we look at the dream content, can you tell me by Chris's clear description of events, which area of the horoscope we are looking at? Yes Stellios.'

'It revolves around his 5th house and the 11th house Linda. The 5th is opposite the 11th; therefore the energies clash. It's like a seesaw. Mars, the sex planet, is in the 5th house, the 'fucking' house, in secretive Pisces. The Moon very closely linked, she clouds the issue, but she can expose the infidelity too. Of course, the fifth house rules the heart and acting.'

'Brilliant Stellios, Yes, betrayal of loyalty is filthy and degrading,' she shouted, almost frothing at the mouth. 'Is there anything else before we move on?'

'Jupiter is in Virgo on the other side of the seesaw. It exaggerates the stab in the back. It can involve a conspiracy as the 11th house rules friends and co-workers. Virgo rules work and cleansing; Jupiter in the 11th links to new age groups and Aquarius, the water bearer, lords over both.'

'My word, we've all been researching, haven't we. Excellent, Lance. It all sounds gruesome, doesn't it? Gangs, conspiracy, betrayal of loyalty and sordid affairs; Does any of this ring any bells Chris?'

I felt like I was in the dock and she was leading The Inquisition. Oh my God. Oh my God! The Strafford life all came seething back to haunt me. The elements were all there. Loyal advisor to the king: betrayal and conspiracy by a group of the opposition and the stab in the back. I was stunned into silence. I scanned the room. Were they all conspiring to topple me? Were my so-called friends and spiritual brothers going to betray me?

I looked at her: that sardonic smirk and the glint in her eyes. Claire's angelic face shone bright; it was the only glimmer of hope for me. I was even suspicious of Stellios, my trusted right hand man.

'Yes Linda,' I answered. 'It's very accurate. I wish I had this information before hand. Maybe I could have foreseen the consequences and changed the outcome.'

She was on a roll now. I could feel her homing in for the kill.

'Okay, the first dream, who wants to get the ball rolling?'

'Well, the bath is Jupiter and the 11th house,' said Jeremy. 'They rule all containers as they link to the Aquarian water bearer who pours out water from a vat. The water is stagnant, full of fag ends and filth - that's Mars and Moon in Pisces. A young girl is helping Chris to clean up using a scouring pad. That's the Moon again; it rules young virgins. The scouring pad is a combination of it all. Mars is abrasive, Moon and Virgo are cleaning and scrubbing.'

'You've got it in a nutshell. But what does it mean?' Linda probed.

'He's trying to clear his life from stagnant, negative emotions, which are swamping him and restricting his union with his inner partner, his anima.'

'Absolutely brilliant Steve Absolutely brilliant,' Claire applauded.

'The saving grace here is there is hope,' Claire spurted. 'He is taking positive action by cleaning up his act and his anima is supporting him. She is youthful, pure and full of life. What a superb analysis. That's the depth of esoteric astrology. It provides objective and subjective directions and solutions. Isn't it awesome?' Claire was gushing in adulation of the wisdom. She really was a sweet, soppy, sentimental girl.

'Right, who would like to grapple with the next image? We can see a similar theme here. Imagine having Margaret Thatcher in a dream; that would be my worst nightmare,' Claire spouted giggling in starts and fits.

'The party is Jupiter in Virgo in the 11th. It rules friends and relatives. Socialising is Jupiter and also the fifth house, the natural home of playful Leo. Margaret Thatcher, well that's Mars and Moon, a powerful female leader. Thatcher is Scorpio ascendant and her sun sign is Libra. It's the same combination that Chris has.'

'Great observation Lance,' barked Linda. 'That's acceptable because Libra ascends and Chris's Sun is in Scorpio. Thatcher is also a powerful political leader, linking to his Uranus in Leo and Libra ascendant. Excellent. She's alone and she's been neglected. Chris recognises her and offers to serve her, but all the glasses are filthy. Can anyone tell me what astrology links we have here?'

'Linda, it's the same as the first dream.' I interjected without hesitation.

'Wao, we've got a budding astrologer here, have we? Okay, explain, explain!' She was out to embarrass me and insult my intelligence. I sensed it.

'The filthy glasses are Moon, Mars in Pisces opposite Jupiter in Virgo. The Moon's symbol looks like a glass and its quality is transparent. It's also a receptacle of spirit; that's the whisky. Pisces also rules alcoholic beverages. I offer to serve her, that's Jupiter in Virgo, it rules service. Hey, wait a minute, Thatcher links to the young girl in the first dream. Thatcher is my ultimate anima figure. Powerful, respected, wilful, she's *The Iron Lady*. I'm getting the words of a song,

Onwards Christian soldiers,
Marching as to war,
With the sword of Jesus,
Going on before.

'It's the Crusades. It's the march to the Holy Land to liberate Jerusalem. It's also The Arthurian quest for the Holy Grail. It's the vessel of rebirth and pure spirit. Oh, my God. Oh my God!'

I had a waking vision. I knew it was linked to past life memories. I looked around me to see their faces were all glazed over. A hypnotic trance had beguiled them. Even the girls were stunned, standing there, with their mouths gaping in disbelief of my interpretation.

'I don't know where it came from. Honest, I really don't know anything about it. It just flooded me, something took my mind and body over.'

They were flabbergasted. Claire and Linda started muttering to one another. The boys just stared at each other with vacant expressions.

'I think we need another quick break class. We'll resume in 10 minutes,' Claire concluded.

There was a rush to the door. I calmly rose with poise and dignity, glanced at her, turned my chin up and strutted out. The boys had congregated in the hall waiting for me.

'Chris, Chris, where did it come from? Have you been studying like mad? God, did you see their faces? You were bloody marvellous, just bloody marvellous,' Lance said, singing my praises.

'That was sweet revenge, Lance. It just came through me, from some other dimension. I felt the energies. I smelled the dust, the awesome human effort, the blood, the battles, the defeats and the victories. I sensed the Holy Land and the Grail; yes the quest to restore King Arthur and heal the land.'

'Fuck sake,' Lance gasped. 'You really sorted her out. I'd love to be a fly on the wall in there now, just to hear their reactions.'

'What a scenario, I can see it all!' Stellios said launching into a dialogue. God what a piss-artist he was!

'Linda, where's he getting it from? That's not even in the books.'

'Claire, it's just a fluke. It's a one off; he's no astrologer.'

'But, it's all there, the Crusades, the Grail, Onward Christian Soldiers, it's all there, Linda. I think he's possessed. I don't know. I really don't know.'

'He's different, that's for sure. He's grown so fast; it's not normal. He's freed himself from his entanglements and he's stood up to DB. It's taken everybody years to integrate; look at him, he's done it overnight.' Stellios squawked, imitating Claire and Linda's Yankie cackle. They were in stitches.

'God, I can't wait for the final episode. What are you going to pull out of the hat next Chris?' Jeremy asked.

'Jeremy, it was totally intuitive. I had no control over it. I knew the dreams were linked, but some force overtook me. I felt I was only a vehicle for its expression.'

'Quick, let's get back in there. I can't wait for the climax,' Steve shouted.

'Settle down now, settle down now. I'd like to thank you Chris for your stunning interpretation. Where did it come from?' Claire asked.

'It was nothing, really. I've just been doing a bit of reading, it's all in the books.'

Linda looked evil. If looks could kill, I'd have been dead by now. I body-swerved her daggers.

'Chris linked the Moon first to a glass and then to a cup, the Grail Cup,' said Claire. 'He said the hieroglyph looked like a cup, quite right. What do we call that kind of link?'

'It's called morphology,' Stellios offered. 'It means an object that looks like an astrological glyph, relates to the energy of it. For example, a circle looks like the sun; therefore all circles are related to Leo and the sun's energies. Look at a roundabout in a playground. It's all sun and Leo: children, play, going round and round, sunshine and sweets.'

'Brilliant explanation Stellios,' said Claire. 'You really do surprise me. Have you been eating magic mushrooms again?'

'No, Claire, I'm on what Chris is on.' The whole mob was wasted in laughter. Linda just cowered and seethed in the background.

'Right, let's get to the final dream; it's getting late. Who's going to start us off?' Linda snapped. 'Chris is on a narrow ledge carrying a book. There is chaos all around him. People are falling off into a deep abyss. The book is Libra ascendant by morphology. Open a book and lay it on a table with the spine facing up. See it looks like the hieroglyph.'

'The narrow ledge and people falling off is Neptune in Scorpio in the 1st house,' ventured Jeremy. 'Neptune rules falls and the abyss; Scorpio rules death. Neptune also rules clutter and ornaments. Uranus is precarious; the intercepted sign is the narrow ledge. It's in the 10th house that rules mountain paths.'

'Exactly right,' Linda answered. 'Who would like to conclude the analysis?'

It was Lance. 'Chris holds on, but loses his book. That's Neptune; it rules losses. He goes back and rummages through new boxes of knickknacks on the ledge. New knickknacks are Uranus, but also Venus in Libra. They are boxed up. Libra rules all forms of wrappings. He eventually carries off two pieces of expensive, rare porcelain. Duality's are Venus, but I'm stuck on the last bit.'

'Great effort Lance, Who can finish it off for him?'

'Leo in the 10th, with Cancer mid-heaven is the expensive porcelain,' I interjected. 'The rarity is the intercepted sign. Venus is also sextile my Uranus, they indicate specific spiritual gifts; that's the whole thing in a nutshell.'

The room went silent again, and then the boys stood up and clapped. They went wild with support. Claire gushed along with them, but Linda's face went blue then red. She pulled at Claire, swamping her with heavy frowns.

'Settle down now, boys, settle down,' Claire sang, as Linda charged over to me, raging like a bull.

'Okay, Smart Alec, what does it all mean then?' She blasted. Her eyes fired and her nose flared. She poked the pointer at me as if it was a lance and she was going to run me through. Her negative energies tried to bombard my solar plexus, but I was protected. She was shocked and in horror when I rose, snatched the pointer from her and marched over to the board.

'I am on the path of self-discovery. It's tough. I lose my book. People fall off, but I hold my ground. The book symbolises my relationship. I let it fall off the end into the abyss. It's a struggle, it sets me back, but I eventually uncover new gifts and talents. These are unique, rare and special. They are spiritual gifts, which I win as rewards for my efforts.'

'Fantastic! More! More! More! We want more, we want more!' The boys went wild, standing up on their seats, waving and shouting.

'Right, that's enough. That's the last class I ever take. You're beyond teaching you undisciplined bunch off losers,' shouted Linda, and she stormed out.

I had completely demoralised her. I got my revenge and it felt so sweet, especially on a subject she knew back to front. The boys calmed down and filtered away to the kitchen for a nightcap.

'Chris, see you in five, okay? We'll get refreshments ready.'

'Okay Stellios, Oh, we've got to discuss policy later. Don't let any of them slide away.'

'Chris, I don't think there's any fear of that. They're all itching to know how you did it.'

'Did what Stellios?'

He waved me away as Claire approached me with my chart.

'Well done, I've never seen anyone do so well in their first lesson. I didn't realise DB picked up on your astrological talents and lecturing gifts.'

'What do you mean? He never said anything of the sort to me?'

'I turned your chart over and there it was, in DB's scrawl. It said brilliant Uranus to Venus aspect indicates a master esoteric astrologer. Writing and lecturing will follow. I'm surprised Linda hadn't told you about it before. We're the only ones who can decipher his doctor's scribble.'

'Claire, she looked at my chart at least three times, but not once did she tell me what the writing on the back meant, even when I asked her.'

'I don't know Chris. Anyway, I was impressed by your Crusades and Arthurian quest theme. Come on, how did you get it? It's not really in the books.'

'Claire, I don't know, it just welled up inside of me. It flooded me; it flowed through me from some other dimension. I can't explain it. Do you know what it means?'

'Well, these themes are deeply ingrained in your chart, they are archetypal.'

'What does that mean?'

'Archetype comes from two Greek words, Arche and typos. I'm sure you know what they mean, don't you?'

'Yes, the beginning, the origin, but that doesn't mean a thing to me?'

'It's a phrase coined by Jung. You should read his awesome book on the subject. He states it's a primary cosmic force from a deep, psycho-spiritual source, which flows through an individual, bathing him in inspiration, motive and direction. For example, we talk about the Hero archetype embodying the sign of Scorpio. Therefore Scorpios are saturated by this archetype and express it through heroism, challenge and growth. Ultimately they succeed in the battlefield of life. Read DB's book, Beyond The Intellect. It's a fantastic overview of the esoteric significance of archetypes, you'll love it.'

'I'll do that Claire, but I can't understand why I picked up on those two archetypes?'

'There could be a number of reasons. One is previous life connections.'

'What, you mean in a past life I could have fought in the Holy Wars and I have a connection with King Arthur and the quest for the Holy Grail? Surely that's just mythology?'

'Chris, there was a historic King Arthur. He was a 6th century Romano-Celt warlord. His mission through Merlin was to spiritualise the church and hold the balance of energies of the Christ Light. Can you imagine the heroic effort, holding the bridge open? There were knights, but there was nothing chivalrous about them. They lived in bloodthirsty, barbarous times, where the sword was justice and the law. They held allegiance to Arthur, who united the clans. They held off Saxon and Pict invasions long enough for the Christos energy to be channelled and anchored in Britain. If you're really interested, read the epic Welsh poem, *The Mabinogion*; it's one of the most authentic sources of Celtic-Arthurian history. It was handed down through word of mouth. The Celts thought it would lose its magic if it were written down. Oral wisdom was the only way to keep the energy flowing and untarnished. Our modern druids still hold the same oral traditions of their ancestors. The Knights of the Round Table, the quest and that romantic vision, all came later. It was the same archetype of Arthur, the saviour of Britain, which animated the shining chivalric knights on their way to the Holy Wars. It's the same archetype which flows through all great British leaders in time of great national need and struggle, Lionheart, Cromwell, Kitchener, Churchill, even Thatcher.'

'Claire, it's way over my head. I can't cope with more previous life stuff. I can just about handle this one. I'll keep it on the back burner for now, maybe, one day I'll delve into it, when the time is right.'

'Whenever. Keep up the good work; I'll keep the class going, even if Linda opts out. She's not a bad soul, she's just got a lot off issues she's battling with at the moment, just like all of us.'

'I understand. Thanks for the encouragement. I really do appreciate it. Listen, I'm meeting the boys to discuss the new reforms I negotiated with DB. It concerns all of us, I'd like you and Linda to attend.'

'I'll be there. I'll ask Linda, but don't bank on her attendance.'

'Okay. See you in 15 minutes in the dining room. Thanks again for your support.' She trundled off upstairs humming and whistling. I liked her playfulness and lightness; she was a great inspiration to me. I triumphantly marched into the hallway to await my hero's welcome.

CHAPTER 30

They were all laughing and slagging off Linda when an almighty roar rattled the room.

'Bloody brilliant Chris, You're the dog's bollocks, man,' Steve shouted.

'Yes Chris, you never cease to amaze me,' Lance gasped.' How did you manage to defend yourself against her solar plexus bolts? I felt her emotional thrust standing behind you; it hit me for six.'

'Easy boys, look.'

They were in stitches, on the floor, almost peeing themselves. I had wrapped a few sheets of aluminium foil around my abdomen and chest, very similar to a breastplate, before I went back in for the final conflict.

'Christo, you're full of ideas. Where did that one come from?' asked Stellios.

'I don't know, it just seemed logical at the time. I reckoned it would protect me if she started projecting her vile, emotional vomit at me and it did.'

'Did you see her face when you got up, unaffected and disarmed her? I wish I had a camera. She was completely taken by surprise,' Steve blasted, in a fit of laughter.

'Yes strategy and ingenuity are very effective devices for winning battles, don't you think?'

'I'm sure you're tapping previous life memories. Moves like that and specific idiosyncrasies stem from deep within the psyche. DB calls it atavism.'

'Atavism? Jeremy, explain that to me in layman's terms. I'm still struggling with all these new words and concepts.'

'We bring back deep memories of past life activities. Strange things like dress code, hairstyle, facial hair, hand writing and all sorts of habits.'

'You mean to say my habits are carry-overs from past lives?'

'Yes, they are specific to you only. Let's say your siblings were all raised the same way, under the same environmental factors, with the same privileges and limitations. Yet their habits are all different.'

'Yes, I can see where you're coming from, but I'm not totally convinced.'

'Okay, lets have some examples guys, to illustrate atavism.'

'I loved wearing flouncing white shirts, with wide collars. I had a life as a poet in the Romantic period,' Lance said. 'I also loved wearing my hair shoulder length and always sported an earring in one ear.'

'Lance, that must have been years ago. Look at you now, you've only got a few squiggly strands on top and two patches around your ears that look like Brillo pads,' Steve laughed.

'Don't take the piss Steve, even that's atavistic. I've had lives as bishops, cardinals and Franciscan monks.' He had us rolling around again. He was a fantastic antidote to the drudgery and misery around here.

'Look at Claire. She wears her hair short and bushy. She also loves wearing big masculine collars and loose tunics. She was Samuel Coleridge in a previous life,' Stellios interjected.

Is that why I love wearing round, army-style, granddad-collared shirts? My favourite colours are light blue and khaki. It may be a carry over from the Kitchener life, it must be, I thought.

I also loved wearing black or dark blue sweatshirts over tennis shirts. That reminds me of the print of Strafford on the front cover of the biography. He was wearing a black or navy breastplate with a high Royalist collar, just like my sweatshirts and tee shirts. He even had a goatee beard and I'd had one for years. I've also inherited his beautiful, elegant hands, of all things. People always compliment me about them. Even Queen Henrietta Maria complimented Strafford on the beauty of his hands. That's where I must have got the idea to use the foil protection.

'Let's take Mike. He's a cockney through and through. Look at him; he doesn't look English? He looks more Mediterranean than I do,' Jeremy continued. 'His olive complexion, dark eyes and dark hair. He's had a life as a Greek philosopher and Spartan soldier. He was one of the 300 brave soldiers under King Leonidas who held back the might of the whole Persian army at Thermopylae. He was thrust back there as Lord Byron during Greece's fight for independence. He loves Greek mythology, philosophy and food: the whole country in fact, more than the UK.'

'Remember Pete's stutter, where did that stem from? What about Steve's love of big, fat, bulbous women with massive tits? It's all atavism, all of it,' Stellios said. We all burst into laughter again as Steve mimicked his ideal mistress with his hands.

'Talking about big, bulbous women,' Steve said, 'change the conversation, I can hear Claire waltzing downstairs.'

The room was in uproar again when Claire bounced in.

'I hope you've not been talking about me behind my back. You know I'm psychic and never wrong,' she joked.

'Sit down Claire; we've just been explaining Atavism to Chris. We've given him a few examples of it, from knowledge of our previous lives. I hope you don't mind, we told him you were Coleridge in a previous life.'

'Oh no Stellios, that's fine. He would have found out sooner or later.'

'Claire, I never realised we bring back so many characteristics from previous lives,' I said.

'Chris, you inherit the weirdest things. I'm the spitting image of Coleridge. I wish I could write like him though. I'd need to take a bucketful of laudanum for that. You know he was addicted to the drug? I sure eat like him; that's the only addiction I've got. I've inherited his wicked sweet tooth. I love all those dainty English pastries. Linda and I often disappear to Barnet and indulge in tea and cakes at our secret teashop.' She had us all in good humour and her spirits were high. 'I just want to congratulate you on your great contributions to the class,' she added. 'You're really gifted. I wish I had access to that source of yours. What's the secret?'

'I don't know. It just filters through the ethers, when I least expect it. I suppose it's my Daemon contact. Anyway where's Linda?'

'Oh she's got one of those migraines of hers. She sends her apologies for not attending. I'll tell her all about it Chris. I'm going to take notes, if that's alright.'

Headache my arse; she was licking her wounds and no doubt plotting her next attack on me. I got the meeting into action.

'Right we've had a really eventful day, what with our rude awakening and tonight's events. First, thank you all for supporting me. I'm happy to say I've won some concessions for us, but at great expense to me, which I don't mind.'

'How did you manage that? Asked Steve. 'We were sure you were taking a heavy beating when you were marched into the lounge.'

'I won all the issues I needed for us, but I promised DB we'd all get our act together here. That means organisation, domestic responsibilities and hygiene, and that means personal too.' They weren't too pleased at first. I sensed their objections and reservations, but when I mentioned beer money, they all threw their concerns to the wind, shouting, stamping and singing my praises.

'Listen, before we celebrate, I want to tell you what I'm in for. I've been allocated fly-leafing duties on my own.' They all stuttered into a steely silence, glancing at each other and murmuring.

'Yes, I can't say I'm looking forward to it, but it's all part of how we communicate DB's lecture.'

'Chris, it's hellish out there,' Jeremy warned. 'Dodging in and out like a common criminal. Eek, yuk, all that slimy stuff; it's really revolting, it gets everywhere, on your clothes, in your hair and it looks like you've been playing with yourself.'

'Thanks for the graphic details Jeremy, He also wants me to head our festival campaign. I'm looking forward to that. It's a challenge and I'm sure I've got a gift for it. I know what he's up to. He's trying to alienate me. It's a kind of sideways promotion to Siberia, so I'm not interfering too much in how he runs things around here.'

'He's trying to grind you into the ground Chris,' Lance stated. 'The last lad who was sent out fly posting on his own was never heard of again. He must have ran off with the paste brush and bucket and started a decorating business.'

'Lance, don't take the piss.'

He smiled at me. 'Chris we've all done it, sometimes it's fun, really. I've been all over the country, this bar, that pub, this historic town, that castle, it's fascinating.'

'Thanks for the encouragement. I've also negotiated more involvement in policy making. There are issues we won't know about; they are privy to the inner circle. But direction of the work, new projects and ideas will be shared with us. If I'm not around Stellios will deputise for me. Does anyone have any objections to that?' They showed no outward signs of disagreement, but I wasn't sure.

'Good, we will also have more esoteric instruction. The class tonight was as a result of my intervention, now it's your turn to have your say.'

There was silence in the ranks, a few nervous glances, then muttering. I could see the majority was in favour, but some were not happy. Claire winked at me; I had her support at least. Stellios Greek slang sang against a sea of gruff, gravelled sighs and murmurs. He was orchestrating the mob into agreement; I could sense it.

'All right Chris, it's not been an easy decision, but there's something else we want before we agree. We want a clothing allowance. Look at us; we're all in rags. You can't expect us to smarten ourselves up wearing this lot.'

'You've got a point. I'll see what I can do. I'll try to get you at least one new shirt and a pair of jeans. Keep those for public events, but wear your rags until they fall off your back.'

The room hit the roof. Thank God Dick was out and Linda was in a mood. That was all settled then, the first democratic meeting of the outer circle. They had accepted my proposals, but with a few reservations. It was all right in theory, but to implement the changes would be another matter. There was also the issue of Linda. I was sure she'd do anything to scuttle my plans and undermine my authority.

She was a conniving bitch who'd do anything to discredit me. She would try her best to get them to conspire against me. She was threatened by my presence here. I had the potential to take away the mantle of astrology teacher from her and she knew it. That was the only reason why she didn't tell me of DB's comments on my chart. I was a threat to her supremacy. I had to find a way to positively work with her or she would always be my enemy, a lethal thorn in my side. She was DB's loyal agent after all; he needed to know what was going on in our ranks.

I left them still laughing at Linda's expense. They were all trying on my foil breastplate for size and prancing around with the pointer poking it in the air as if it was a lance. It was like a fancy dress party in full swing. Claire followed me out into the hallway.

'Chris, I'll support your plans; it's a breath of fresh air having you around. It's taken a lot of pressure off me, I can tell you. They never really listened to Linda or me. I'll try to talk sense to her; she's extremely highly strung most of the time.'

'Thanks for the help. I really appreciate it. If you could get her to meet me at least half way, then we could work things out I'm sure.'

'I'll try, but I can't give you any promises. She's a complex kettle of fish, with loads of hang-ups, like most of us here. See you tomorrow; bet you're shattered.'

'Good night Claire, thanks again.'

I turned to make my way to the back door, when Dick and Barry slipped in past me. I got an icy cold shoulder from them as they slid past, completely ignoring me. The racket in the dining room ebbed to an uncomfortable silence and then loud jeers exploded with intermittent slow claps. I plodded back to my empty, cold den, in the darkness of night, mulling over the day's events. There was no Elena's bosom to melt into anymore. My only bedfellows were the stark, clear, glassy sky and a glint of the new moon. As I approached the caravan, it thumped and trembled to the din of music and the lights were full on in Steve's partitioned part of the caravan. He must have been really on a bender this time. The Police hit single *So Lonely* billowed out from the open door on wafts of incense and dregs of air tainted with dope.

"So lonely, so lonely, so lonely,
So lonely, so lonely, oh so lonely."

The song echoed into infinity as I dragged my sorry soul, drowning in memories, through the sombre arch leading to my partitioned pit and slid into my solitary, Spartan bed, fully clothed. I left the dim light flickering to the lyrics as I nursed my bruised ego. As I crouched up in a wretched ball, the scent of her sweet body on the sheets tantalised my senses. My insides wrangled, my heart crashed and my groin gasped for her embrace.

'Bloody bitch, Elena. Fucking hell! Why did it have to be this way?' I sobbed uncontrollably like a wimp with no backbone. Pull yourself together Kasparis, for God's sake. What the fuck is happening to you? She shat all over you; she debased your honour. The bitch is shagging that actor while you're crying in your solitary confinement. Come on, get your shit together, there's work to be done. My alter ego bombarded me with bolstering words of reality.

'Oh, but I miss her touch, her warmth, her sensuous, curvy body, her succulent lips, her...'

No you don't. Don't be fooled, she'd have you on a ball and chain, tied around her little finger. She's a selfish, devouring bitch only after glamour and money. The battle in my head raged to the muffled echo of *Wrapped Around Your Finger*. I eventually slid into a deep slumber and woke to the dappled rays of dawn and sweet melodies of nature's morning calls.

I was sent out that morning and every other day, fly-posting the length and breadth of the country. DB followed, giving lecture after lecture. Leeds, Doncaster, Peterborough, Manchester, Newcastle, Liverpool, most of the northern towns and cities, flashed by me, like a film in fast forward. Weeks bled into months. I became an adept posterer, but I was out on a limb.

I attended a few exhibitions too. My esoteric understanding and confidence was blossoming into full bloom. DB had sorted out the insurrection his way after all. We didn't get half of what was discussed. He did, however, buy them a set of new clothes and treat them to the occasional curry at the Bilash in Potters Bar. I consoled myself in my work. I didn't miss Elena that much. Stellios had gone to visit and she went to Cyprus for a spell.

Roy, the lad from Birmingham, had settled in. When I first set eyes on him, I felt I'd known him. Maybe I'd met him at one of DB's lectures; I couldn't be sure, but I knew him from somewhere. He was tall, built like an ox and had long, reddish brown hair and dark brown eyes. He wore a full beard or goatee most of the time. We hit it off together, I don't know why; we were miles apart in mentality, culture and age.

My spiritual life stammered into periods of alienation and inspiration. I persisted with my diary, recorded fragmented dreams and did what I could with my meditation. DB's plan to isolate me from the group had worked in his favour, but it had instilled in me a strong self-belief and an even more focussed will. I knew I had to win back my place in the group. I'd had enough of my enforced exile.

One freezing, cold morning, I was swishing the paste mix and getting ready to go to York when Linda trotted into the kitchen. I had a balaclava, scarf and an old pair of holey gloves on. My ragged clothes were caked in hardened paste from weeks of fly posting. I looked and felt like a tramp. I had let my hair grow and even had a shaggy beard. She shoved past me in an arrogant mood, giving me a gloating glint from those beady eyes of hers.

'Hi Chris, are you still with us? I haven't seen you in ages. I thought you'd left ages ago, pining after Elena. Are you enjoying your fly-posting trips? I hear you've become a pro at it. I think I'll tell DB you love it so much you want to do it for a further six months. I told you not to cross me, didn't I?'

The sarcastic bitch was in fine, vengeful form, bubbling over and rubbing my face into the paste. The scheming cow had engineered it all. I thought it odd when I was ordered to fly-post indefinitely. I was supposed to bring order to Claregate, not to be sent into exile. I knew her every move now, but she always tried to demoralise me at any given chance. I did not fall for her bait; I ignored her.

'Cat ran off with your tongue then?' She rattled and flitted off back to her office with a cup of tea.

It was then that I decided that this was my last posting session. I was going to confront DB after York. I was eager to visit York because Strafford had lived there, when he was Lord Lieutenant of the North. It was a long trek there and back. By the time I returned to Claregate, dinner had been cleared away. A few embers flickered and glowed in the blackened, wrought iron grate. I was drenched in sweat, rain and freezing paste. My hands were blue; my fingernails were so cold that they shone with ghostly illuminated hues. My toes trembled in my soggy old socks as I wrenched my squelching boots off. After a while, my circulation started to seep back to my frostbitten digits. I found the leftovers of a Claregate broth in the fridge, which I microwaved. I chucked a couple of logs on the hungry fire and guzzled the homely concoction. I fired myself up as the inferno raged in the grate and in the pit of my soul. I was going to reclaim my rightful position in the group. I had learned my lesson. I had been humbled, but the fire in my belly raged for recognition. I marched back to my lowly abode, fully aware and confident of my direction.

CHAPTER 31

The morning heralded a new dawn for me. I was going down to LE to fight for my rightful position after months of being exiled. I had been at Claregate more than a year now. A significant series of waking dreams proved it was to be my turning point.

> *21st April 1984, 7am.*
>
> *Sitting at a table with DB and Barry waiting to be served food by Dick. He places a plate in front of me, which has very little curry on it. DB senses my disappointment and gives me some curry from his plate. I notice that I am sitting on DB's right hand side and Barry is on his left. I am now driving DB's car down to Potters Bar.*
>
> *Dick has left his room at Claregate and a young lad is going to take it over. He is playing darts alone in a pub, because no one will play with him.*

I had a fair idea what my dreams were telling me, but I wasn't sure, anything could happen. One thing was clear, there was movement; Dick was out of favour and I was sitting at DB's right side.

I marched to the outside toilet and had an invigorating shower and shave, leaving my moustache bushy and curled up at the ends. I was in Kitchener mode, clad in my battle tunic. I wore a light blue shirt, hanging loosely over a pair of beige trousers with razor sharp creases. I slipped on my glazed, black Oxford brogues with steel heel clips and charged into Claregate. I bumped into Stellios in the hallway. I hadn't seen much of him over the last few weeks.

'Christo, God you look so different all dressed up and cleanly shaven. What a transformation from your down-and-out disguise. Where are you going?'

'I've re-invented myself. This is the new me and there are going to be major changes around here; do you hear me?' I thundered at the top of my voice. Doors creaked open, steps echoed from above and Linda's head slid around the dining room door, hissing at me.

'What's all the racket this early in the morning? Oh I might have known it was you. You've decided to chance your luck again? So you want another bout of exile do you?'

'Stellios, call the boys together after dinner. I want a full report on the situation here. Linda, I'd like a word with you in here, now, or we can have it out in full view of the others.'

'Who the hell do you think you are, marching in here and shouting your head off?'

'I've had it up to here with you: you scheming bitch. I've tried the diplomatic way but it doesn't work seem to work.'

'Oh, spare me the insults. You don't worry me in the slightest.'

'Right everyone; I'm going to tell you all a few home truths about our Linda. Do you know she hid DB's advice from me? He had scrawled some notes on the back of my horoscope, relating to my gifts and talents. She knew it, but even after asking her, she brushed me off, saying it wasn't important. Claire, what did it say? You read it to me.' She cowered into her shell as Linda blasted her with a torrent of emotional venom. She almost dried up in fear, but her sense of justice and fair play took the better of her.

'Yes, you are right Chris. She did hide it from you. I'm sorry Linda, but I've got to follow my conscience.' Claire was roasting by now from Linda's searing glance.

'Tell them all what it said. Go on, tell them.'

'It said Chris had the gift to become a brilliant astrologer and lecturer.'

Linda was horrified. Her face blasted hot and cold as their gaze focussed on her.

'She even plotted to expel Elena because she was lapping up the limelight,' I added. 'The bitch knew I was a threat to her, so she set about to destroy me. She sent me into exile all these months, because she knew she was losing control here. But I'm back and here to claim my rightful position in the group.'

She melted in front of everyone with her head bowed in admission; she never even attempted to retaliate. She knew she was finished. Dick rose to her defence, but his frantic antics held no sway. He was a lone figure, completely alienated and isolated. Barry just walked out to a waiting car that sped in the direction of LE.

'Right, now that we've established a new broom around here, we're going to get this place in order. You must all help me turn it around for our benefit. Lance, do you want to come down to LE? I'm leaving in the next car. I've got some unfinished business with DB.'

'I wouldn't miss this for the world. I'll be out now.'

'Chris, can I come down with you?' asked Roy. 'DB wants me to finish off some set building.'

'No problem, jump in the back.' In minutes we were on the way for my confrontation with DB.

'Chris you look like a sergeant major in those clothes; you even sound like one. What prompted the transformation?'

'Lance, I had enough of being subjected to weeks of alienation. I was exiled for no reason. I also had a series of waking dreams this morning, which reinforced my position.' I relayed my dreams to them in graphic detail.

'DB's going to promote you to the inner circle,' Lance gushed. 'You're going to take over Barry's position. He's going to feed you wisdom and more responsibilities. He's a symbol of the psychopomp in your dreams.'

'Psychopomp? What does that mean? I'm lost.'

'The psychopomp is an inner or outer reflection of your soul. It can be a symbol or person who beckons you in a dream and leads you back to your higher self. When you are on the path, you first confront all your fears and phobias. The concretion of these energies forms a loathsome entity we call *the Dweller on the Threshold of Consciousness.* It bars the way to the inner worlds, but ultimately we dispatch the entity, after resolving and understanding our negativity. A radiant being of light is born out of the ashes of *the Dweller - the Angel of the Shining Presence*. This positive *Solar Deva* becomes housed in our psyche. Through continued inward focus, it is transformed into the anima, or animus if you are a woman. It's the female/male inner partner. She or he leads the way to the inner realms of the higher self.'

'Lance, I've lived through hell and back battling my *Dweller*. I've beaten the bastard, I'm sure. I've experienced that state of inner calm, where I have encountered my *Angel*. I am plagued with dreams in which I'm uniting with female forms. You know, I've even had Margaret Thatcher as an expression of my ultimate anima figure.'

'I am sure you have. But the next evolutionary sequence is union with the psychopomp. He is the true inner guide. In ancient Egypt and Greece his archetypal form was Thoth-Hermes. In Rome, he was the god Mercury. That's why in astrology the psychopomp is linked with the planet Mercury. In our dreams, he takes the form of any symbol that leads the way or points direction. He may manifest in the outer world as a guru or spiritual teacher, but he is never a so-called *spirit guide* contacted by mediums.'

'So DB is a manifestation of the psychopomp? He's regularly in my dream life. Lance, Roy, this is confidential. Okay? I've had very weird, erotic dreams, where I'm having sex with Baker and he's having sex with me. I was in utter turmoil for weeks. I used to go through hell thinking about it. I really thought I was turning into a poof. Don't tell anyone about this, you two. If it gets out, Linda, Barry and Dick will have a field day. Lance what do you think that means?'

' Oo, who's a lovely boy then? Go on, give us a kiss.'

'Lance, stop fucking about, I'm serious. Do you think he's been having sex with me in the astral world?'

'Chris, you should be privileged to get the attention. I've never had anything of that sort. I only have boring straight sex with my anima, and she's normally an ugly pig of a woman.'

'Come on quit it, Am I in the shit or is it a kind of psychopomp union?'

'Exactly Chris, You are being primed for the work. He knows you have what it takes, spiritual guts and staying power. The union is symbolic of your relationship with your soul. The psychopomp eventually transforms into the Master. You are in union with your *Daemon*, your Master.'

'Well we'll soon see if my dreams are prophetic or not. I'm not going to beat around the bush. I want answers and I want action.'

We dodged the menagerie of cats and dogs in the forecourt. The upstairs window curtain swished open. I could barely see DB's silhouette and someone else's. They were having a meeting. I presumed it was Barry updating him. The boys went to their duties and I stormed into be confronted by John.

'What's all the rush this morning Chris? God it's nice to see someone is making an effort to smarten themselves up. I wish you could get that lot to do the same.'

'John, if I wasn't sent to outer Siberia over the last few months, I would have whipped them into order, I can assure you.'

The ceiling above began to tremble and the lights flickered under the stress of DB's hobnail shoes. He always wore them when he wanted to kick arse. My arse was on the line as he clumped downstairs, with his little lapdog behind him.

'Hullo strawberry bollocks, so the prodigal son returns. What news of the northern territories; I hope we are fairing well.'

He was full of bullshit, as usual. Barry and John sat there with smug looks on their smarmy faces.

'So, what do you want then, charging down here in your Kitchener uniform, all buttons and full of hot air? Aah, so you're fed up with posting, are you? That was a lesson for you in detachment, humility and staying power. It tested your resolve and toughened you up for the important work ahead.'

'That bitch Linda set me up. It was all her scheming, wasn't it?'

'Chris, do you think I need a woman to hand out my tests. I know how to mould you. I know your strengths and weaknesses. I'm here to promote them and iron them out. By all accounts you are ready to taste the fire. Barry told me how you completely demoralised Linda. She deserved it, filling my head with conspiracies and plotting against you.'

'The bitch gave Elena her marching orders, didn't...........'

'I gave her her marching orders. I knew her motives and she's still at it, behind your back,' he blasted in a bombastic outburst that rocked the whole household. The dogs whimpered; the cats cowered and an unsuspecting sparrow thudded against the window. I'd never seen anything like it before. The pure force of his voice created an external wave of psychic energy that ripped through the atmosphere like a nuclear explosion. I had become immune to that sort of emotional haemorrhage. I had Linda to thank for that.

'Fire Chris; yes fire!'

What was he inferring? He was so cryptic sometimes.

'You are to take over the reigns from Barry; he's got a lot of post film production to organise. John will take you under his wing for a while, until you settle in. He'll give you projects to initiate and goals to achieve.'

'Now wait a minute. Do you honestly think I'm going to take orders from John? I've seen the lists he gives to the boys and they hate it. They don't respect him at all. He's never around when the shit hits the fan. No thanks, and no disrespect to you John. I'll do it my way or nothing.'

DB sat shifting in his seat, building up to a confrontation; I sensed it brewing. He rose on his hammerhead fists and peered over his bi-focals. His searing, brown eyes pierced my soul and he jutted forward as if he was going to launch himself at me.

'Ah, ha, ha! Fantastic, Chris! That's my boy, exactly what I expected.' He exploded in a fit of laughter. Even his lapdogs were taken by surprise.

'What do you mean? Fuck sake, you've been testing me again, haven't you?'

'Do you think I could trust someone who's got half a brain and no balls. I want someone to stand up to me. I want someone to use logic, willpower and diplomacy. John's a good kid, but he's got no man management skills, nor staying power. But he is loyal and I trust him with my life. Barry is my right hand, or was my right hand, but even he lacks the skills necessary to wield the fire and use it. He's not ready and he never will be, but his skills as a negotiator and diplomat are excellent. He's a devoted servant, but even he knows he's not ready for *the Burning Ground.*'

What was all this talk of fire? I didn't understand DB's continuous reference to it. I looked at him in confusion.

'You'll know it soon enough. You'll understand, I'm sure. By the way, Dick is moving out. He's got himself a bitch with money. That's what he's always worshiped, women and money. He's sold his soul to the highest bidder, the mercenary. He'll still be printing for us. His potential father-in-law has a thriving print works. The boy's got his head screwed on. He needs it, what with his deprived childhood. You do know I picked up Mike and him when they were snotty little runts in the East End. I adopted them and pulled them out of the squalor of London's slums. Yes, he craves money and a settled lifestyle. Who can blame him?'

That answered my question; my waking dreams were precognitive. I had tapped into my source; I was being bathed in light and energy. I felt Him stir deep inside of me. He was always there, to cushion my falls, to give me encouragement and to goad me to more effort.

'Right boys; Leave us now. I want to have a word with Chris in private. Tell Lance to put the kettle on. We need a cuppa after all this excitement. You know you were with me in the Crusades, don't you?'

'DB, don't bullshit me. I've had enough to last me a life time.'

'Linda told me how you plucked it out of your chart.'

'It just came seeping through the ethers. I could smell the sand saturated with the stench of decaying corpses, hundreds of them. I saw the standard of Lionheart fluttering in the wind. I felt the deadly, desert sun scorching my skin red raw. I saw it flash and glint on the helmets and armour of the Crusader knights; it sprayed darting rays on their white tunics emblazoned with the red cross of the Lord. The Crusaders and Infidels fell in there thousands, loyal blind souls, fighting for their beliefs. All their blood gushed like crimson rivers, flowing into a vermilion sea. They all perished, for nothing, absolutely nothing.'

'Chris, you don't understand. Lionheart was a Nirmanakaya expression. His task was to hold and secure the Christ Light in the Holy Land. All those brave souls fought under the banner of Christ Consciousness. If it weren't for their efforts, we would be in darkness now. Yes, I picked it up in your chart ages ago. Even the Fertile Crescent is there, and those looped, razor sharp Muslim sabres. That's your Moon, Mars in Pisces in the fifth house. Mars and Moon morphologically represent the sabre. He burst into the first verse of the epic psalm,

Onwards Christian soldiers marching as to war,
With the cross of Jesus going on before!'

Lance popped his balding head around the door. His beady eyes and ears were alert as usual. He was always on the lookout for some spiritual carrion to gorge on.

'Hope you haven't scoffed the dogs Lance. Where are they?'

'Oops sorry DB, I forgot them in the kitchen. I won't be a minute.'

'Lance, you'll never change.'

He walked in sporting a cheeky grin, plonked the dogs down and hopped out.

'DB, how are you certain I was there? How can you be sure?'

'Trust me, you were there all right. I've given you enough clues. You'll have to find it out by yourself.'

'How can I do that? It's not as if I can pluck it out of thin air.'

'Research the period. Get to know as much as you can about the prominent figures involved. Study their names, their clothing, and their standards. Immerse yourself totally in the period. Then watch your dreams, ask questions and meditate. The unconscious is a vast, living ocean of meaning, energy and fire. If you proposition it, it will throw up a pebble, a trinket, or even a name. That's the law of magnetism.'

'You mentioned fire on a few occasions. What did you mean?'

'You'll know soon enough. If you are really interested read my book *The Diary of an Alchemist*. The ancients called it Serpent Fire, Fohat or Kundalini. References of it are in the books. There's no secret about it. However, there are only a few rare souls who can withstand *the Burning Ground*. It's connected to their past lives.'

'What do you mean?'

'If you have won the right to wield the fire in a past life, you will have opportunities to access it again. It needs a highly disciplined, soul infused personality, dedicated to the path, just to survive the experience, never mind use it.'

This fire business was way over my head. I decided to take things as they come and get into a rhythm with my studies, meditation and my service work. I also recorded everything religiously in my spiritual diary.

'Go on then, hop it. I've got urgent business to attend to. Oh, before I forget, *Beware the Ides of March*. Watch your back, there's a bad apple in the basket. John, Barry, let's get down to it. Come on, my time is precious. Chris, I want you down here with Barry and John every morning. Get Gerald to find you an old banger to get around in. You can drive can't you? Right, off with you.'

The doors slammed behind me and DB started ranting and raving. They were under financial pressure; I could feel it in my bones. I trotted outside to mull things over. I could see Roy, Steve, Stellios and Jeremy hammering away merrily on the set. I cast my mind back to what DB had said about Elena and the veiled warnings of betrayal of trust. What did that all mean? I hadn't a clue. Obviously I had to unravel it on my own. It was my personal karma. DB could have no part in it. It was my freewill and my responsibility to explore it. I felt like a million dollars: promotion to the inner circle and a company car. I was in favour. I wasn't doing too badly in the materialist's eyes. I was a high-flying executive with a six-figure salary. The only problem was it was all in the cosmic bank.

CHAPTER 32

M y thoughts meandered back to my personal tête-à-tête with DB and the rotten apple in the basket. Who could it be? Linda? Dick? Yes, it's Linda of course; she spews her rot all over Claregate. It's difficult not to become plagued by her infectious energy.

'*You can't ripen an apple with a blowtorch,*' bellowed in my ear. I tingled all over, as **His** vibration trickled from the top of my head to the base of my spine. It was one of DB's favourite sayings. I was beginning to feel like that apple. I knew I was not yet ready for the blowtorch. DB's reference to *the fire* and *the burning ground* really intrigued me. I had read something about *Kundalini Fire*. The effects of long-term meditation ultimately led to the stirring of this divine force deep within the base of the spine centre. Surely to God he was not inferring I was ready for that.

Now that I was at LE I decided that I might as well research The Crusades. I was sure DB would have books on the subject and there was bound to be references in Britannica too. I trotted off to pick Lance's brains; he knew where all the books were.

'Lance. Hi, got a few minutes spare? Could you direct me to DB's books on The Crusades.'

'Crusades? Crusades? What are you up to now? Bloody hell, that's not fair. You're not researching another past life, are you?'

'Lance, you were in class when I got it through.'

'Yes, I suppose so. But it's still not fair.'

'I can't help it, Lance. My *Daemon* floods me with knowledge. I'm not in control of it; it comes out of the blue.'

'That's your bloody Neptune in Scorpio in the first, with Libra ascendant.'

'Just cut the bull and show me the section. I promise to tell you if I uncover something. You never know, you might have been around then.'

'Not likely, I haven't got a Crusader bone in me. I'm a pen-pusher, not a jouster.'

'Oh well, maybe you were a scribe at the time. Someone had to record the bloody events, didn't they?'

'I may have been a pope or a powerful bishop?'

'More like a court jester I'd say; all stories and trickery.'

'Many a true word is said in jest, I'll have you know. They could even poke fun at the king without getting flogged or beheaded.'

'Come on, you ditherer, show me the section and give me some peace and quiet.'

We slid quietly into the stale, silent room and he left me to it. Every time I sat here the pungent scent of antiquated tomes sent butterflies fluttering in my stomach. It was as if I was entering a time warp.

There were biographies on Henry the 2nd, Richard the Ist, King John and The Magna Carta. What was The Magna Carta doing there? I didn't realise it was connected. I knew very little about it, only that it became England's first legal document and charter, recording civil rights and laws of the land. I had no idea it was at the same time as The Crusades.

I studied for hours in there. There were kings, queens, lords, barons, generals and knights, cardinals and popes. I didn't realise how many Crusades there were. I saturated my brain with The Crusades of Henry the Second and the Lionheart. I reckoned if I had a life then, it would be specifically related to them. King John never visited the Holy Land but his son, Prince Henry did. No, John, the Lionheart's brother had grand designs for the throne of England, Normandy and Aquitaine. He tried to usurp Lionheart's throne whilst he was away fighting for Christendom. What a feuding bunch of royals they were. It was survival of the fittest. Family ties didn't account for much in those, bloodthirsty medieval days.

Lance walked in with a cup of tea and cucumber sandwiches.

'Mmm, Lance, that's thoughtful of you. I hope you've peeled, salted and sliced the cucumber into transparent slithers.'

'What! You think you're DB or something? Anyway, how do you know about 'the battle of the cucumber sandwiches'?'

'Steve told me; what a farce.' He hovered around, glancing his beady, little eyes over my shoulder to see if he could peck up a few crumbs of knowledge.

'Stop licking your lips, I haven't found out anything. There's too much material, I don't know where to start. I've got a stinking headache now. I'll give it another hour and call it a day.'

'Don't expect miracles Chris, it may take weeks for your unconscious to regurgitate some clues. Leave it for now; just keep alert, subjectively and objectively. It will happen when you least expect it. Ask your *Daemon* via your diary. Meditate on it and record your dreams.'

'Thanks Lance; yes, I think I'll call it a day; I'm mentally exhausted. Oh, I've got news to tell you about my new appointment. You were right and my dreams were prophetic. I've told Stellios to get together after dinner to discuss developments.'

'Ooo, I can't wait,' he cackled and he bobbed out merrily, chirping and chuckling.

I decided to wrap it up, but I spied a book on Charles the1st, jutting out of a space on the top shelf. I had a quick read and perused the colour plates of the royal family. Strafford was there and Archbishop Laud, the king's other advisor and Strafford's devoted friend. My mind catapulted me back to the gruesome beheading on Tower Hill. Something inside stirred. I had to visit the site. I had never been to any of London's historic buildings, but I promised myself a day out soon. I had to satisfy my curiosity. I slammed the book closed, gathered my notes and strolled outside. The boys were packing their tools away.

'Coming back with us Chris? I think there's room.'

'Maybe Stellios, I'll just check if DB wants me.'

'Okay, we'll toot when we're ready.' I hopped into the house and shouted, 'DB, do you want me?'

'Shhh, he's resting. What do you want?'

'Sorry John, Does he need me for anything? If not, I'm going back.'

'Oh yes, he wants you to take a trip to London tomorrow, down to Soho. We need to put film in for developing and we've got some to pick up. He said to take Roy with you for company.'

'I've never gone into London from Potters Bar before. How do I get in?'

'Take the train and tube, or yes, I think it's best to drive in. You may have to collect a few cans of film.'

'Drive?'

'It's easy; I'll give you directions. Roy can be your co-driver. I'll sort out a car for you and give you petrol money.'

'Well, it will be an adventure at least. Strange, I was just thinking of a trip into London.'

'See you at dinner, Chris, okay.'

I trundled outside and squeezed into the beat up, old car. There was just enough space; we were crammed in like sardines. Something was wrong; I sensed it. The atmosphere was thick and moody.

'God, quick, open a window, I'm going to die. It smells like a dead cat in here. You all need a good scrub.'

'Hey, it's all right for you, in your pen-pushing gear, sitting supping tea and mixing with the elite,' spat Steve. 'I hear you've become one of them now, another lapdog lieutenant.'

'Stop talking shit, I'll never be that. Listen, you can't change things from the outside, can you?'

'Yeh, but their auras are infectious.'

'Guys, I think I've proved myself to you, haven't I?'

Their faces didn't reflect any confidence in me. There were a few anxious glances.

'Haven't I? Come on, don't clam up on me. You're treating me like an outsider.' There was an awkward silence as we creaked into the drive. They had all slumped into their shells. Even Stellios had sunk to a low ebb.

'Right, I've had enough of this bullshit. What's up with you lot?'

They crawled out of the car and plodded head down into Claregate, with their heavy auras tripping them up.

'We'll talk after dinner. I think we need to clear the air.' They acknowledged me with muffled mutterings and disappeared into their different boltholes.

What had I done to deserve this? I felt betrayed. I could not understand the way they were cold-shouldering me. What had happened in all that time I was exiled? There was a stinking plot brewing and I suspected who was at the centre of it.

I was in deep thought when Roy beckoned me to the library. He was on his own and was eager to talk to me.

'Chris, listen, and keep it quiet. Something's brewing, but I'm not sure what's happening. They've been poisoned, all of them. You've got to be careful, there's a rotten apple amongst them.'

'It's that conspiring bitch Linda, isn't it? How did she get to them so quickly?'

'I don't know, but she called Lance and he infested them with something. I saw them all huddled together just before we got in the car. Their auras were thick with negativity.'

What was going on? What had I done wrong? Why were they treating me like an outcast? I had fought for their rights; I sacrificed my privileges for them. I never let them down.

'Thanks Roy, That's pretty decent of you. By the way, DB wants both of us to take some film into be processed. Fancy a trip to London?'

'Thanks Chris, that'll be great. I've never been to the capital before.'

'Well, we're going to the heart of *sacral city*, Soho.'

'Soho? We're taking the film to Soho?'

'I suppose Barry negotiated a good deal with one of the film developers down there. He probably threw in a couple of massages too. Roy, I don't want you to put your head on the block for me, but it's your choice. If you hear anything, keep me posted. I really can't understand any of it. Even Stellios has gone cold on me. That's really odd.'

He slid out leaving me in a dilemma. What was going on? Factions, betrayal, back stabbings, conspiracies. There were so many splinters, allegiances were broken and alliances sealed. They were all jostling for favours and power. My position of strength had suddenly degenerated into a mish-mash of promises and false hopes. My only option now was with the inner circle. Doors were opening there and I knew my destiny was ultimately linked to the hierarchy. I had to heal my rifts with Dick. I needed to be diplomatic with Barry and John and I had to keep my influence in the outer circle. Maybe Roy could help me there. I needed to tread carefully, but what was Stellios up to?

I retired to the eerie caravan, with haunting thoughts. The door banged in the sweeping wind, creaking on its old, rusty hinges. Leaves and twigs conspired with each other, swishing and cracking around my feet. The dusk calls of birds squawked and chirped as the golden-red solar orb sank into its celestial slumber. I wish I could say the same. Alas, my thoughts rustled around my head sparking off a frenzied emotional dance of my demons. I was in utter turmoil, all alone, with a plot brewing and no one to confide in. Only *He* could help me now, but my mood had muffled his warming presence. I slid into a light slumber, only to be thrust into a horrifying experience.

21st July, 6pm. OOBE
I was plunged into a cesspit of astral crap. I felt myself being groped and tugged by filthy astral currents. I tried to keep my head clear, but grotesque entities swamped me, pulling me deeper and deeper into the bowels of hell. I felt nauseous, as if I was drowning in my own vomit. My stomach began to twist and churn as I fought for air. I crashed out of the experience gasping and chocking; I was sick all over the place. I felt like I'd been kicked all over. My body ached, I was soaked in sweat, my lungs throbbed and my heartbeat thudded in my head. I felt like I had been attacked and vampirised by ghoulish entities.

I was so exhausted that I melted into a deep sleep only to be awakened by Roy.

'Chris, are you in there? Chris.'

'What's up Roy? What are you doing in here?'

'Are you all right? It stinks of sick in here.'

'Yes, I'm okay. I've just got a dicky stomach.'

'You've missed dinner. John gave me the keys to the car, the film and a cheque for tomorrow.'

'Oh no. What happened? Was DB annoyed?'

'No, he was fine. He told them that you had been promoted to the inner circle. You ought to have seen their faces. The whole table trembled in unexpressed emotions. Linda seethed, Claire was indifferent, the inner circle smirked and the boys wore vacant faces.'

'Where are they now?'

'I don't know, they've disappeared somewhere, maybe the pub.'

'I don't like it one bit. Something nasty is brewing. I've sensed it. I've just had a violent astral attack.'

'Attack? What? Do you mean they are projecting on you?'

'Yes, I'm being preyed upon, but I'll be okay, I know how to handle it. I can imagine what it feels like for an alcoholic or drug addict to be in delirium tremens.'

'What are you on about Chris?'

'When they are in a drunken stupor or spaced out, astral bodies of dead alcoholics and addicts vampirise their bodies.'

'Eek, how horrible; is that true?'

'Yes, they roam the astral world in search of victims to feed on. You see, they still need their fix or binge, but they have no physical body to act through.'

'Do you mean to say there are astral vampires?'

'Yes, they attach themselves to the astral body of their host and drain them of their energies.'

'So that's why addicts and alcoholics say they have been attacked by spirits? It's not hallucinations after all?'

'Roy, they are more real than you and I, I'm telling you. I've had a few bad OOBE's. I've been in similar situations.'

'Bloody hell, I can't imagine anything so terrifying.'

'You'll have to go through it Roy, if you want soul contact.'

'I realise that, but I'm not ready yet. I can feel it sweeping in and trying to swamp me.'

'It will come when the time is right. We all have to deal with our *Dweller on the Threshold.* You must not resist it; it will take you. It must, for you to change yourself from within.'

'Chris, I understand. I'll see you tomorrow morning.'

'Be ready to go at 7.30. I don't want to get caught up in the rush hour.'

'Okay, good night.'

He trudged off into the moody, dark night, leaving me with the aftermath of my vile experience. I needed to clean myself up and clear my aura. I changed clothes and psyched up for a meditation. I settled myself and within minutes I had withdrawn into a deeply relaxed inner calm. My heartbeat slowed, my breathing relaxed and gentle tingling energies began to tickle my chakras.

'Wao! I had a sudden vivid image out of the blue.

> *9pm, meditation experience*
> *I was in a royalist tunic, waiting for an audience with the king. The chamber doors creaked open to a blinding aura of light and gold. I hid my eyes from the searing energy. Then a voice from the depths shouted,*
> *'The Roi is here! The Roi is here! The Roi is here!'*

I came round, totally bewildered and zinging with energy.

What was that all about? The light was blinding, the searing aura of the king was awesome; but what did it mean? I was exhausted and brain dead by now. Too many questions bombarded my skull. A mass of frayed ends, garrotting knots, and gaping holes, too overwhelming to mend, tortured my fevered mind. The tapestry was becoming more complex by the minute. Every section completed lead further into infinity. There was no end or no beginning; there was just the now. I had to live in the now. Things were rapidly changing and unfolding around me. I slid into a final slumber with my thoughts on visiting Tower Hill tomorrow and the Crusader research I did today. They all swished together, names, dates, scenes and faces all tumbled in the drum of my dreams, rinsed fresh by sweeping jets of the fountain of life, my subjective paradise.

CHAPTER 33

I woke refreshed, threw on some clothes, gathered my notebook and set off for a cup of tea. As I waded through the dew-drenched green my mind wandered to yesterday's events. My chart, yes, it was all in my chart. That feeling of betrayal in the group; it was true, all of it. I entered the hallway and the phone started blaring. I picked it up in Linda's office.

'Hullo, who's speaking?'

'Is that you Christo?'

'Elena, why are you calling so early in the morning?'

'I wanted to speak to you, it's urgent. I want a divorce. It's been over a year since we split; we can get a 'quickie'. All you have to do is to admit to adultery and we'll get it on the grounds of irreconcilable differences. I also need money, half of your savings. That's what I'm entitled to before you fritter the lot away down the Claregate black hole.'

'What! I have to drag my name through the gutter to protect yours. You fucked off with that bastard and left me. You've got a bloody cheek'

'Christo, if you don't, I'll go crawling back to Cyprus. I'll tell everyone about our split, in the most graphic and dramatic style. You know what an actress I am.'

'You fucking bitch, you expect me to agree to your demands? DB was right after all.'

'Look, the choice is yours. I just have to tell your family and friends that you flipped your lid, had sex with the girls there, kicked me out and gave all your money away. I can just see myself playing the feeble victim, faint and gaunt, and sobbing my heart out.

'He's lost it; brainwashed in that cult. They've sucked him dry of his personality and blackmailed him out of his money. He shacked up with a hippie, American chick called Linda and is high on drugs all the time,' she said in a traumatised tone. God what an actress she was.

'You fucking bitch, you'll destroy me! My Mama, my Yiayia, they wouldn't understand. You'll kill them with your poison.'

'Oh, there's something else. I've heard you're into gay sex too. Now that would be the icing on the cake, don't you think?'

'You fucking whore! I never thought you'd stoop so low. Elena, I lived with you for seven years. We shared the same bed; we struggled through the bad times together. I loved you, I trusted you, but you've shown your true colours in the end.'

'Listen, did you think I'd want to live in rags for the rest of my life? I'm neither a loser nor a romantic, and I'm not a spiritual airhead. I want money, I want glamour and I want a rich man to pamper me. You've got nothing to offer me, you never had. I had to swallow my pride and study catering. I didn't want to end up slaving in a restaurant all my life. I'm going places, I've got high expectations.'

'I'll see you in court, you bitch; I'll have you for slander. You'll not get a divorce nor a penny from me.' I slammed the phone down so hard it almost broke in two. She got to me. I let her get to me. It was all a set-up. She had planned it all. The bitch knew the law back to front. She also knew I wanted rid off her. But I really didn't think she'd stoop so low. Drugs, gay sex, cults, brainwashing and blackmail. That bastard Lance or Roy must have leaked my experience to Linda. The plot was getting thicker every minute. I bumped into Roy in the hallway carrying a cuppa for me.

'Chris, I was on my way to wake you.'

'Thanks Roy, Let's get out of here fast. I can't handle another disaster.'

'What's up? You sound awful and you look all flustered.'

'I'll tell you in the car. Let's get going.'

'Okay, see you outside in five minutes.'

I took my cup and sat outside in the car. What was going to happen next? What else were they going to throw at me? Was this also part of my tests? I was lost and alienated; I could not trust anyone anymore. Roy was a kind soul, but he was green. I did feel there was something weird binding us together; that was really odd. But could I confide in him? I wasn't sure. I could not afford any more disastrous alliances. He skipped out and hopped into the car. Within minutes we hit the M25. It was quite clear of rush hour traffic, but as we approached London it became more congested.

'Roy, fancy going to visit The Tower of London? I'm fascinated by its turbulent history. What do you think?'

'Bloody brilliant,' he said, in his heavy Brummy accent. 'I've always wanted to visit it. Don't ask me why, it's just something I promised myself I'd do.'

'That's exactly what I felt. Isn't that strange? I've got a past life connection there. I just wanted to go and tune into the energies, just to see if I could pick up something.'

'Pick up something? What do you mean?'

'I've read that if you retrace your steps back to a place where you lived before, you can access memories of the experiences left there. It's all somehow recorded in the ethers, in the land and the buildings.'

'You mean to say the walls have ears? I've heard that expression before, but I didn't really think there was anything in it.'

'Roy, some places are saturated with human energies: thoughts, emotions, pain and tragedy, love and happiness, death and destruction. They are never lost or forgotten. That's why the ancients always worshipped in pre-chosen sacred sites. They built monuments to their gods and idols. Churches, monasteries, shrines and temples are saturated by their energies. It's in every brick and boulder. Their sweat, effort, blood and every cell of their bodies is impregnated in each granule of sand and in each droplet of water.'

'I never really thought of it that way, Chris.'

'Roy, it comes from within. I am bathed in light and knowledge. My *Daemon* feeds me with wisdom and enlightenment.'

'Do you mean to say you have a direct link to your soul? That only happens when you have integrated your personality.'

'Exactly. It's not been easy dealing with hundreds of years of shit, but finding *the pearl of great price stuck in the mud of matter* is the ultimate prize. I've had to go through hell and back to be where I am today. That bitch Elena got to me this morning. Now that is one of my most severe challenges; to extricate myself from that scheming, adulterous whore.'

'Elena? Who's Elena?'

'My darling wife; we're separated. Haven't the boys told you about her? I thought they would have, just to drag my reputation through the muck.'

'No. Anyway, it's none of my business. It certainly isn't going to affect my judgement of you.'

'She's blackmailing me. She wants a divorce and half my money or the bitch will blacken my name. She's even using that strictly confidential information I shared with you and Lance yesterday.'

There were a few moments of eerie silence as I waited for a response or an admission. He went taciturn on me. Was the silence an admission of guilt? Or hadn't he quite worked out what was happening?

'Chris, you don't think I had something to do with all that, do you?'

'Nothing surprises me lately. Well, did you? Don't fuck around the bush, tell me straight.'

'Chris, what do you think? Do you honestly think if I had stabbed you in the back I'd come running to warn you about the lads' conspiracy and be here now?'

'Roy, there are so many twists and turns in this arena, it's like *the Labyrinth*, with a grotesque deformed demon at its core.'

'Trust me. I've got nothing to do with it. I never knew there were so many plots and conspiracies in the group. I came here to immerse myself in study, meditation and service work. That's all I'm interested in, nothing else.'

'Well keep you nose clean Roy. Don't get involved in petty squabbles and power struggles. If you do, make sure you're on the winning side.'

'Chris, I'll always support the just and right way. I'm not interested in manipulation, bribery and blackmail. I'm only interested in truth, beauty and goodness.'

'The ancient teachings are here Roy; DB is an initiate. He's the next link in the unbroken lineage of wisdom teachers. It's all here all right, but you'll have to earn you spurs. Wisdom is won, it's not handed out on a plate to be wasted. Remember my dream with DB offering me food?'

'I didn't think it was going to involve power struggles, backstabbing and conspiracies.'

'Roy, it's all part of development here. *Not that we must live in one world less; we must live in both worlds more.*'

We sped into the hub of sacral Soho, the sex centre of London and dropped off the film. We returned after a take-away meal and meandered towards The Tower of London.

'So you had a previous life experience here, did you?'

'Yes Roy, It wasn't a pleasant experience either.'

'Well, aren't you going to tell me about it, or is it a secret?'

'I'm not quite ready to share it with you Roy, it's nothing personal. I need to savour the experience a little longer.'

'I understand, it's personal. Trust and loyalty are so important.'

'Loyalty is sacred, a divine quality. It's tested to the ultimate. Trust, now that's a high order too. Both go together as heavenly bedfellows in my scheme of things.'

We parked the old banger and waded through a sea of flickering, camera-clad Japanese tourists, snapping up every granule of dust and stone. An army of flag waving English school kids marched in from the flanks taking them by surprise. A troop of mounted policemen trotted in between them. It felt as though we were caught in a bloody crossfire. Suddenly the sound of a tumultuous mob crowded my cranium and a severe pain shot through the back of my neck, forcing me to crouch down in a clear spot.

I screamed aloud as my consciousness was thrust back to that terrifying beheading in front of 100,000 jeering, vindictive peasants and noblemen. The stench of the foul deed swamped my emotions and saturated my wounded heart. A soul wrenched monologue seeped into my consciousness and I was thrust into Strafford's wretched body. He coughed and spluttered in his chair, dressed all in black, with a quill in his wracked and wavering hand. The rancid odour of dampness and sweat drenched the stinking prison in the Tower as he wrote:

'May it please your Sacred Majesty...I understand the minds of men are more incensed against me, notwithstanding your Majesty hath declared, that in your princely opinion I am not guilty of treason and that you are not satisfied in your conscience to pass the Bill of Attainder. This bringeth me in a very great streight, there is before me the ruin of my children and family, hitherto untouched with any foul crime: here are before me many ills, which may befall your Sacred Person and the whole kingdom should yourself and Parliament part less satisfied one with the other, than is necessary for the preservation both of King and people; they are before me the things most valued, most feared by mortal men, Life or Death..........So, Sir to you, I can give the life of this world with all the cheerfulness imaginable and only beg that in your goodness you would vouchsafe to cast your gracious regard upon my poor son and his three sisters, less or more and no otherwise than as their (in present) unfortunate father, met hereafter appear more or less guilty of this death.

God long preserve your Majesty. Your Majesty's most faithful and humble subject and servant Strafford.'

A flash of King Charles in the Royal Chamber at Whitehall zapped my fevered mind. He was sitting behind his ornate, golden desk, with his head bowed in his hands. Around him stood a number of guards and noblemen. From outside came the sickening sound of vicious taunts from the marauding multitude smashing the gates.

'Sign the Bill! Sign the Bill! Black Tom to the block! Black Tom to the block!'

The king lifted his sorry head, stretched out his royal, ring-encrusted hand, plucked the quill and swept his signature on the Bill. Filled with anguish and despair, he turned and handed the death warrant to his clerk.

'Oh, my God! It's him! It's him! It's him!' I shouted. The revelation smacked me back to reality. The crowds had shuffled off, leaving me dazed and nursing a blinding headache.

'There you are. I've been looking for you for ages. God, you look awful. Look at you; you're white as a ghost. Are you all right?'

I looked up at him and the sun's rays blinded me. His silhouette was emblazoned in a golden halo. The Roi is here! The Roi is here, blasted in my head. The vision came thundering back from my consciousness. Roy was Charles the 1st in his past life!

'Chris, speak to me. Are you okay? Here, have some water.'

I quenched my thirst and balanced my mind to centre myself. What should I do? Tell him? No, I must wait; he's not ready for it. Yes, that's what I'll do, I debated in my mind.

'Thanks Roy, I'll settle here for a moment.'

'Here, stand up and get some fresh air. Look at the Tower. Isn't it awesome? Can you imagine how many tyrants and innocent victims went to their deaths in there? Hey, look where you're standing Chris.'

'It can't be. It's not possible, is it?'

'There's the plaque. That's the exact spot where most of the executions took place. This was the infamous hill that overlooked The Tower of London.'

'Bloody hell Roy, I can't believe it. I was drawn here, to this very spot. The pains came haunting back, trailing ghoulish memories of the last gruesome moments of his wretched life.'

'Come on; let's get off this spot. There's a monument behind here; let's have a look at it. It's got a list of all the people executed here.'

'Hey, Sir Thomas More; look, even he got his head chopped off here. I didn't know that. I thought Charles the 1st was executed here too. Let's see.... I'm sure his royal head rolled off the block.' Roy said as his fingers cursed down the gruesome list of names. 'Surely to God it must be here.'

'Yes Roy you're right he was tried and executed for high treason and crimes against the realm, but not here. He was beheaded on a special scaffold erected outside the banqueting hall at Whitehall

Palace. He followed his most loyal and trusted servant, the Earl of Strafford, who was beheaded here.'

'Strafford, Strafford? Yes, there's his name all right. Beheaded, May 12th 1641. God what bloodthirsty times they lived in. Didn't the Civil War follow all that, Cromwell and things?'

'You've studied the period then?'

'No, not really; we once had a school project to prepare; it fascinated me. I enjoyed the intrigue, the power struggles and the battles.'

'Let's get cracking Roy; we've got a hornet's nest brewing back at Claregate. I'll need my wits about me. Talk about civil wars; we're in one at the moment'

'Chris, you can trust me, honest. I have faith in you. I know you'll do what's best for all the group.'

'Thanks for the vote of confidence. I'll need a lot more of that. What with the Elena situation, Linda's plotting plans, and DB's tests and trials, it's all a bit much. Even Stellios gone cold on me.'

'I'll support you all the way. Maybe it's a good idea to keep our relationship secret. That way I can feed you with information if it comes my way.'

'Great idea Roy; You're not so green after all, are you?'

'That's my cover Chris. I'm Virgo. I come across so pure and innocent, but I'm Leo ascendant; that's power, loyalty and confidence.'

'You're certainly a cautious mix. I'm glad you're on my side. Virgo is dutiful, devoted and hard working. I like that. You know my Jupiter's in Virgo? That makes us a good match.'

'Mmm, where's Leo in your chart?'

'It's intercepted in the 10th. I've also got Uranus retrograde there.'

'That's the power behind the throne, isn't it?'

'Hey, you've been doing your homework.'

'I love the astrology; it's so meaningful. It works on so many levels.'

'Have you posited your soul's purpose aspect in your diary yet?'

'No. Is it important?'

'Yes, it should give you an idea of your direction, gifts, karma and past lives.'

'I'll do it tonight, when we get in.'

We got to the car, squeezed through the rush hour and hit the M25. It was chock-a-block and it took us hours to get home. Rain lashed against the old banger, leaking in from dodgy door seals and wonky windows. The passenger seat was almost waterlogged. Roy squelched his soggy feet, took off his socks and wrung them out. We arrived back in a bundle. The wipers ripped with the sheer volume of rain battering the windscreen. The engine sizzled and the headlights flickered. It was so symbolic of my fragile situation. I needed to weld my personality, seal out the leaks and get my engine all finely tuned up.

We had missed dinner. Totally exhausted and hungry, I said goodnight and retired to the caravan. Steve's light dimly flickered in his condensation-drenched window. The sickly stench of stale socks intermingled with incense and dope hit the back of my throat. Maybe it was symbolic of his aura, all seething and stinking of negativity. I was beginning to wonder if he had done it on purpose, as a sign of indignation now that our friendship was in doubt. I peeled off my sticky, damp clothes and swooned into a deep, soothing slumber.

CHAPTER 34

I woke up to a lonely, freezing caravan. Steve had stolen out in the early hours for his ritual encounter with the teapot. My breath bellowed hot gusts into the icy air and my body crystallised as I swished away my freeze-dried bedclothes. My tingling feet magnetically attracted my sodden, threadbare slippers, hiding under the bed. I creaked over and wiped my warm hand over the frosted window. God, it was so cold, the ice caked the inside as well as the outside. My breath blasted burning holes in the glazed, intricate patterns of divinity. The warming rays of the sun glinted sheepishly through the gaps, blinding my sleepy slits and defrosting my thoughts.

'Chris? Are you in there?'

'What's all the racket? Who's there?'

'It's me, Roy. Quick, open the door, it's bloody freezing out here.' A bolt of glorious, golden light beamed in as tongues of warm and cold air jousted for supremacy in the ethers.

'Shut the door. What's so important that it can't wait for later?'

'I'm so sorry Chris. I'm so sorry; I betrayed you, I betrayed you,' he cried and fell to his knees, begging for forgiveness.

'Roy, what the fuck are you on about man? Pull yourself together. What are you sorry about; tell me?'

'It's a horrible nightmare. All of it is?' He was delirious.

'What nightmare? Roy, speak to me. Loosen up and calm down. What's happened?'

He eased up as beads of sweat trickled down his nerve etched, pale face.

'I was there, Chris!'

'Where? Where were you? You're still talking gibberish.'

'I felt as if I was a prisoner, but I was in a vast, ornate gilt chamber. Its opulence was reminiscent of a king's palace. I was aware of being held against my will. Guards watched over me restricting my movement, but the environment I was in was familiar to me! I was then swished around in morbid sea of inconsistent dream visions, before waking up soaked in sweat and trembling with fear.'

'What's all this gibberish Roy. Calm down; pull yourself together. It's all right now. Tell me what happened.' I cradled him in my arms while he unfolded his aura and proceeded to share his experience with me.

'I noted my soul's purpose astrological aspect in my diary, before I dozed off. I didn't think I'd get anything back, not that quick. Suddenly my consciousness was thrust into a feeble, decrepit body. I felt his anguish, despair and sorrow, but somehow an overwhelming sense of pride and authority oozed from him. His garments were made of the finest silks and embroidered in gold braid, frills and baubles. He was like a caged lion, strutting to and fro in his auspicious cell. Haunting echoes and chilling cries from the square below flooded his ears, as he awaited his fate. Then I was flashed back to a scene where he's in full regalia with his sword raised in his right hand.

'God, he's a king! He must be a king! I thought, as he was about to knight one of his most trusted subjects.

'Arise, Sir Thomas Wentworth, Earl of Strafford,' he said. 'May the good Lord grant you a long life in the service of my crown and the realm of England.'

Roy paused for a moment and looked at me with such anguish in his eyes. 'Chris, it was you! You were The Earl of Strafford, weren't you?' he shouted in a tortured wail. 'Tell me it's not true. It's just a bad dream, isn't it? Tell me.'

'Roy yes, you're right; I was Strafford in a past life. It's true! It's true! Remember when you found me in a bundle yesterday, by that gruesome execution spot?'

'I remember. You were in a terrible state, all seized up and in shock.'

'Well, I had past life recall there. I had a vision of King Charles signing Strafford's Bill of Attainder, his death certificate. Roy it was you; you were Charles the 1st in a past life. I also had a meditation experience of an audience with the king. I was dressed in royalist garments. The words *The Roi is here! The Roi is here!* Blasted out from the majestic awe of a glorious, golden aura. I was puzzled about the words, but now it's all clear. Roi is the French word for king. Your name is Roy, isn't it?'

'Bloody hell, I can't believe it. There must be some mistake.'

'Calm down, Roy there's no mistake. I wasn't sure myself, but you have confirmed it. You were Charles the 1st, there's no doubt in my mind.'

Roy's eyes were all glazed and his consciousness was in no man's land.

'It's all so vague and confusing. I felt his strong presence overwhelm me. I was walking in a vast park, casually taking in the crisp, early morning air. It was a bleak and chilly day. Then, in an instant I was being marched out, surrounded by foot guards on either side as drums thumped and flags fluttered in an icy, ill-fated wind. In a flash, I'm walking out onto a high, wooden scaffold, drenched in black, funereal drapes. The dreaded blood-saturated, the executioner's block and axe jutted out centre stage, like the last tooth-stump in a death-decaying jaw. The multitude below swayed in adulation of me, cursing the injustice served by the rogue parliament. They prayed for mercy and cried for my redemption. With great dignity, I calmly asked the executioner to raise the block, before pulling off my cloak and Order of St. George. With my eyes staring skywards and hands raised, I placed my royal head to rest on the cold, stark block, awaiting the heavy, bone- crushing blade to sever my neck from my shoulders. Do you know what my last thoughts were, just as that awesome axe, crushed my spinal cords sending excruciating pain, riveting through my wretched frame?'

'What were they Roy?'

' I offered my soul to God's will and prayed for forgiveness for the great injustice thrust upon you, the Earl Strafford, my loyal servant.' He was trembling all over and on his knees he shouted, 'Chris, I'll make it up to you, I will, I will. I'll do anything you ask of me. I'm indebted to you. Please release me from my anguish, please.'

'Roy I forgive you, if it makes you feel better; but you're not directly responsible for events of the personality of Charles the 1st. You were not his personality; you only shared the same soul. Granted, you will still have memories of some of his traits, idiosyncrasies and ideas. You will have to balance out the karma of that life now. That's why we've been thrust together in this life. Bloody hell, DB must have known of our link; he wanted you to accompany me to London. It was all somehow set up. He wanted us to meet and unravel our karmic link.'

'Chris, Chris, what do I do now, I'm scared shitless.'

'I suggest you note your experience in your diary and analyse the feedback. Research his life and the Civil War period. You may even uncover more connections. That's how it works you know. Don't tell anyone of our link. I'm not sure why DB thrust us together, but there must be underlying reason for it I'm sure.

'Thanks for the confirmation. To think it surfaced just because I posited my Soul's Purpose aspect from my chart. It's so uncanny this astrology.'

'Roy, nothing is unbelievable in this place; everything is miraculous and for a deep reason. Hey, have you seen any of the boys yet?'

'I heard their voices in the dining room. They are having breakfast.'

'That's my next task. I need to get to the bottom of this conspiracy. You take some time out; I'll tell DB you're resting today.'

'Thanks Chris, I'll be in my room if you need me.'

'I'd rather not involve you, not just yet. I need to have it out with Stellios. I wonder what he's up to?'

'Be careful, Chris. They're all after your blood, I can sense it.'

'I'll be fine really; it's Strafford against the mob, only I won't make the same mistakes again. I've learned from his disastrous relationships.'

Roy disappeared into the early morning mist and left me to plan my strategy. I needed to get to Stellios first; he was the key to this mounting insurrection. I threw some clothes on and waded through the morning fog. It mirrored my predicament completely. I was in deep confusion. My thoughts collided against monstrous mists in my mind as I trudged to the back door. They're not going anywhere in this weather, I murmured. The conspiring mob was in the kitchen plotting amongst themselves. I sensed the stench of their seething auras as I popped my head around the door.

'Anyone for a cuppa?' Silence reigned and I was completely ignored. I felt a surge of rage in my belly as I poured myself a cup of tea. They were huddled around the log furnace with their evil thoughts.

One by one, Steve, Lance and Jeremy left their seats, leaving Stellios, perched by the blaze, warming up for an attack.

'How was your trip into London? What's it like to be a top, lap dog now?' He didn't waste any time throwing down the gauntlet. He wanted me to respond in anger and rage. I waited for a few moments, the atmosphere was charged to explosive levels. It just needed one tiny spark to ignite it.

'Stellios, do you remember the early days in Brighton, the plotting, backstabbing and blackmail? Do you recall our promise to each other? What's changed? What's so different now?'

He sat in deep hesitant thought, measuring his retaliation.

'You've changed. You're one of them now, you've betrayed us. We put you where you are. Now you've kicked us in the teeth.'

'Come on, you knew were I was heading. You all knew I would win entry into the inner circle. Stellios, you're almost there yourself. What have I done wrong, tell me? I've slaved for months, in exile, fly-posting and manning exhibitions. I've endured Linda and Dick's taunts; I've been humbled by DB's tests and had to swallow humble pie, by following Barry and John's orders.'

'That's just it. You'll become one of them, all hot air and bullshit. It stinks of double standards. We're not happy at all. Steve is thinking of leaving, Jeremy is just clinging on and Lance has sunk into a deep depression.'

'Don't blame me for their shit Stellios. *Each one is his absolute lawgiver, the decreer of his glory and gloom, the dispenser of his life, his rewards and his punishments.*'

'Don't get all-philosophical now. I'm so unhappy, but I can't leave here; they've still got me by the balls.'

'I said I'd help you, didn't I? I'm in a much stronger position now.'

'Maybe, but I don't trust them one bit. They're all assassins, ready to stab us in the back.'

'Talking about assassins. I had an early morning call from my beloved Elena yesterday. The bitch is blackmailing me. She wants a divorce and half my money. She's threatening to blacken my name in Cyprus by spreading gossip and lies about me. She's using it all against me. What do you know about it Stellios?'

'What do you mean? Are you blaming me for the leak? I'm no backstabber!'

'Who is it then, Lance, Dick or Linda? It's Linda isn't it? She leaked it to Elena and she's using it as a stick to beat me with.'

'Chris, I don't know where Linda got her phone number. I never gave it to her. Anyway, I thought you wanted rid of her?'

'Yes, but not with me over a barrel and on her terms. After all, I didn't do the dirty on her, did I?'

'Christ, just give her the divorce, good riddance; get her out of your life for good. She'll plague you forever otherwise; this is your chance.

'You're right, but I'll have to give it some thought. That's better, you're back to the Stellios I know and trust. Get the boys together and tell them the change is for the better. I know you can bring them round.'

'I'll try, but I think Steve's definitely decided to leave; he's had enough. He wants to get Pete's book published and there's no chance of doing it whilst he's in here.'

'It's his freewill. Nobody can dictate our lives but us. He's a good kid, I hope he finds success out there and doesn't end up like poor Pete.'

'I'll really miss him if he goes. He's been my confidante here for years; I'll be lost without him.'

'You'll be just fine, I have confidence in you.'

I managed to offset the factions in the outer circle, although Steve did eventually leave us. Over the next few months Jeremy shot off with a Scandinavian traveller. She hooked him at a New Age exhibition. I don't think he had ever been with a woman; he was so taciturn and naive. She sorted his lower nature out all right: sex, drugs and rock'n'roll! I heard that he married her, but it didn't last. He was too much of a free spirit to be tied down for long. He did pop in once or twice whilst on his travels, just to keep in touch.

Steve wandered into a big black hole of obscurity, never to be seen again. Stellios and I never really go it back together again, but he still lingered on. Something was brewing with him; I couldn't quite put my finger on it. I confided in him, but never in personal matters, nor anything spiritual. Roy became my closest ally and confidante. I trusted him implicitly. Our bond was so close, the group used to tease us with homosexual innuendo.

Claire managed to placate Linda. She was my shoulder to lie on when I was feeling lonely and lost. Her sweet bosom was so comforting when I ached for female company. There was nothing sexual about it, just two souls in the thick of psychological and spiritual warfare sharing deep, heart-rending feelings.

I patched up my differences with Dick too. We became friends in the end. I took control of the business, which meant book distribution, sales and development. That was his baby, but we carried it together. We both knew it was more important than filmmaking. He used me to get to Barry, John and the rest of the psuedo-film producers and directors.

My alliance with DB grew stronger. Barry and John hovered in the distance, just close enough for comfort, but not too close to interfere in my work. I had successfully managed to bridge both the inner and outer circles together. There were minor incidents, but they were few and far between.

I had become an adept in esoteric astrology, even taking the odd class and lecture. My esoteric understanding had multiplied a thousand-fold since the early days of pitiful mutterings and blocked expression. I had gone through two dairies of spiritual writings. My dream-life was phenomenal, brimming with energy and meaning. I had perfected a meditation plan, which began to stir the divine, fiery energy from within. My previous life research was throwing up all sorts of connections, some very obscure, but some uncannily clear.

I eventually conceded to Elena's demands, but only after months of threats and counter threats. She got her way in the end and I got her completely out of my hair. Something still bugged me about the whole sordid affair. I knew it was not over; there were going to be repercussions; I felt it in my bones.

Four new recruits filtered in. James Plaskett was a British chess Grand Master and he was a weird one at that! He was all intellectual bullshit and kept running his life as if it were a chess game. It was all black or white! I didn't think he had a spiritual brain-cell in his cranium, what with all that strategy mangling his mind! I couldn't fathom out why he had decided to come here and live in squalor. We attracted all sorts, but Plaskett wasn't your run of the mill looser.

Pete Woods was a troubled soul, wandering in and out of society, searching for his ultimate path. You could hardly determine his expressions because he was always hiding behind his tufted, sprouts of facial hair. I never trusted bearded guys, I was sure they were concealing something sordid under all that fluff. He walked around as if the world was perched on his shoulders. He'd had a history of depression, which served him well in his profession. He was a psychiatric nurse. I don't know who needed more help, him or the patients he was nursing!

Then there was a middle-aged, Irish guy called Paddy Cleary. Now what was he on our doorstep for? He was a strange kettle of fish. He had gone from relationship to relationship, home to home, group to group. He hadn't found his niche yet. He was still plagued by his strict, Catholic upbringing and desperately clung onto his ingrained religious dogma. It was a loadstone, which plunged him into the depths of conscience and despair, every time he tried to reach for the spiritual realm. There was something menacing in his eyes. They were so black and penetrating. I felt so uneasy in his presence. It was as if he knew me intimately!

Last but not least, there was Andrew Griffiths. He was a highly-strung, young lad from the Welsh valleys with a lot of shit to sort out. God he was built like a Whippet and bounced along all over the place, in spurts of erratic, nervous energy. He was a time bomb ready to explode at any time. He had the deepest, soulful eyes I had ever experienced. Now he was spiritual, but he could not hold his shit together long enough. He was in constant inner conflict. One can only imagine what wars raged in his head. Guess what? He moved in with me in Steve's pokey little hole. That was all I needed, a neurotic puppy to look after.

CHAPTER 35

I woke up one morning shouting, screaming and holding my chest. It was on fire; my heart was racing, lungs blowing and my nerves spasmed. It felt like I had a gaping, bloody wound.

Bang! Bang...Bang! Bang! Oh no! Oh no! I was catapulted back to a terrifying waking dream.

> *27th Aug. 1984, 8.15am.*
>
> *I see a dangerous looking man wearing a black balaclava running towards our car. I am driving and DB is in the passenger seat. We are stuck in heavy traffic. Suddenly he pulls out a gun. He's going to shoot DB! I jump out just in time; grab the gun before he can fire. We fall to the ground, fighting, kicking and punching.*
>
> *Bang! Bang! The gun blasts a couple of rounds while we are rolling round. The fight eases to an eerie halt; one of us has been shot. I could see the glint in his eyes. He was possessed. I knew those deep, penetrating eyes. I felt a gush of warm, vermilion, blood ooze from me. Oh my God I'd been shot.*
>
> *He tried to push me off, but as I turned I grasped a hold of his balaclava and yanked at it. He turned just before wrenching free.*
>
> *'Bastard!' I shouted. I just caught a tiny glimpse of his murderous face, but not enough to identify him. I slouched forward, nursing a gushing chest wound, tears of anguish and disbelief flooding down my face.*

'Why didn't I see his cowardly face?' I shouted and thumping the dust with my fist, the life force began to drain out of me. DB came running to my rescue. He knew what to do, of course he did, he was a doctor.

'Didn't I tell you to watch your back? Didn't I warn you,' he shouted as he sutured my wounds.

I felt physically sick; the whole experience gored me through. The ugly scene left a foul stench in my mouth. Some one has it in for me, I thought. It could be anyone, but why? I had patched up my differences within the group. I had no quarrels with anyone at that moment.

Then another thought entered my mind. He was going to assassinate DB and I got the brunt of it. I saved him; I was his loyal bodyguard. I needed to keep my wits about me. Maybe it was one of the new recruits? It wasn't from the inner circle, that I was relatively sure about. I had to get to know the new blood. There was a traitor amongst them and I had to flush him out.

As I dressed I heard Andrew muttering something. I could also hear him pacing up and down, like a caged animal. It was doing my head in.

'For fuck sake boyo, give it a rest. You'll wear a trench in the carpet if you continue your schizoid behaviour.'

'Grrr.... grrr... grrr...grrr...' he grinded, in a growling attack. 'Fuck off! Mind your own business, you 'greasy bubble'.

I could have grabbed him by the jugular, but I felt sorry for him. Something more terrifying had him by the balls. He was battling his *Dweller* and it was beating the shit out of him. I called him Griff from that day on. I was sure he wasn't the assassin. He spent most of his time assassinating himself. Poor Griff, he was so self destructive, but he had tons of energy, when he could project it.

I met DB down at LE for our morning strategy session. We had breakfast and I was given the orders for the day. James Plaskett lived down there with him. DB always interrogated potential talent before he let them loose at Claregate. He wouldn't have me there because I was hitched with Elena. He couldn't handle her 'squirting ovaries', as he used to say. I hadn't had much to do with Plaskett. I was always busy with the mountain of Claregate business and he used to shoot off to chess championships all over Britain and even the world. He could do damage, if he wanted to. He was one to watch all right. I took the chance that morning to probe him.

'Hi, James, I've seen you around, but not really met you properly.'

'Jim, call me Jim. You're Chris, right?'

'Yes. You must lead an interesting life, what's the pull here? Haven't you got enough excitement in your chess tournaments? What are you after?' I didn't beat around the bush. I knew I had to attack him first. His mind was razor sharp.

'What do you mean? What are you doing here? Haven't you got better things to do, rather than duck and dive in this commune? What are you running away from?' Check! He was just as I had anticipated; question after question, followed by an attack.

'Checkmate James, I'm no match for you on an intellectual level, but I can beat the shit out of you on any other level.' I laid down the gauntlet. He knew I wasn't a pushover. He hesitated for a minute and before he replied, DB interjected.

'James, don't test your metal on him, he's hard as nails man. You've got no chance. He'll swallow you whole and spit you out in little bits.'

We all burst into laughter, dispelling the tension and acknowledging each other's strengths.

'Believe me James, you got off lightly. He's a bulldog, this one. He doesn't give in, ever! I'd recommend you withdraw gracefully, before your honour is dragged through the muck.'

'DB, it's all right. I'm only playing with him. James, you're a bit fucking weird, but aren't we all around here. You're all right, as long as you don't cross me. I'll have your balls if you do.' He didn't know if I was serious or not, but he got the message. He was a strong character, but I sensed he was harmless. Anyway, if he were a threat, DB would have flushed him out by now.

'So where are you off to next then James?' I said just to irritate him.

'Jim, Jim's the name. Can't you get it in your thick...'

'James, don't fuck with me. Listen, I'm only testing you, don't get all touchy and defensive.' There was a moment's silence. I had him stumped already. He didn't know how to take me. I had messed up his logical thinking process with my crude, bombastic approach.

'Chris, please call me Jim,' he pleaded.

'Alright Jim, where are you competing next?'

'Actually, I'm practising for the English Championship in Hastings. It's an annual event held every autumn. Hopefully I can raise my ranking. I've been so unlucky there you know. Every time I play there I seem to fall ill. I don't know why. I arrive fighting fit and the day after, I fade away with bad health. I even ended up in A&E once. I was rushed in with a ruptured appendix. It almost killed me.'

'That's really weird. Have you got to the bottom of it? Is it a nerve thing?'

'I really don't know. I'm a diabetic, so that may have something to do with it. I'll have to ask DB.'

'Jim, I'm off into battle, the bank needs covering. I've got bills to pay, old projects, new projects and I've got to keep them all going.'

'Good luck Chrissy babe; I'm glad I'm not in your shoes.'

'Hey, stop fucking around, Chris is the name.'

'Ha, ha! Just testing,' he laughed.

He was all right, a breath of fresh air around the place. I could take the piss out of him and he equally riled me. He was a professional. He didn't hang around feeding off other people's auras like most of the boys. He had his shit together.

'Right, I'm going back. Do you want me for anything DB?' He trudged downstairs with his threadbare red dressing gown on.

'Chris, come into the lounge for a minute. Lance, I need privacy for a while. Jim, go on, piss off and scratch your balls somewhere else. Go on hop it, I need to speak to Chris in private.' The door thudded behind me and he sat in his old rocking chair.

'I've got news for you.'

'What news? Is it bad or good?'

'That was Stellios on the blower. He's decided to piss off out of here. He couldn't face you. I suppose his conscience got the better of him.'

I was in shock. My face drooped and my eyes glazed over.

'Bloody hell, that was out of the blue. I had a good heart to heart with him not so long ago. I can't understand why he's left us. Maybe he's missed Steve. He was very close to him.'

'He was a bad influence in the group, good riddance. He's off back home to lick his wounds. Let him get a job in catering. He won't last long and that'll be that. He won't get a work permit over here now. I was working on it for him, but that's the end of that.'

'No problem DB, There is plenty of new blood out there to replace him, Roy's showing a lot of promise.'

'Yes, I knew you'd hit it off with him. You've got close karma to work out.'

'You knew all along, didn't you? You knew he was Charles the 1st.'

'Chris, if it's beneficial to both parties to have knowledge of past-life karma, I'll help it to be revealed. I only threw you together; you both unravelled the pieces and finished the puzzle.

'Anyway forget about Stellios. He was tumbleweed, a hanger on. He won't amount to much out there. Now Roy, he'll need breaking in you know. I don't think he's ready, do you?'

'Well almost,' I answered. 'I'll take him under my wing, just to sound him out. Listen, DB; there's something else. I've been having strange energy transfers during my meditations. I'm buzzing all over. I come out almost on fire, it's amazing.'

'Chris, I told you to be ready to wield it, didn't I? You're obviously prepared for it now.'

'Prepared for what? Tell me?'

'You'll know soon enough. Patience, persistence and endurance, your time will come. Ah… *the burning ground, the burning ground!* Go on, off with you, you've wasted half an hour of my valuable meditation time.'

I strolled to my beat-up limo and putted and puffed up the lane to Claregate. *The burning ground?* It had been ringing in my ears for ages. I had flicked through his book *Diary of an Alchemist*, but it was way over my head. I knew I was going through a spiritual transformation. I could feel it in my bones.

Claregate was like a morgue when I arrived there. Stellios hasty departure had left a gaping vacuum and the void needed to be filled. Would Roy be up for the challenge? Was someone else going to emerge? I hopped upstairs towards my office. Pete Woods appeared from the upstairs living quarters with a couple of cups in his hands. I hadn't given him any time yet. He kept well away from me and I was always rushing here and there.

'Pete, Pete Woods, come in, I want a word with you.'

'Me, now?'

'Yes. Who do you think I meant? God forbid, there's another one like you around.'

'Oh, Okay. I'll just take these downstairs, I'll only be a few minutes.'

'You better be quick. I've got loads to do, so don't piss around. Oh, you might as well bring me up a cuppa whilst you're down there.' He nodded and plodded downstairs with his aura around his ankles. He'd been ducking and diving for weeks, doing the odd job here and there. Now that he'd been 'called up', he was shitting himself.

'Come in, come in, and stop dithering like an old monk. Put the cup down here.' He was a nervous wreck, fidgeting all over the seat. His sweaty, little hands twitched nervously and he splashed tea all over himself.

'Sorry. I'm so nervous,' he panted as I seared his face with a laser glance. He was a small, sickly, pale lad. His mousy hair and a full beard conspired to veil his piercing, beady little blue eyes. I looked right into them, penetrating his soul. I saw something, something overpowering. The zinging buzzed in my head as *his* vibrations flooded me.

'Ahh...ahh...' A bolt of light flashed through me, knocking me off my seat. As I lay on my back, he dashed over, propped me up against the table and raised my legs in the air.

'Chris! You all right? Don't worry, I'm a nurse, you've just blacked out. You'll be fine in a minute.'

' Ahh...ahh! I was blasted into another dimension.

I was kneeling in attendance of a holy presence, eyes closed in prayer. All I could feel was a golden, heavenly aura bathe my whole being. As I opened my eyes, I saw the back of an Archbishop or Cardinal facing his altar. I was in royalist tunics. It was a snippet of the Strafford life.

'Arise, Sir Thomas. With this Holy Communion, I bless thee with the blood and body of Christ, Our Lord.'

I opened my mouth, gazing intensely into his open face.

'Oh, my God!' I shouted and lashing out, kicking Pete into the cabinet.

'Chris! Fucking hell. What's the matter? What is it?' He rushed back to my side again.

'No. Don't come any closer. Leave me alone. Please, leave me alone.'

He backed off, slowly retracing his steps until I had calmed down. I was still stunned and in a bundle on the carpet.

'It's okay Chris; you just had a bad turn. Do you suffer from epilepsy? You kept shouting a name or something. I might be mistaken, but it sounded like, *my Lord, my Lord.*

I managed to clamber up to my chair and balance myself. I felt so weak, frail and lifeless. I lifted my hanging head and glanced once more at him.

'Oh my God, it can't be. It can't be,' I murmured.

'Can't be what? What are you trying to say Chris? I think you need to lie down for a few minutes. You still look pale. I'll get you a hot, sugary tea, that should sort you out.'

Thank God he went.

'It was him! I can't believe it! It can't be surely to God!' I muttered whilst centring myself. 'Jesus Christ, he was dressed in those ecclesiastical robes. He gave me communion. I saw his bearded face, his eyes, yes they were unmistakable!' He had come back as well! By all accounts he was Strafford's main ally in the Realm. He was also his closest friend and confidante! He was Archbishop Laud, Charles the First's other main advisor. 'It wasn't possible, I must be mistaken, it can't be.' I said whilst the door eased open revealing Pete's reassuring face and nurse's aura.

'There you are, you look a thousand times better already. Your colour is starting to flush your cheeks.'

'Thanks Pete, At least you've brought some useful skills with you. Most of them here are unskilled, undisciplined and hangers on.'

'I've nursed for ages. I'm a qualified psychiatric nurse, but I hate the clinical set up. It's all drugs, drugs and drugs. That's why I turned my back on it. I love the existential psychology of Maslow, Krankl and Jung. I met DB at one off his talks and loved his pragmatic approach.'

'Pete, you're a handy man to have around here. What are your plans?' As usual, I probed him intensely.

'Well, I'm really interested in esoteric astrology and esoteric healing, especially how DB's co-related the astrology with the Bach Flower Remedies. I love his work on bio magnetic fields. Have you read how he used to treat patients with electro-magnetic pulses? It's revolutionary and it really works.'

'It's ground breaking teaching, all right, but I'm not into the healing aspect of it. What about Claregate? Are you going to fall by the wayside after the first hurdle? It's a hard life in here. You've got to have balls to survive the onslaught.'

'What do you mean? I'm dedicated to the path. I'm loyal and trustworthy, but the onslaught, what does that mean?'

I sighed for a moment. Here we go again, another dithering, green tumbleweed destined to battle with is *Dweller.* He was in for a hard time.

'Pete, I hope to God you succeed in subduing your negative astral shit. You know, the *Dweller on the Threshold of Consciousness?* If you can't handle its vile energies, you'll be no good to anyone. It's a fucking living nightmare for months. How long have you been here? Three, four weeks?'

'About six weeks and it's been hell. I don't know what it is; I've got no major attachments, no domestic ties, but I feel as if I'm being consumed with negativity all the time.'

'Tell me about it. All I can say is it gets better, but you need to let go of everything to ultimately find your true self. That's the prize, finding *the pearl lost in the mud of matter.*'

'I'm quite persistent, detached and analytical. I'm Virgo with Leo rising.'

'You'll need all the help you can get, believe me. But, you'll have to deal with your hang-ups. Keep your diary religiously, practice meditation, study the wisdom and work hard at your service to humanity. That's the secret of fulfilment and spiritual development here.'

'Chris, I'll try my best. I really will.'

'And don't get dragged into inter-community factions either. Steer well away from Linda's poisoning fangs. Be wary of Lance too. He's a laugh, but he's always leaking secrets. Keep yourself to yourself and you'll be alright.'

'Thanks for the advice. I think I'll stick close to you, if you don't mind?'

'Pete, my daily schedule is daunting. Sometimes I do 16-hour days. But I'm happy to offload some of my responsibilities to anyone who can handle them. I don't suffer fools gladly though. I'm a perfectionist and really thorough in everything I do.'

'I'd be happy to help out in any way possible.'

'Okay, but don't let me down. I won't tolerate excuses.'

'Chris, why don't you go for a rest, you need to recuperate after your ordeal. Is there anything you want me to do meanwhile?'

'I think I'll go for a quick meditation. I'm sure I'll be back to normal soon. No Pete, you can't deal with anything yet, but thanks for offering.'

He retreated upstairs, leaving me to my fevered mind. I could not reconcile my thoughts. I was still in awe of the experience. I needed to brood on it for a while. I certainly couldn't tell him who he was, not just yet. He had to earn his spurs like the rest of us.

I plodded downstairs and out to the gardens. The late summer's multi-coloured blooms flashed at me as they swayed in the warm gentle Zephyr. Reds, pinks and golden yellows merged with brilliant whites, blues and violets. What a masterful pallet of textures, scents and colours they were. Delicate butterflies dallied in on spurts of breeze, pirouetting to the delight of exposed, floral genitalia. Sparrows zigzagged in and out in never-ending, aerial dogfights. Two graceful turtledoves glided on the jet-steam and settled on the boughs of an old, wise oak. There he was; Orion, the Solar Architect and artistic genius, bathing all of his creations with divine love-wisdom and flooding them with life and fiery energy. Dylan Thomas's poem danced gaily into my mind as I waded into the grassy, verdant lawn.

> *The force that through the green fuse drives the flower, drives my green age;*
> *That blasts the roots of trees, is my destroyer.*
> *And I am dumb to tell the crooked rose my youth is bent by the same wintry fever.*

> *The force that drives the water through the rocks, drives my blood red; that dries the mouthing streams, turns mine to wax.*
> *And I am dumb to mouth unto my veins, how at the mountain spring the same mouth sucks.*

> *The hand that whirls the water in the pool stirs the quicksand; that ropes the blowing wind, hauls my shroud sail.*
> *And I am dumb to tell the hanging man, how of my clay is made the hangman's line.*

> *The lips of time leech to the fountainhead; love drips and gathers, but the fallen blood shall calm her sores.*
> *I am dumb to tell a weather's wind, how time has ticked a heaven round the stars.*

> *And I am dumb to tell the lover's tomb*
> *how at my sheet goes the same crooked worm.*

It rang in my ears, conjuring up Stellios sudden clandestine escape and Elena's warm embrace. She still tickled me inside, although she hurt me so much. I eased into the caravan. God it was a furnace in the mid-morning sun, even with all the windows open. I stripped and slid into my meditation.

CHAPTER 36

'Oh my God! No, no! DB, don't, don't...Ahhh!!' I jumped up, swiping fading chimeras in the ethers. My lungs exploded on impact with the sizzling air. My heart pumped its blasting beat in my head and through my convulsing frame.

> *27th Aug, 11.45 am. Meditation vision.*
>
> *DB's standing behind me as I am sitting in my favourite meditation chair. He squeezes me carefully and lovingly around my shoulders, relieving me of tension. I shrug him off, but he resumes his embrace. I feel his face and breathing close to me; God he's going to make a pass at me, he's going to kiss me! Oh, my God! Zap. Zap!*
>
> *He gently placed his thumb on my forehead and I was flooded with an intense flash of light that penetrated my whole being.*
>
> *'Yes Chris, yes!* **The burning ground, the burning ground**, *you're ready for* **the burning ground**,' *he muttered, nodding his head.*

What was happening to me? Why did he come to me? What did he do to me? I felt like I had been tampered with. That light, that energy, what was that all about? My mind haemorrhaged and climaxed during the experience. As I lay there, in a relaxed repose, my consciousness swayed into esolepsy. I was fading into an altered state; I sensed it.

'Wao! Wao! Ahh!

I shuddered as a fiery force blasted through me, sending my body into spasms. The force was so intense my head and feet met each other in mid air. It went as it came, suddenly and abruptly, leaving me in a mangled heap on the bed. My insides hurt so much it felt like I had been kicked and punched. My lungs, heart and head were on fire. The whole experience lasted only a few seconds. It was awesome.

I could not move; my body was in catalepsy. I dare not stir, I didn't know if I survived the experience. Was I in the astral? Had I passed over? Was I still on the earth plane? I built up the courage and pinched myself.

'I am still alive and still Chris Kasparis,' I shouted, and then painfully rose from my fiery bed. It was the divine fire, I was bathed in light; DB prepared me for the event. I had my first super conscious experience. I had visited *the burning ground*! Of that I was sure, but why me? What had I to offer? What was my destiny? What was going to happen next? Would the experience come back? I trembled at the prospect of another baptism of fire. I was shit scared; this was not normal, I must be a freak. Nobody else in the group has had anything similar. I wanted it to come back; it must come back. Maybe it was a 'one off', a figment of my fertile imagination. Yes, I faked it all, all of it! But it wasn't a dream or just a vision; it was more. It felt I was in the presence of God.

'My God is an all consuming fire' blasted out from the pit of my mind. Yes, that's exactly what it felt like; I was being consumed from within.

'Is that the time? Bloody hell, my duties, the bills, the bank,' I shouted glancing at my clock. I threw my rags back on and bolted into battle fortified with the charged energy of the gods. I knew then I was special, but for what? All I knew was that I had to serve the path, the land and the Lord in his divine plan for the planet.

I managed to race through my duties with great power and renewed enthusiasm. There was a vast shift in energies. The new blood was flooding the group's aura, but all was not right. My emerging lieutenants were still not at ease with the task ahead, but I could not expect miracles.

My consciousness had expanded a thousand fold since the experience. I savoured it for a couple of weeks, but I needed to share it with someone. I couldn't tell anyone here, I knew they would shoot me down with accusations of glamour and delusions of grandeur.

One afternoon, after I despatched my duties, I decided to seek an audience with DB. He was the only person I knew on the planet who would understand and not ridicule me. He was taking in the mid-afternoon sun on the forecourt. He stood in the flowerbeds in his gaudy, threadbare red gown that was almost see-through in places. It was quite embarrassing seeing his buttocks fade through the meshwork of frayed strands.

'Oh, my babies, my babies, nobody cares. Call yourselves spiritual you lot! Look at them, there're all gasping for water. How would you like it, if you were deprived of food and water? Lance, Lance, get out here now you dithering donkey. Bring the hose; I want all the beds drenched or I'll have your guts for garters,' he blasted.

'It's all right, it all right, uncle DB is here, it's all right,' he mumbled, conversing with the plants. He bent down on his haunches and his robe rode up over his buttocks. Now I knew why they called him '*Little Elephant*'. What a sight.

'DB, can I see you for a minute? I know you're busy, but I won't take up a lot of your time.'

'Chris, is that you? Hi, strawberry bollocks, what's up? Bad news? Is it the bank?' God, he was such a laugh sometimes, with his dry Caprcornian humour. Lance plodded up struggling with the hose as if it was a writhing cobra.

'Fuck sake, Lance, give it here, the bloody thing doesn't bite. Go and turn the water on. Well, what do you want? Come to talk about your fire experience, have you? You've sat on it long enough; I had expected you sooner.'

'All these mornings you knew of my experience and you didn't let on? You sensed something was bothering me, didn't you?'

'Of course I did, but I can't interfere with your shit. I can only do so if the *Hierarchy* instruct me, or you approach me.'

The *Hierarchy?* What do you mean?'

'You should know, if you've studied the teachings. The Masters, the Great White Brotherhood, Lord over the whole planet and solar system. *The Hierarchy* are the divine guardians of the Plan. They hold the Knowledge; they channel *the fire* and bathe us with love and light.

> *From the Point of Light*
> *Within the Mind of God,*
> *Let Light stream through*
> *to the minds of men,*
> *Let Light descend on Earth.*
>
> *From the point of Love*
> *Within the Heart of God,*
> *Let love stream forth*
> *Into the hearts of men,*
> *May Christ return to Earth.*
>
> *From the Centre where*
> *The Will of God is known*
> *Let purpose guide*
> *The little wills of men,*
> *The purpose which the Masters*
> *Know and Serve.*
>
> *From the Centre which we call*
> *The Race of Men,*
> *Let the Plan of*
> *Light and Love work out,*
> *And may it seal the door*
> *Where evil dwells,*
> *Let Light and Love and Power*
> *Restore the plan on Earth.*

You know *The Great Invocation?*'

'Of course I do DB, but what does my experience mean? You were there weren't you?'

'I was instructed to prepare you for the event, which I did. They, *The Lords of the Flame*, bathed you in fire. You've tasted a little of what's to come.'

'What do you mean? There will be more?'

'More, that's just a trickle; they wanted to see if your body was ready for it. They tell me you're strong and prepared enough to withstand *The Rod of Initiation*, the real *Burning Ground.*'

'It was awesome; it came out of the blue, just like a bolt of lightning. I was baptised from head to foot. I was fucked up for minutes afterwards; I couldn't move, my body was in catalepsy.'

'Chris, I know. I was there with you; I nursed you through the whole process. Oh, it brings back distant memories of my first stirrings of *Fohat*, the Divine Fire of *Samadhi*.'

'Is it Kundalini, DB, is it?'

'Calm down, calm down, I know what it feels like. You're literally on fire aren't you?'

'Yes, it's been with me every hour, every minute, every second of the day since. Sometimes in meditation it rages into a furnace, but thank God, it eases into a trickle, with tickling sensations charging my whole being.'

'Wonderful Chris, to harness and use it continuously. You'll have to dedicate your life to the service of the Masters. There will be no second chances; it's now or never. Dedication, devotion, sacrifice, loyalty, endurance and trust are the pre-requisite qualities required for adept-ship. Are you willing to take the challenge? Are you strong enough to carry the Torch of Light into the darkness of materialism?'

'DB, I don't know. It's happening too quickly, all too quickly.'

'You never answered my question, is it *Kundalini Fire?*'

'It may be the first stirring of the *Coiled Serpent*, hidden in the core of the root chakra. She is unleashed in an act of attraction when her partner *Solar Fire* is thrust into the consciousness through *the Crown Chakra*. The union of both creates an electric orgasm a million times more ecstatic than a human one.

'I'm scared, I have my doubts; what if I'm not ready? What if it all goes wrong? Will I be physically, emotionally and mentally scarred for life?'

'Chris, it will only come to those who wielded the fire in past lives. But, having said that, anyone can win the right to access the *Divine Fohat* through sheer effort, focus and dedication. Don't worry, it will happen naturally, when the time is right. Just persist with your disciplines, you're right on track.'

'I don't know. Will I have the courage, the staying power to retain and endure it? I really don't know!'

'Chris, it's in the lap of the gods now, don't worry, just relax and let it happen. Believe me, you'll come through just fine. Don't panic, you've been prepared for the event. Now off with you, get those new recruits in order. I'm planning a major assault on the festival circuit. You must be ready now to start astrology interpretation and lecturing? Why don't you start at the next festival; I think we've got one soon in Birmingham.'

'Yes DB, I'm ready all right. I just wanted you to give me the all clear.'

'Chris, **the Kingdom of Heaven is taken by storm.** Remember that.' He turned towards the house. 'Lance, turn the water off; I'm moving the hose to that flowerbed over there. I hate waste, hate it. Oh, before you go, I want you to come to the main building. I need you there; I think there's a traitor in the ranks. Move into Stellios old room. I'd gut it out first if I were you, he was a messy slob.'

'All right, I feel the same way. Something's brewing, but I can't put my finger on it. See you at dinner.'

I hopped into my banger and putted back to Claregate. I was glad to being ridding myself of Griff. I was beginning to feel his rancid aura seethe closer to me. I needed a new environment and a fresh start now that Stellios had deserted me and I was on my own. I trotted into Pete's broad, bushy face.

'Pete, what are you doing? Anything important?'

'No not really, I'm doing some book collating for Dick. He's printed the new *Jewel in the Lotus*. It looks fantastic.'

'I'm moving out of the caravan into Stellios old room. It's about time I put my energies into the main building. Winter's on the doorstep and I've had enough of sleeping in cold storage. Come on give me a hand.'

'Alright, I'll be out in a minute.'

'Tell you what, I'll pop up and see what state he left the room in. I bet it's a tip.'

'You might find Roy up there, he's popped up for a rest.'

I trundled upstairs and bumped into Linda coming out of the toilet. Our relationship was cool, but I could at least talk to her now. There was no more astral crap gushing from her anymore.

'Hi Linda, I'm moving into Stellios old room. Just in time before the frost starts biting again.'

'You'll have to fumigate the place.'

'Well I don't mind, I'll redecorate it.'

'Good luck; you'll need it.'

'Linda, how are the new ones settling in? What do you think of them?'

'Well, they're okay, nothing special. They'll need a lot of breaking in.'

'Is there anyone iffy? You know what I mean?'

'Iffy? What? Weird, cranky?'

'Yes, is there?'

'Chris, if they were conventional, we'd be in trouble. They're all nuts, a few pennies short of a pound. I'll keep an eye out for you.'

'Thanks Linda, you're a gem.'

Boy, she's changed her tune, I thought and I pushed my way into the room. I had to shove hard as the old carpet had snagged on the door. 'What a fucking mess! How could he live like this?' I shouted in total horror. Old socks, rags, old shoes, mouldy cups of stagnant coffee and a stained old bed stared me in the face. The stench of damp saturated the space. He had left all the windows nailed closed and old plastic sheeting peeled off them; it was a DIY trick to keep out drafts. I tore it all down and opened the creaky old frames to let in some fresh air. It took me days to make it habitable, but it was worth it. Pete and Roy gave me a hand. They were getting on just great. Little did they know that they had close past life karma together.

I thought about feeding Pete some clues, but decided against it for the moment. He had not yet earned his spurs.

The Birmingham festival was only days away. I was prepared to give my first astrological analysis and lecture and I had primed Pete and Roy to come with me. Roy was delighted; he hadn't been back to see his folks for ages.

The night before, after dinner, they helped me pack the old box van with our POS materials, books and tables. The atmosphere was great, full of enthusiasm and laughter.

'Dring, dring! Dring dring!'

'Bloody hell, who's that at this time of night?'

'Chris, it's for you. It's your stepfather, and it's urgent!' Claire shouted, popping her curler-infested head over the banister.

'Take it downstairs Chris, it's more private there.'

'Hullo Ernie, what's up? Why are you phoning so late?'

'Chris, I'm on my way to England with Elli. She's lost it all together.'

'What do you mean Ern?'

'She's had another nervous breakdown. She's lost so much weight and she's melted into a deep depression.'

'Bloody hell Ern, will she be okay? Where are you going to stay? How's Mama taken it?'

'We'll stay in Worthing with your uncle. He's got her signed on at his GP. Hopefully, he can sort her out. She's in a hell of a mess. It's that bastard, her husband. He's made her life hell and he's taken her kids away from her.'

'Is Mama okay? How can I help?'

'She's worried sick, but she feels better now we're coming back for treatment. The Cypriot doctors are useless; they haven't got a clue. Elli keeps on asking for you. I don't know why, can you help her?'

'Come up when you get time Ern. I'm not sure what I can do, but I'll try. I've got her horoscope cast, perhaps I could see what's bugging her, I don't know.'

'Mmm, well we'll see you soon. I'll call you when we arrive.'

'Okay, tell her not to worry. I'll do my best to help her. I know lots of healers and complementary therapists.'

He clicked the phone off. He didn't sound impressed. He was a Roman Catholic before he was baptised Greek Orthodox. He didn't believe in all this 'mumbo jumbo', as he called it. I had lost contact with my family over the last few years. They all thought I went mad and was brainwashed. My poor Mama couldn't even bring herself to talk about me. They all thought I was a lost soul, bound in a hellish inferno. To them astrology was the work of the devil. Meditation, even worse! They got the inferno bit right, but that was of divine origin.

What could I do for her? Why did she ask for me? It was all really strange. I hadn't spoken to her in years, but I did have her chart. I decided to submit her Soul's Purpose aspect to my higher self. Perhaps *He* will give me guidance through my dreams. I could only try.

'Right lads, see you eight o'clock sharp in the hallway, ready to go.'

'No problem, are you okay?' asked Roy.

'It's my sister Elli; she's on her way to the UK for treatment. She's had a hell of a life, breakdown after breakdown. Now she's even starving herself.'

'What sort of treatment? You can't help her can you?'

'I don't know Pete; all I can do is do a bit of subjective work on her chart and meditate on her. Maybe I can send her some absent healing, what do you think?'

'Healing? You? You don't know the first thing about healing. You said it wasn't your cup of tea, remember?'

'Yes, well, you're right, but I can visualise her in my mind's eye and focus the second ray of healing and love-wisdom, from my heart to hers. DB says if you're not sure where the damage is, focus on the heart chakra.'

'Maybe I can sit with her? I've got tons of experience in psychiatric and conventional fields of medicine.'

'Thanks Pete, but I think we'll leave it to the professionals. If I could give her spiritual support and possibly find a complementary therapist, I'm sure that would help. That's the least I can do.'

I trudged to the kitchen for a nightcap, poured a cuppa and retreated to the dining room. The last few embers of the fire glowed and sparked and I sat there reminiscing over my inner experiences.

The burning ground, the burning ground. Was I ready for it? Did I want it to happen? I had a choice in the matter. Of course I had. I could give it all up and lead a normal life. Yes, children, a mortgage, the family car, holidays, a gorgeous wife on my arm. Mmm, did I really want that again? Could I handle another rejection? All I knew was that I was lonely, extremely lonely. Elena had fucked off with that bastard; Stellios had disappeared into thin air. He was the so-called spiritual one, not me.

But the fire, yes the fire, that was unique. I had accessed it. Maybe it was all a mistake, all of it. But I was on fire from within; that was no illusion. It's all in the Wisdom Teachings, I contemplated. I nursed my cuppa as all sorts of thoughts collided in my schizoid cranium. I plodded upstairs to bed. There was no end to my fevered mind. I shook my aching head, summoning the end of my frenetic, brain bashing.

I managed to locate Elli's chart. I posited her Soul's Purpose aspect as well as her Saturn aspect. It was heavily restricted in her health area of the chart. I knew he was goading her. His crushing energies were triggering off this depressive-anorexic state she was in. I turned off my little table light and melted into a deep, soothing slumber. Thank God, my inner fires settled, like the dying embers in that glowing grate downstairs. I couldn't handle another active night, not tonight at least.

CHAPTER 37

I woke up to a dream that I struggled to recall at first. I knew it was connected to Elli's chart. Fragments were surfacing; the restaurant, the staff, the neglect, yes. It was all seeping back.

I looked at the clock. The others would be waiting for me. Shit, I was so knackered. I slipped into my slick, festival clothes and trotted downstairs.

'Hi guys, ready to go?'

'Yes, have you had a cuppa?'

'I'm too excited Roy, man. I'm buzzing all over. I can't wait to get behind that table and do my first professional consultation. So let's piss off out of here before Griff gets us. He's on one of his benders; I can sense it coming, the full moon is looming.'

'Can I drive up Chris?' Roy asked. 'I know the way like the back of my hand.'

'Sure. Bet you're excited too. When was the last time you saw your folks?'

'Oh, over a year now.'

'God, have you been with us that long? Doesn't time fly when you're having fun.'

'Give us a break Chris, we're still battling with our shit; aren't we Pete?'

Pete looked awful. His stony face was slashed by painful, deep ravines, which reflected the claw marks of the beast within. A steady trickle of cold sweat leaked from his tortured forehead, mirroring his raging, inner torment. I feared he wasn't strong enough to come through.

'Uh, what did you say?' he mumbled, then added 'yes, that's putting it mildly.'

We sped up the M25 and hit a bad patch just before the M1 turn off. To make matters worse, it started to lash down. Traffic slowed to a monotonous crawl, just as depressing as Pete's persona.

'Guys, guys, I forgot to tell you; I had some feedback from my sister's chart last night. It's so revealing, but I'm a bit puzzled about one part of it.'

> *10th Sept. 7.15am, waking dream*
>
> *I walked into Stenos; the restaurant wasn't busy, only a few tables were taken. I noticed a couple on the window. They were trying to get the attention of my staff, who were all sitting down, drinking coffee and chatting. I approached them, asking if I could help in any way.*
>
> *'Yes, can you get me some English mustard; I've been waiting so long for it. I did ask a waiter, but he must have forgotten.'*
>
> *'Sorry sir, I'll get it immediately,' I said, turning and rushing towards the kitchen hatch. My staff still sat there doing nothing. They didn't care about the neglect, nor had they any respect for me. I managed to serve the couple the English mustard, which they appreciated.*

'That was it guys. It was telling me that there was neglect of responsibilities, but where? Mmm, I suppose she left her children in the care of her in-laws? They were holding it against her. The husband refused her access to them. God it must have torn her apart. Yes, that's her Gemini sun-sign, being torn apart. Her Cancer ascendant rules family, neglect and depression. Saturn's placement in the 6th house rules heavy backbreaking karma, taking responsibilities and harsh health issues resulting in wasting disorders. The English mustard though; what was that all about?'

'Chris, you've lost me.'

'Roy, it will come to you sooner or later, I promise you. It just needs practice.'

'Pete, what do you think?' I asked. He'd shrunk into his face and buried himself in his beard. He was in a state of turmoil; I could see it in his eyes. His *Dweller* was beating the shit out of him.

'Pete, come on pull yourself together man. Don't dwell on it; it feeds on your feelings of insecurity and your disordered thoughts. It will consume you if you let it. Live in the now, come on, get clarity. Live for today, never mind tomorrow. Come on, shift it.'

I shoved him. He was like a tattered, old, lifeless punch-bag. He slouched there with no means of defence. He had no will, no energy; he was an empty shell.

'Roy pull over now!'

The van screeched to a sudden halt on the hard shoulder. I sprang out and dragged Pete out into the fresh autumn air and cutting rain. Cars swished by, lashing us with motorway muck.

'Pete, Pete, fight it man; don't let it get to you. Fight it! Talk to me, come on, talk to me!' I thumped him against the beat up old van, hoping to get a response. 'Come on, you fucking loser; shout, get it all out! Don't internalise it, don't let it gnaw at you.' I slapped him again and again. He was like a cadaver, pale and clammy, with almost luminous skin. He was soulless and dead to the world, with his life force draining away on the hard shoulder.

'Right, have it your way, just fuck off here. Roy, let's get the hell out of here, I'm not taking any losers on board.' I jumped into the van and got Roy to rev up.

'Chris, you can't leave him here, that's cruel, it's inhumane, you just can't!'

'Roy, I'm trying to get him to pull his shit together. Have you got any bright ideas?'

'You can't leave him here in the pouring rain. Come on, how about a bit of 2nd ray compassion?'

'Oh, all right, I was just trying to shock him into action. If I could get him to retaliate, that would be a result.' I squelched out into the driving rain. He was a sorry, solitary figure, head hung low and crouching in a mangled mess of depression. A mass of drenched, crinkly cut hair, cascaded into his wretched face and his saliva-saturated beard obscured his gaze.

'Pete, pull your self together, please. I need you; I can't do all this on my own. I need you by my side again, just like in the days of Strafford.' There was an eerie silence before he slowly raised his weather beaten face. His eyes tinkled in heavy sockets, like a beat-up old doll.

'Strafford, Strafford, by his side again? Who's Strafford? What do you mean?'

'Nothing, it was just a slip of my fertile mind, but at least it's got you back in the land of the living. I thought I'd lost you. Come on get in the van. Look at you, look at me. Fuck sake, it's all right for you, you'll be hiding behind the stand. I'm drenched from head to foot. How am I going to front this stand looking like this?'

Eventually we got going. The traffic was still bad, but it was easing off slightly. He had come to life; the cadaver had come to life.

'So, what's this about Strafford then? Who was he? Tell me?'

Roy glanced at me, sending the van into a sudden swerve.

'You didn't tell him about us did you? You didn't!'

'Roy, bloody hell you'll get us flattened; keep your concentration on the road.'

'What's he talking about? Us? You mean to say you've got a connection with Strafford too?

'Pete, who told you, you've got a link then?'

'Guys, guys, you've lost me now,' Pete said. 'Roy, pull over, I need to talk to both of you.'

The van screeched to a halt once more. I could see lines of flashing headlights, blaring at us, like searing rods of red-hot iron.

'Right you two;' I shouted 'I hadn't planned on telling you anything about our karmic connection. It just slipped out, in amongst that fucking scene out there. I'm not going to tell you who you were Pete, that's too easy. You'll have to show me you've got your shit together first. I want more effort on your part before I share this with you.'

Pete's enthusiasm trickled away, but the light in his eyes was back.

'Thanks for the kick up the backside,' he said. 'I needed it. I know I'm not ready for past life information; I can't whip this one into shape yet. But, give me time; I won't disappoint you.'

'Roy and I had a past life together. He's aware of it, aren't you Roy?'

'Yes, I got it confirmed not so long ago, the experience was awesome.'

'So, you believe we're all linked by previous lives of the same period? You're having us on aren't you Chris?'

'No, Pete, it's the truth. Strange as it may be, it's all true.'

'Bloody hell, I must admit, Pete and I get on really well,' Roy said. 'We just hit it off the first time we met.'

'You do know you're astrological twins?'

Pete was bemused. 'Astrological twins? What do you mean?'

'You've got the same sun signs and ascendants.'

'So we have,' said Roy. 'No wonder, we're so compatible.'

Pete was showing more interest now. 'You haven't answered my question; who was Strafford? Who was he? Tell me?'

'Read up on the events leading to the English Civil War,' I told him. 'Now, can we now get back on the road? We've got a stand to set up and just look at me; I'm soaked to the skin. Roy, if I'm still soaked by the time we get there, I'm swapping clothes with you.'

'No chance, no way, my clothes will be too big for you anyway.'

'I'm not wearing any of Roy's, he's a short arse, look at him, he looks like a down-and-out.' I managed to keep Pete's sagging aura pumped up. He looked a lot better and he even started conversation.

'Chris, you know your dream? I think I've got a clue what English mustard is referring to.'

'Oh, so you weren't a complete cadaver after all, were you? Well what do you think then?'

'Have we brought Esoteric Healing Part 3 with us?'

'It's in that box behind us.' He clambered into the back and fished out a copy.

'Have a read of that,' he said. 'Does that sound like your sister's symptoms?'

'English mustard,' I exclaimed. 'Of course, the Bach Flower Remedy, English mustard; Pete you're a genius, I'd would never have thought of that connection.'

'Well, does it fit? Does it?'

'I'm not sure. I haven't spoken to her or seen her. It's got to be linked with her condition, it's got to be.'

'Where's all this coming from?' asked Roy. 'Your higher self is even giving you remedies for healing now.'

'I don't know, but ever since my fire experiences, I've been bathed in light and knowledge. I know very little about the Flower Remedies, yet my soul flashed English mustard to me.'

'Fire experiences, what fire experiences?'

'That'll have to wait until you're both ready to hear it.'

'Chris, don't be a kill joy, tell us; we promise we'll keep it a secret.'

'No it's not important now, we've got a festival to attend to. How much longer to go Roy, any ideas?'

'Yes, we've just past the Leamington Spa junction, it's only another 20 minutes.'

'Brilliant, don't go anywhere near 'Spaghetti Junction' Roy, that'll tangle us up for hours.'

Roy gave me disdainful look. 'Chris trust me, this is my old stomping ground.' Within half an hour we were at the back doors of the town hall. All the weird and wonderful New-Agers tinkled in and out with their spiritual paraphernalia. What a sea of activity; it was awash with colour, sound, scent and individualism. Bawdy yellows and oranges of the Hare Krishna devotees clashed with the blacks of the ebony-clad Wiccans. Healers and psychics glided in like prima donnas wearing rainbow satins, ethereal silks and pure white cottons. Every single soul, unique in their note, sounded like a finely tuned instrument playing in a divine orchestra. Yes, we were all different, but we were all jewels in the vast, multi-faceted New Age, crown of consciousness.

It didn't take us long to set up our stand. Everything went according to plan. I had a pivotal position, piercing the centre. On the flanks, the Claregate banner and standards fluttered in the sweet-smelling, aromatic air. Chimes, bells, drums and cymbals beat up a frenzied attack as we charged our chakras and adjusted our auras. I scanned around to see the competition. It was going to be hard to make an impact, but I was confident of a good result.

'Hey Pete, Roy, look over there. Do you see what I see, or am I going nuts?'

'Oh my God, they get weirder all the time,' answered Roy.

'Are you a Star Person? Do you fit into this list of criteria? Let Michael El Legion explore your inter-galactic vibrations!'

'Hey Roy, look at him,' I shouted. 'Fancy being analysed by that? Talk about space cadets, he must be an alien or he's beamed himself down from the star ship Enterprise, light years ahead of us.'

'He must be the man! Michael El Legion, in the flesh,' Roy said. 'Look at him prancing around in that figure-hugging, silver space suit. Boy, is he a megalomaniac. He must be from the US. Nobody else would dream of appearing like that, even in here.'

A gorgeous, violet-clad temptress flounced out from his stand. She bounced gaily around the milling crowds, like a hot air balloon jostling in the tops of trees.

We had a slow start, but by the end of the day I had interpreted four horoscopes and we'd sold quite a few books. Just as we were packing up for the evening, the voluptuous, violet vixen, crept towards me, flashing her beguiling lashes.

'Hey guys, I'm Aurora, I'm American, we're Star People, Michael and I!'

'Hi, Aurora, this is Roy, Pete and my name is Chris, we're Earthlings. Do you come in peace?' Roy glared at her and retreated into the stand. Pete melted and his face flushed fiery red. God, what a shower of cowering, dithering introverts I was surrounded by.

'I must apologise; they're only let out once a month. They can't really cope with the exposure, but I'm trying hard to rehabilitate them.'

'Hey, Esoteric Astrology, I've read of it, but never came across anyone who could use it. Didn't Alice Bailey start it?'

'Yes, the new Esoteric Planetary Rulers were given to her by The Tibetan Master, Dwal Kul. His wisdom flowed through her.'

'Didn't she say that astrology was soul-centred and could not be used to analyse personality issues?'

'True, but Douglas Baker's new approach has taken it to it's ultimate level. He's devised a system that unifies all wisdom, all knowledge and all understanding into one wondrous astrological tapestry.' I had her hooked by my esoteric charm and eloquence. I was on a roll, buzzing all over.

'Chris,' she smiled. 'I've got a deal for you. Do me an interpretation and in return, I'll get Michael to do you one of his psychic channellings.'

Psychic channellings by Michael El Legion? Who could refuse a galactic encounter with a star man?

'Alright, let's arrange it for some time tomorrow, when it's quiet.'

'Fantastic Chris, oh I love your accent. Are you from Edinburg?'

'No, I'm not from Edinburgh, I'm Glaswegian.'

'That's nice. I'm really looking forward to the readings, I can't wait.' She gushed all the way back to the Star stand and whispered into Michael's cyber ear. He gave me a Star signal. God it was just like *Star Trek*. I returned my terrestrial thumbs-up. We had sealed our fate; the deal was done.

'Come on boys,' I said. 'Let's get out of here before we're abducted.'

As we were wrapping up I heard a female voice ask Roy about an interpretation. I was ducked behind the stand, unplugging the computer. Her cheery chitter-chatter caught my ears and I listened as I heard Roy tell her about me.

'Oh there's Chris, he'll tell you more about the astrology. Chris, this is...what's your name again?'

'I don't give my name out to strange men, but I'll make an exception this time. I'm Alana.'

'Ahh, bloody cables, it's like Spaghetti Junction under here. Roy, quick.... oh no!'

Crash! The bookstand fell over; posters flicked in the air and the incense rack tipped on the table. I clambered up from behind the tabletop to be met by the most clear, piercing blue, wide eyes

I'd ever encountered. My heart started trembling and my muscles all tensed up as *His* powerful vibrations raced all over my body. The laser blasted in my ears, knocking me off balance. Down I went again, ski-ing around on posters, books and cables. My face roasted the back of the stand. It was on fire. I was on fire! My whole body was in shock. Roy and Pete were killing themselves. I felt like the early days at Mind Body and Spirit. She was beautiful: long curly, auburn hair, pale freckly, Celtic skin and a beaming heart-stopping smile. My solar plexus gushed at the excitement and my sacral centre cranked into a grinding, groan. God, I hadn't felt this way in years. My rusty lower chakras churned into spasm, sending mega desire signals to the higher ones, short-circuiting their spiritual fuses. I had to get myself together. She had awakened my Scorpionic passions and dowsed me with her angelic presence. I was overwhelmed; I was jelly in her hands.

'Roy, Pete, don't just stand there, splitting your sides, give me a hand, will you!' I shouted, asserting what was left of my authority. Who was she? She pierced my armour-plated heart. I had thrust my potent desires deep into a secret box in the unconscious years ago. Pandora, oh Pandora had found the key to my torn, tattered, emotions.

'Hi there, I'm Chris, sorry for the mess, we're just packing up for the night. You're interested in the astrology?'

'Yes, I've studied orthodox astrology, but I've been looking for a more holistic approach for ages.'

'Well, you've come to the right place, maybe it's meant. Nothing happens by chance.'

She stared into my eyes, God, she knew.... I knew there was a spark between us. Fuck sake, I was jelly from the waist down. I had no control over my body. Thank God she couldn't see how my legs were jittering. I was a love-lorn romantic. My voice sweetened as she spoke in her mild, Welsh-Brummy accent.

'Alana, listen, what are you doing tomorrow? I'd love to chat to you about your interest in astrology.'

'Well, I hadn't planned coming again, but there was a lecture I was interested in.'

'Good, see you tomorrow then.'

'All right, it will be late though; I've got to rearrange my schedule. See you then.'

She flashed her eyelashes at me and a waft of her etheric fragrance swept like tidal waves over my lonely heart.

'Chris, Chris come on, they're going to shut us in here for the night. Let's get cracking,' Roy shouted anxiously.

'Where are we staying tonight? Have you organised anything?' Pete said in a desperate tone.

'Staying? What? Where?'

'Chris, what's the matter with you? You're not making any sense.' Pete replied squinting his face.

'I know where I'm staying,' grinned Roy. 'I'm off home for the night. Ooo, mum's home cooking, my old bed and room. You're quite welcome to come back there. I'm sure mum wouldn't mind.'

'That's great Roy. Are you sure there's room?'

'Pete, there's room, loads of room.'

'Roy, take Pete with you, I'll kip in the back of the van. I don't trust them up here, it reminds me of my childhood days in Glasgow.'

'Chris, don't be a fool. It'll be freezing and so uncomfortable.'

'I'll be okay Roy, go on. See you in the morning. Don't be late!' I waved them off and closed down the stand. I just managed to escape the hall before the caretaker grinded the lock and bolted the old door. I wandered back to the van to think over my romantic liaison. Was it possible she was just playing; that she wasn't coming back? I had seen it all before. At least I knew I was human: my lower chakras needed servicing, even if I was not using their energies.

I popped into a chippy for some food. The euphoria of the festival had kept me going but now I needed something. I plodded back to my box with my chips wrapped up under my arm. I felt like a New Age traveller, all I needed now, were dreadlocks, a few body piercings and a couple of old dogs for company. I faded into a deep, soothing slumber, with no recall of the day's events.

CHAPTER 38

'Chris, are you in there? Open up, it's freezing and it's pissing down.'

'What's all the racket out there?'

'Chris, we've got something to show you, open the door.'

'Roy, it can't be that important. Set up the stand and I'll see you in 15 minutes.'

'Hey, have you got that girl in the back?'

'Don't be stupid.'

In minutes I was up and out in the early morning mist, with my toothbrush in my mouth and a towel tossed over my neck. As I walked towards the town hall I passed a procession of drug addicts and alcoholics huddled up in their bed-sit cardboard boxes. The stench of cheap wine and hair lacquer, bellowed from their mouths, like the puffs of rancid pollution gushing out of inner city factories. One lad lay there; piss trickling down his filthy trouser leg onto the box he was laying on. The urine spread underneath him like a psychedelic fractal image.

'Ahh, no! No! Get way from me! Get away from me! Ahhh... leave me alone! Get off of me, get fucking off me!' he blasted as he swished around, swiping the air with punches. Wails, tears of despair and sheer terror erupted from his tormented soul. His body contorted and twisted into a mangled frame. I knew he was possessed; I could not help him. Astral vampires were consuming him. They were shells of soulless alcoholics and addicts that were stuck between world's, searching for sub-humans to feed off. It was sickening to hear the poor sod's screams echo in the mist. Nobody understood or realised what the victims of the vampires were really going through.

Passers-by zigzagged past their shantytown to the wails and outstretched hands of their social conscience. I sent them my prayers, hoping that these lost souls on both sides would be released from their anguish and incessant cravings.

I jogged down a lane, like a boxer on his early morning run, dodging piles of black bin liners seething with decomposing swill. That's how they must feel, I thought. Their insides were rotting; they were mutating into the living dead, destined to wander in filthy lanes and back streets in search of a quick fix. I trotted into my paradise from that purgatory out there. If they only knew that salvation was feet away from their hell. If they only knew a safe haven brimming with lightworkers was on their doorstep.

'Chris, look, you'll never believe it.' Roy handed me the Sun. 'Turn to page six.'

'You're right, I can't believe it.'

Star People amongst us. Michael El Legion, a self-professed, Starman, tours the UK.'

'Look, there's Aurora, standing next to him. Hey, these people are famous, man.'

'They're also appearing on TV AM too!'

'Chris, call the Birmingham Post. Get a reporter down here.'

'Come on guys. I don't want that type of publicity. Get me a coffee and something to eat Pete, I'm going to freshen up.'

The exhibitors slowly filtered in, tarting up themselves and their stands. Hare Krishna drumbeats, chants and chimes belted out and the devotees danced in ecstasy. The Wiccans lit their heavy incense and worshiped their Pagan deities. Others prayed, meditated and stretched out in Yogic postures. The New Age machine sparked into gear and the loud hailer announced the festival open to the public. Michael and Aurora beamed down from the ethers. They greeted us in their familiar Star People's peace sign. I sat in my chair and withdrew into a short meditation. The boys wandered off for a quick 'reckie' before it got busy. Whilst in meditation, I heard a rustling sound and opened my eyes to a little Hare Krishna boy

fiddling with an incense holder. He couldn't have been more than 10 years old. He looked so cute in his orange and yellow robes, head shaved apart from his ceremonial little ponytail. He raised his painted gaze up to me. God, I felt his deep, soulful, brown eyes, penetrate my heart. He stared at me, stony-faced, with a pitiful expression. He was in pain; he was suffering. I felt his loneliness and his isolation. The lad seemed content enough, but something wasn't quite right; he wasn't your normal 10-year-old boy, full of life and energy. I smiled at him, thinking I'd get a response.

'Hi, my name is Chris, what's yours?' He didn't respond; he just fiddled nervously with the holder. 'Do you like it? It's pretty isn't it?' He stood there, in a starchy pose with his thoughts in a straightjacket. 'Are you enjoying the festival? Do you play any instruments?' He just stared at me, probing my words with his senses. I felt so inadequate; maybe he was deaf.

'Have you got *In the Steps of the Master*? I've been looking for a copy.'

'Yes, I think we have. Isn't it out on the shelf?'

'Oh yes, there it is, thanks. Can I flick through it?'

'Be my guest, sir.' My little friend had scampered, leaving his pouch of meditation beads on the table. By now the stand was inundated with interest. The boys had come back just in time. I had a few astrology charts to do. Time whizzed by so quickly; the morning bled into the afternoon. I took some time out before my consultation with Aurora.

I located the Hare Krishna table and stopped to chat to the devotees there. They were lovely souls, a young couple in their twenties. A little girl sat behind the stand with her mother. She resembled my young friend; I was sure she was his younger sister; she had the same austere look on her face. Her soul cried out for something as she buried her angelic face into her mothers' bosom.

'I think your son left his meditation beads at my stand earlier. I've got them in my pocket.'

'Oh thanks, Tarakanath is always forgetting things; he's so spaced out.'

'He's not deaf is he?'

'God no, he's very timid though. They don't get much exposure; they rarely leave the community.'

'Oh, anyway, tell him I came by. He must have been worried about losing his beads.'

'Hare Krishna! Hare Krishna! Hare Rama! Hare Rama friend, walk in peace.' I left them to their ritual chants, chimes and drumbeats. When I got back, Aurora was wedged into the chair waiting for me.

'Hi there Chris; How you doing?'

'Brilliant Aurora; you didn't tell us you were celebrities. You're in the national newspapers.'

'Oh, it's Michael's PR agent; he's switched on. Yes, we're doing a tour of five countries; it's hard work being on the road.'

'Bet it is. Anyway, let's get down to business. Have you got a chart cast already?'

'Yes, I have. Can you use it?'

'Yes, I'll get one of the lads to transfer it onto one of our chart wheels. I'm used to the format.' The reading went well and afterwards she floated off to tell Michael all about it. She had exhausted me; I gave her half my solar plexus and it felt like it to. Michael beckoned me to his stand.

'Chris, thanks for doing Aurora's chart, she's thrilled to bits. You made an impression on her. She's always wanted a Soul's Purpose chart.'

'It was my pleasure Michael. She's a bundle of creativity and she's got stacks of energy.'

'Tell me about it, Chris. Have you got time for your galactic channelling now?'

'Yes, I've called it a day, the boys can man the stand in my absence.'

'Good, settle down, relax and sit there. I'm going to do some Kinesiology on you first, just to get you in the right frame of mind.' He spent 15 minutes re-arranging and balancing my energies. I felt totally relaxed and primed up for my channelling session.

'Right, today's date is the 12th of September 1985; this is a galactic channelling session by Michael El Legion,' he said into the microphone. He proceeded to tell me that I was a very advanced soul, who was responsible for setting up energy systems in Atlantis. I was a scientist and elder; I had used the astrology then as well as divine alchemy. I was connected to Artcurus, a sacred planet in the Bootes constellation. To tell you the truth, I hadn't a clue what he was on about, but I didn't want to stop his flow.

'Oh, you're going to meet and work with a cosmic being, Rawena, Lady Rawena; she's a master astrologer and Arcturian high priestess. In one of your past lives you were a Druid high priest. You were responsible for holding the light at Stonehenge, Avebury and other Druid sacred sites in Wales. You had a powerful life with King Arthur and the Nirmanakaya Merlin, who was St. Germaine in a past life.'

Rowena? Merlin? King Arthur? St. Germaine? It was getting ridiculous. Here I was trying to keep my feet firmly on the ground and he was saying I was virtually a god. He babbled on about my Dharma and Karma.

'Your soul has chosen this life to balance energies on the planet, preparing it for its immense transition. You will be travelling abroad to ancient sacred centres, triggering off healing energies by using divine invocations and meditations. You are one of *the chosen ones*, who will prepare the planet for it's upgrading as we enter the New Age of Aquarius.'

I started to buzz all over. My head went into severe cramp spasms as he described the Strafford and Kitchener lives.

'You have been unjustly put to the sword by your peers. Conspiracies and betrayal were instrumental to your downfall. You died in a warship. Ooo.... I'm getting an icy sea; God I'm there, it's so cold, ooo... It was a set up; you were set up by MI5; they wanted rid of you because you caused too many waves.'

By this time my hair was all pricked up and my chakras were churning. God, he was picking up past life details I had suspicions about. This information was top-secret and certainly not researchable.

'Beware, beware, even now, in this life, you are being conspired against. Yes...betrayal of trust, loyalty and honour. There's also a deep personal wounding you're carrying. You've been stabbed in the back by a lover's adultery. Great care is needed, something's fishy, they're not telling me anymore.'

Where did he get it all from? I was disappointed in the beginning, with all that inter-galactic crap; but he was so accurate on the past life stuff I was beginning to wonder if the 'space shit' was true too. He clicked off the tape, centred himself and opened his eyes.

'Oh, you're a Star Person too. Did you know that?'

'Michael, that was fantastic; I must admit the inter-galactic stuff was way over my head, but I could identify with the rest. Thank you very much and I wish you both success in on your tour.'

'The pleasure's mine, brother. Go out and express your divine purpose. You are one of the rare *Chosen Ones*. You are blessed with universal power, love and understanding. Go forth into the galaxy and multiply.'

I got up, still in awe of his channelling. I had my reservations about mediums, clairvoyants and psychics. Perhaps I needed to keep an open mind in future. I wandered back to the stand, head down, brooding on Michael's reading.

'Hi Chris, you okay?'

'Oh, hi there... Hi, I'd almost forgotten all about you. Great to see you Alana, I thought you were just pulling my leg yesterday. I really didn't think you were coming back.'

'I was busy, but I rearranged my schedule and managed to get a few favours from my colleagues. You look spaced out. How was the reading? It looked so intense.'

'Alana, I need a coffee or something. Do you want to join me?'

'Yes, all right, as long as I can buy my own. I'm an Aries, with Virgo Ascendant, a perfectionist, very independent, fiery and extravert.'

'Okay, come on before I collapse. Roy, I'm just off to get my bearings back again. Pack up the stand and I'll see you in half an hour.'

'Ooo, Chris don't go all soft and sensitive. She'll reduce you to a mere mortal like the rest of us.'

'Go on, off with you; I'm no different to you, Pete and the rest of the Claregate mob.' I picked up a couple of holders and a few of packs of incense. We made our way to the Hare Krishna stand. They were breaking down their table.

'Hi, is Tarakanath around?' His little ponytail bobbed up from under the table. 'Hi there, here's a little something for you and your sister.' His wee face sparked into light and his eyes shone as I placed the gifts in his little tender hands.

'Thank you Chris and thanks for bringing back my beads.'

He looked so pleased as he showed his parents. It had made his day; it had made my day too, just to see his wee face light up like that.

'I don't think he's ever been given a present before, do you? They must have a very strict upbringing at the community.'

'I don't think it's proper, you know, being thrust into community life, without having a choice in the matter,' answered Alana. 'It's not normal; kids need to experience growing up in normal environments. They need to play, watch TV and socialise with normal kids.'

'Yes, that's what's missing. He's not had a childhood; he's grown up too quickly. He hasn't explored the joys of play. He's been thrust into worship, prayer and discipline. At least I chose my path in life, but what can he say or do? He'll be set in his ways soon and that will be that.'

'Maybe he'll turn out happy and content. At least he's receiving true spiritual values, not the crap our kids are exposed to.'

'Possibly, but there's got to be balance. If you don't experience black you will never truly know white. Come on, I'm parched; let's get to the bar before they shut.'

'Hey, I thought you lot were supposed to purify your bodies and raise your vibrations.'

'Yes, but a little spirit always helps and it goes down a treat. Why, don't you drink?'

'Yes, yes of course I do, but my liver's like a piece of old leather. I have to be really careful now.'

'Old leather?' I asked, rather confused. 'You drank that much? No! I would never of guessed, not you, in your white clothes and multi-coloured bandana. You look more like a 'fluffy bunny'.

'Ha! Fluffy bunny my arse; I'm a WRAF, I've had to keep up with a squadron of hard drinking boys.'

'Well, you do surprise me Alana, I'd never of guessed. What else are you into, apart from astrology.'

'Mmm, I love Ufology. I've just started a course on colour healing and I'm a psychic, but I rarely use it.'

'How did you get into Ufology?'

'Well, shhh.... This is hush-hush. I trained in aerospace systems operation. No end of times I'd be sitting tracking an unidentified object on my radar screen and then blip, it would vanish into thin air. We'd get reports from local residents confirming sightings, even a police patrol car sent us a report once.'

'God, that's exciting. So UFOs really exist?'

'Not according to the government! We were always told to file this type of information in the 'no need to know' drawer. I guess it was just swept under the carpet.'

'That's disgusting. This government stinks.'

'It'll come out sooner or later, I'm sure. I've read stacks of UFO books; I'm into cosmic connections, galaxies and life on other planets. I'm reading a book on Arcturus in the Bootes constellation. It's really interesting, the book reckons the planet is highly evolved and some initiates are actively involved in the Earth's evolutionary plan. Chris, are you okay? Help, someone help, he's collapsed! You! Run to the Claregate stand; tell them Chris has passed out, quick!'

Alana shouted to another onlooker, 'you! Get me an ice bucket, a cloth and some drinking water, now! It's all right Chris, it's all right, you've just fainted. You'll be okay soon.'

My consciousness faded back to my crumpled body with Michael's voice shouting, Arcturus, Arcturus, Rawena, Lady Rawena. The words echoed in my head, bringing me back to full consciousness. As my gaze cleared, I was wrapped up warm in Alana's embrace, my feet were raised and I had an ice pack on my forehead.

'There we are. Thank God you're back. You scared the shit out of me. Look boys his colour is flooding back to his face. He'll live to fight another day.'

'You okay Chris?' Pete enquired. 'How do you feel? Alana, he's fainted on me too; it's his party trick. I'm sure he's a closet attention seeker.'

'Ohh come on, give me a break Pete. He's exaggerating; it's not like that at all.'

'You just calm down. Roy get him a sandwich and a hot drink. Bet he's not eaten all day, have you?'

I didn't reply but she knew by my sheepish expression that she was right. I just lay there completely in awe of it all. No, no, it was all a fluke, a coincidence, I thought; she's not the cosmic being Rawena from Arcturus, she was Alana from Newport, South Wales.

'Let me sit up Alana, I'm feeling a lot better now. Thanks for the first aid, I couldn't have picked a better person to faint on, could I?'

'Ohh, that's not fair Chris, you've made me jealous. I thought you liked my sweaty old beard close to your face.'

'Piss off Pete, that'll be the day.'

'Right you guys I'm off, I've got a bit of socialising to do. Just keep him steady for a few minutes. He's not to drive anywhere, okay? Maybe see you all next time you come here.' Before she left, she passed me a little note and whispered, 'give me call if you need more first aid in the future'.

I clambered up, devoured my sandwich and guzzled a cuppa.

'Are we all packed up?' I asked.

'Just a few boxes to go and we'll be ready.'

'Good Roy, leave me here to recharge my batteries. Come and get me when you're ready.' I sat there in complete confusion. I thought my life was mapped out for me: all I had to do was perfect my ancient wisdom knowledge, become an adept esoteric astrologer and lecturer, and eventually take *The Kingdom of Heaven by storm*. She had short-circuited my vision. All my plans went up in flames. She stirred something deep inside of me, something I had buried under a heavy tombstone. Rawena, Arcturus, cosmic being? El Legion had implanted seeds of contradiction in my fertile mind. It may be a load of bollocks, but he got my past life profile to a tee.

'Come on then, let's get cracking. Are we going to have our celebratory curry?' asked Roy. 'I know a great one just around the corner.'

I didn't talk about my reading or my experience with Alana. I needed to brood over it. She did give me her number; she must have fallen for me. I don't know why, I was in rags, penniless and with no material prospects. Maybe she just felt sorry for me. Yes, that was it.

We left the curry house and began our journey home to Claregate. The road back was clear, in an hour and a half we trundled into the driveway, safe and sound. We left the van as it was, we were all too knackered to walk, never mind unload it.

CHAPTER 39

'Rawena! Rawena! Arise Christos arise! Beware! Beware!' The words thundered in my head as I bolted upright with sweat oozing out of me and the bedclothes strewn all over the room. I had my sodden pillow in a stranglehold with feathers floating in mid air, tantalising and teasing me back to a vivid waking dream experience.

> *13th Sept. 5.15am. Waking dream.*
> *I am in a lift with a mother and her two little girls. We want to go up, but the buttons are labelled in an obscure code. I press one at random, the lift goes up first, and then it drops downwards with great speed. We are being dragged down deep into the earth's bowels. The lift suddenly comes to an abrupt halt. The doors open into a tunnel. We cautiously peep out; the walls are decked in ancient hieroglyphs, which looked Egyptian, but they could have been more ancient in origin. The tunnel leads us into an ancient burial chamber. I am approached by a high priestess clad in a large, jewel encrusted, golden headdress. She is dressed in beautiful, white silk ceremonial robes, with lush gold braiding and lashings of trinkets. She's holding a golden sword in her right hand, high above her head. As she gets close to me she points the sword at me and I catch a glimpse of her face. It's her! Alana, I'm sure it's her. She taps me on either side of my shoulders and offers me the sword. As I take it in my hand, it surges me with energy and power.*

'Christos, beware! Beware!' Echoed in the ethers as I was swished back into full consciousness still wrestling with my pillow.

I lay there for a while, brooding on it's significance. I was in a state of *psychopompia*, on the knife-edge between both worlds. Suddenly, I was thrust into a vivid vision.

It was a meeting of lawyers or something similar. Rows and rows were jammed packed, some jeering, some in deep thought, some cheering. The smell of damp and antiquity wafted into my consciousness. Coughs, sniffles and snorts echoed amongst the monotone of babbling low voices.

'Thud, thud! Thud, thud! Order, order! Order in the house!'

My focus singled out two faces in the crowd. It was Elena and Stellios. They were dressed in robes and high collars. There was a call of execution against an unfortunate soul being tried for treason. The whole arena erupted into frenzy. Suddenly, my brow exploded into specks and flashes of colour, flowing from the periphery to the centre like a kaleidoscope. Ordered patterns merged into the most vivid, beautiful, multi-coloured, patterns of divinity. They ebbed and flowed into cosmic design after design. It must be Ajna, the brow centre unfolding, I thought, as my waking consciousness eased back from the inner worlds.

I lay there in complete awe of the experience. The courtroom drama? Elena and Stellios? Why were they there? Who was being condemned? It was all very weird. Oh, the mandalas, wao, that experience was awesome.

Was it another extension of consciousness? Possibly, the El Legion channelling...Wao, my dream, the high priestess, the warning! Rawena; she looked exactly like Alana.

I got up, sorted myself out and trotted downstairs for a cuppa. I didn't expect to see anyone that early. The doors were ajar, a taxi with its doors wide open waited, ticking over. Who was leaving? Why all the secrecy? The lounge door bolted open; there she was, with all her meagre belongings, sombre faced and heavy souled.

'Claire, what's up? Where are you going?'

'I don't want to talk about it. I've had it; I can't cope anymore, I can't.' She sobbed her heart out as she waded past me into the cab.

Her *Dweller* had consumed her. She was a mental and emotional wreck. 'Chris good luck, you're a brave soul. You've got what it takes. You're ready for *the burning ground*. I'll send you my deepest thoughts and support. Bye.'

The cab's tyres screeched, gravel sprayed and clouds of dust bellowed. She was gone. Claire was my only female confidante in the group. She looked after me; she was my go-between. She buffered me from Linda's wrath and negative projection. How was Linda going to react now? Anyway, where was she? Had Claire not told her of her intentions? Bet she didn't, Linda would have persuaded her to stay, if she'd known.

God, I'm away one weekend and everything falls apart. Well, I know I'll be summoned to give account. I'm sure DB knows of her clandestine escape. He'll be so down; Claire was his head secretary; how is he going to cope? Who will take over her duties? I jumped into a car and sped down to LE. His light was on upstairs. I trudged up; the steps were heaving with heavy energy. He knew she had gone all right; his negative Capricornian aura tumbled down like a ton of bricks, crushing my ascent.

'So you know then?'

Silence reigned as he rolled over in his creaky, old bed. Reams of astrological charts hung over the top of his headboard and masses of research notes swished to the floor. His rickety, relic of a typewriter lay smoking, in a mangle, too stressed out to endure another hammering by his index fingers.

'Yes I know, I bloody know, of course I know. I tried to dissuade her, but she's lost, consumed in self-pity, drenched in negativity and devoured by her *Dweller*. I thought she had mastered its awesome energies; I thought the *Solar Angel* had penetrated the heart of that demon. I was mistaken; another unfortunate soul with great potential lost to the jaws of the beast. She could only cope by *spliffing*, you know that?'

'What, Claire? I would never have guessed DB. She didn't look the sort; she was so prim and proper.'

'It's her past life as Coleridge. He was an addict. Laudanum, you know, Opium. She struggled to bring back his creativity, his awesome talent, but she just couldn't access it without that dreaded weed. They don't have the staying power, these kids. They're all on some bloody thing. I've told them again and again, *you can't ripen an apple with a blowtorch.* It's their freewill at the end of the day. I hope you're not on anything, are you?'

'You must be joking; I don't even smoke, never mind *spliff.* I've accessed my source through sheer will, focus, dedication and discipline.'

'Chris, your time is imminent, it's brewing. You'll need your wits about you. Be prepared. Claire's departure will hurt, but we'll manage somehow. Filming is over. We've only got postproduction to worry about. Money, it's money we need. How did the exhibition go? Did you bring back any money?'

'Yes DB, it was a success. But it's never going to make millions, is it?'

'Did you interpret any charts?'

'Yes, 15 in total, it was a brilliant experience; I loved it.'

'Did you lecture?'

'No, but I was over the moon with my interpretations. They just flowed so easily. Myths, symbols, objects for meditation, chakra indications, karmic connections, it was awesome. I felt like I was a channel for a higher intelligence. It flooded me with energy and wisdom.'

'You're tapping into the Nirmanakaya's collective consciousness. Work at it, study, meditate, and dedicate your life to the service of humanity. You'll be noticed, you'll be head hunted, the *Hierarchy* need souls pure, tried and tested, to take on part of the Plan for Earth.'

'Don't overwhelm me. Please, I'm not ready for this, not yet.'

'Mmm, what's on your mind? You're not copping out like the rest of them, are you?'

'No, of course not, but I need time, don't push me. I'll do it myself, okay?'

'Okay, okay tiger; I get the message. Make yourself a cuppa and breakfast if you want. I'm not coming down, I've got loads of work to attend to.'

As I pottered around in the kitchen James popped his head around the door. He was buzzing with excitement.

'Mine's tea, milk no sugar; I'm just going for a quick slash. I need to talk to someone, what an experience.' He trotted off to the loo and in minutes was bounding all over me. 'Chris it was awesome, it was so clear, so vivid.'

'Jim, what are you on about? You're beginning to sound like Lance. Come on, spit it out, what was so awesome?'

'Chris, I've had previous life recall. I've never experienced anything like it before. It was so real, so alive, so overwhelming.'

'You should brood over it and ponder its significance before you share it.'

'I can't, it's so relevant to my life. It answers so many questions. You know what I'm like with questions.'

'All right, come on, spill the beans.'

'Chris, it's all about Hastings. It's so uncanny, and it's unbelievable.'

'What about Hastings? What? You won the chess tournament? Congratulations.'

'No! No! I had this waking vision a couple of days ago.'

'Come on, put me out of my misery, I've got a business to attend to.'

'Well, I'd been studying chess strategy; it was quite late. My head was buzzing with knight to king, check; bishop to king, checkmate; suddenly I was thrust into the thick of a gruesome battle scene. Hundreds of medieval soldiers were being butchered; limbs severed and bludgeoned heads littered the place; torsos lay ripped apart and crimson rivers of blood oozed everywhere. The battle cries of knights on horseback echoed in the distance and flashes of that blood red morning sun glinted on razor sharp swords. Lances piercing plate armour like pincushions; the skies were blackened by swarms of deadly arrows. I was wading through corpses, on horseback, fighting, defending, and wielding my heavy broad sword. Then agony, an excruciating pain seared through the side of my head. My vision bloodied red, then black. I crashed to the ground with an arrow embedded in my left eye. It had found it's way through my protective visor. Chris, I was there, lying in full armour, blood gushing from a face wound, sprawled over my dying horse.

'The king is down! King Harold is down!' thundered in the distance, as my brave soldiers tried to defend me. I managed to clamber to my feet, but I was cut down by a knight's lance. The fatal wound gashed my right side. Chris, the stench of stinking corpses and those bloody scenes were awful. I was there! Men dying of horrific wounds, the cries, wails and shouts of womenfolk tending their brave, dead husbands. It was sickening. The whole event was sickening. I was King Harold.'

'Bloody hell, Jim, that's amazing. I can imagine how you felt. I've had similar recall; it's so real isn't it?'

'Chris, look... look above my left eye. See, I've got a birthmark, look at it. That's where the arrow pierced my skull and took out my eye.'

'For fuck sake Jim, you're right.'

'Not only that, do you remember me telling you about my mysterious ruptured appendix, when I was playing in the British Chess Championships at Hastings? The lance gouged my appendix. It all makes sense now. The pieces all fit together.'

'Jim, you go back there, year after year, to engage in battle, where you were struck down. Have you ever won there?'

'No never, No matter how hard I've tried, some mishap always scuttles my attempts.'

'Sit down Jim, here's your tea. I think you deserve it. You'll need to think up another strategy next time. You may even win, now you have past life knowledge. There is a lesson you've not learned and you're still making the same mistakes.'

'Maybe you're right. I'll have to think about it. I'll research the life, I think it's all wrapped up in it.' He was inspired, we talked for ages, exchanging views, glancing attacks and probing past life experiences. God, every conversation was an epic chess match.

I had to get my act together, the bills were mounting up and I sensed a backlash in the air. Claire's sudden departure left a gaping hole in Claregate's aura. That vacuum had to be filled. Who was going to take her place? Linda was the only candidate capable of taking it on. She was more dangerous than ever. She had a monopoly over DB now. She had the power she lusted over. I knew how her devious mind worked; I needed all my wits about me. She had recruited Lance, Cleary and Griff into her gang of conspirators.

I held the fort with the help of Roy and Pete until Pete fell victim to his *Dweller.* He just fucked off without even a warning. I was virtually alone and Roy eventually began feeling the pressure. He was swayed by the mob. I was outnumbered, but I had maintained my link with Alana. She had become my confidante, my shining light, and my saviour.

My sister Elli visited me and I advised her to take English mustard and gave her an astrology reading and organised for her to see a therapist. She was on the mend, taking orthodox as well as complementary medicine.

My spiritual experiences heightened more and more as I used astrology, studied mythology and symbolism. I did an intensive study of out-of-body experiences, which led to hundreds of astral projections. I was swimming in the astral currents. I had almost mastered astral consciousness. The higher realms beckoned my focus. I woke one morning with an extraordinary dream.

15th Dec. 1985, 6.30am, dream.
I am sitting at a poolside with Elena. Half of the pool is full of muddy marsh. Big Negroes are pulling people out of the bog. They have to pay Elena for the Negroes saving their lives. She tosses me in. I'm sinking deep into the mud and my throat is filling with stinking sludge. Suddenly a big, black, hand pulls me to safety. My throat is caked with chunks of hardened mud, which I slowly clear. The pool and bog transforms into a black and white dance floor. I find a suitcase with my name on it. It's got a British Airways logo on it. Elena is sitting with a hooded male. She changes her ring from the left hand to the right.

It was so clear and vivid. The throat was emphasised. Elena tossed me in the shit; she's paid money. Fortunately, a Negro saves me. I almost drowned. I cleared my throat, digging out caked mud from it. I knew that it meant I was ready for throat chakra stimulation. My sacral energies had been subdued and channelled towards my throat.

I had paid my dues, released myself from Elena's merciless clutches. But what was the suitcase with the BA logo all about? What about the dance floor and Elena's link with this mysterious hooded man? Changing her ring over? I hadn't a clue what that meant. Perhaps it was prophetic? Maybe, but I had no plans of leaving.

I got dressed and planned my attack on the day. It was going to be a tough one. My fund raising attempts were almost all redundant. I had reached the bottom of the barrel. Irons were in the fire, but things were getting desperate. There was a riotous mood in the ranks. I had battled on, virtually unaided, for months. The film had been completed, sales were in the pipeline, but our immediate cash flow had all dried up. Maybe my dream reflected the situation I was in. I needed someone to pull me out of the shit. I was drowning; I couldn't cope. I plodded downstairs with the world on my shoulders, no hope, no support and a gaggle of hungry geese snapping at my heels. I mustered up my reserves, prayed for divine help and exhorted a final surge from my broken soul.

Linda and her plotting flock sat around the breakfast table, backbiting each other. The din slowly slid into a deadly silence as I walked in.

'Good morning guys, what's on the breakfast menu today then?' They were not impressed, at all. They waited for Linda's lead.

'It's all your fault we're in this state. You're to blame. It's your responsibility to raise funds. Look around you, they agree with me, don't you?'

They had inherited 'the nodding dog complex'. Even Roy, my trusted friend and karmic link, had deserted me. He sat there in disgust, knowing, once again, he had betrayed my loyalty. Cleary had wormed his way close to Linda over the last few months. His aura stank of insurrection and conspiracy. He had it in for me from the start, but I didn't know why. He sat there on Linda's right, with a smug expression on his face and menace in his eyes. He nudged Linda, goading her into action. Lance sat on her left, drooling at the prospect of my downfall. They all expected me to buckle under the pressure and concede to them. I stood up calmly and put my cup on the table.

'Right, it's obvious you are unanimous in your decision to oust me. I'm all for democracy. Okay, who's going to take on the fund raising? Oh, how about you, Lance? Oh, Griff, you can organise the next lecture tour, it's only 50 venues this time. Cleary, I'm sure you'd love facing the bank, creditors, debt collectors and magistrates. Linda, do you have the balls to co-ordinate this lot? Oh, you've got a meeting with DB in 10 minutes. The shit's hit the fan big time. Harness, the landlord, has taken out a high court injunction. He wants £20,000. Oh Roy, King Roy, the fat cat, sitting there hiding behind your treacherous beard, what delights shall we bestow on you?'

You ought to have seen their faces. Some sank into pools of withdrawal; others glanced around nervously. They all melted into a quagmire of uncertainty, indecision and sheer fear.

'Right, I'm off back to bed, for a lie in. Actually, I think I'll stay in bed all day. Tell DB I'm not appearing today or tomorrow. In fact, I'm taking a week off. I'm sure you'll manage all right. Bye.' I trotted outside, into a beautiful, pristine, white blanket of driven snow. I left that pirate with her treacherous mutiny, in the black slush of their devious deeds. Squabbles raged, fists thumped and voices screeched.

Dring-dring, dring-dring, dring-dring!

'Hullo, Claregate College, may I help you? Oh, hi DB… Where's Chris? Just one moment, he's outside. I'll get him for you. Chris! It's DB, he wants you.'

I sauntered in; head high, with a broad smile beaming from side to side.

Isn't victory sweet? I love the odds, five to one, that's fair, isn't it? I called out to Lance 'I'm not answering it; the ball's in your court. I'm off to bed.'

'DB, I'm sorry. Chris is off back to bed… Right DB, I'll get them all assembled for you.'

I left them all running around like scared rats. He was coming up to give them a pounding. In 15 minutes the door slammed open and I heard his hobnailed shoes clump in.

'I'm here. Right you lot, in here, now!' He gave them the most horrific roasting I'd ever heard. It lasted at least half an hour.

I heard his hammerhead fists rage down on the table. He crunched up and down on their feeble egos. Not a whimper or squeak came from them.

'Chris, I want a word!' he thundered at the top of his voice. I never flinched or acknowledged his call. 'Lance, get your filthy butt up there now. You better practice licking on the way up, cos you've got a lot of arse to clean ahead of you. You all have, all of you!'

I eventually surfaced. They bowed down to me, begrudgingly. It turned out that Cleary was the 'bad apple'. He had tried his best to discredit me, but he had failed miserably. He was expelled off the premises immediately. The rest were on final warnings. Linda cowered for ages afterwards. She wasn't finished yet. She knew she was indispensable, at least for the moment.

CHAPTER 40

'Oh no. No! Get off of me. I'm not ready. I'm not ready!' I bellowed as I emerged from a frightening waking dream, holding my head and throat. I was soaked to the skin, mouth agape, throat deadly dry and heart thudding against my ribcage. I thought I was going to die; it was an awful experience.

> *16th Dec, 5.45am. Waking dream.*
> *My head and neck are wedged under a lorry tyre. It's crushing me; I feel an immense pressure in my skull; I think it's going to splatter like a watermelon. Suddenly, someone's penetrating me from behind; it's not painful, it's pleasant. I know it's DB; I ejaculate after a few seconds. He is now penetrating my throat with his fingers.*
> *'I'm preparing you for throat chakra energisation. You are ready for the fire!' he shouts.*

My dreams were getting weirder and weirder. It seemed they were preparing me for something wild. I'm going crazy. Anal sex? Was I turning gay? I had not been with a woman for ages. Was he shagging me in the astral? It's happened before. Who could I talk to? Stellios had fucked off; Roy the deserter had defected; Claire had been devoured; whom could I turn to? I sank into a deep pit of self-pity. Nobody cared. I was battling alone, against all odds, doing *The Lord's Work*. No praise, no shoulder to cry on, no support. The group, my spiritual brothers, wanted my head. I sank into a state of deep self-pity, mulling over the injustices and humiliation I had to endure.

Why must I suffer this way? Why the torture, the injustice, the betrayal? Why? Why? Why? I shouted out loud in anguish and banged my fist on the wall, then fell back to sleep to nurse my battered ego. So much sacrifice, so much effort, something must come of it, something. We were only a few days away from the annual celebration of Christ's birth. I felt so lonely and isolated; I was an outcast. Suddenly an angelic voice sang out from my pool of despair.

'You have come to be the saviour of the Christ child; his life was littered with suffering, injustice, betrayal and misunderstanding. You, my devoted servant, must persist on your path. Know that I am near.'

I surfaced buzzing with light, love and power. It was my *Daemon;* he had responded to my lament. *He* was with me, flooding me with encouragement. I knew I had to forgive my group brothers. I had to refocus and express the *Will of God.* With renewed vigour and vitality I threw on my rags and set about rebuilding my shattered position in the group. I had to get close to them; I needed to understand their feelings, their needs, and their insecurities. Roy, yes Roy, I'll start with him, I thought. Ultimately, I'd need to make my peace with Linda; she was the kingpin. I had to win her over. She was my biggest antagonist.

The festive season loomed; it was a blessing in many ways. No bills to pay, no bailiffs to fend off, no court battles and no heavy work schedule. We didn't celebrate Christmas; it was Western glamour according to DB. I'm sure it was. Imagine how much capitalist money is gobbled up by Christmas fever. It was obscene; the whole thing was anathema to the true message of the *Christ* child. The season of goodwill and love to all men? Ha! That was a laugh. After the New Year everyone would be back at each other's throats.

The pressure was still on us though. One evening, about a week before Christmas, the electric was cut off as we sat down to the evening meal. We were left in complete darkness. The boys scurried to the kitchen, lit little night-lights and sprayed the place with them. I knew right away what it was. I had sent the Electricity Board some post-dated cheques, in the hope they would be lenient. But the cruel, insensitive bastards cut us off. Christmas spirit? We spent the next couple days in darkness, with no lighting, nor heating; thank God the cooker was gas. We huddled up around the hearth of the dining room's open fire. There was something magical about the whole thing. We were insulated from the gluttonous excesses of the outside world. Candle lights tinkled and flames flickered to stir our highest emotions.

The Christ child, heavenly star, the lowly manger, animals providing body heat; we felt that warming angelic glow and humility, huddled up around that burning bush. I didn't need to utter a word of reconciliation. We had all bonded together, sublime in our moment of shared misery. Things could only get better; we knew it, and we believed it. It must, it would. It united our spirits, our hearts beat as one, and our souls sang a divine soliloquy.

Miraculously, two days before Christmas the lights came back on and never went off again throughout the holidays. I couldn't explain it; it wasn't supposed to happen, but it did. I didn't question it; it was a brilliant Christmas present. We all rejoiced at *The Lord's blessing*.

I had a welcomed break. Some went home, some stayed huddled up in their holes, hibernating for days. I caught up with my astrology research. My dream life was explosive, deep and energising. Something was moving and growing; I was being reborn within. The *fires* still flashed through me. I was enthused, elated and completely consumed in my esoteric world.

4th Jan. 1986. 5am. Super conscious experience.
I surface from a few muddled dream fragments. I lay on my right side, thumb pressed against my forehead to stimulate Ajna. My left side began to throb and powerfully vibrate. A thrust of energy blasted from there up to my brow. I experienced a phenomenal flash of light flood my whole being. The energy persisted; I thought I was going to project into the astral. Then my mind opened up into the most beautiful, ethereal landscapes,

*all vividly expressed in bright colours. The experience gradually
faded away and I centred myself.*

Was this *The Burning Ground?* Whatever it was, it was
awesome. I was stunned and overwhelmed by the experience. The
aftermath was just like heaven with angelic essences, rainbows and
vibrant sashes of spiritualising energy dancing through the inner
realms. It was mind expanding.

I was all fired up for days afterwards. Roy and I had patched
up our differences. I was with him in the office planning next year's
lecture tours, exhibitions and film production. The phone blared
abruptly and interrupted our conversation

'Hullo, Claregate College, may I help you?'

An excited voice, blasted down the handset. 'I need to
speak to Chris, quick get me Chris; I need to speak to Chris. It's
important.'

'Who wants to speak to him?'

'It's Pete, Pete Woods.'

'Hi Pete, it's me Chris. What's up? You sound like you're on
fire. Are you okay?'

'Bloody marvellous, Chris just great! Something phenomenal
has happened to me. I've been reborn.'

'Reborn? You mean you're a Born Again Christian? You're
not on a mission to convert me, are you? I'll pass you over to Roy,
maybe he'll want to be born again.'

'No, no, I've had a spiritual experience, a previous life recall.
It was so clear, so vivid. You were in it, you were there.'

'Sounds interesting; you found out you were Archbishop
Laud then?'

'Yes Chris, I did, I did. I was in a suicidal mood one day,
contemplating my demise. Something inside told me to visit
Canterbury Cathedral. I'm not too far from it; it's only a bus ride
away. Well I got there, strolled into the main hall, head bowed and
tiptoed to the altar. It was eerie and completely empty, just a silent
colossal monument. I hadn't prayed in years. Dreadful thoughts
swamped me. I had deserted him; I wasn't worthy of his grace. I
wasn't a Christian; I didn't know what I was. I was worthless, a

burden to my family and society. I stooped there with a heavy head and broken heart. Then I recited *The Lord's Prayer*. Suddenly, I was thrust into a vision; I was in front of a Holy altar, dressed in red and gold robes. I had a glorious, jewelled mitre on my head. I was preparing communion and then I turned:

'*With the power vested in me, I, Archbishop Laud, give you, in the name of Lord Jesus Christ, his holy blood. Arise, Sir Thomas, Earl of Strafford.*'

'You were kneeling, head bowed, waiting for my divine grace. I was filled with light and love from above as I held up the chalice. My whole body was bathed in his presence. Heavenly melodies echoed as angels swooped down, raising my lost soul out of the quagmire. I fell to my knees and my consciousness rushed back into me. The words 'Service! Service! The Lord's work! The Lord's work! Your brothers need you to do the Lord's work', echoed in my head.'

'Pete, that's an awesome experience. Do you want to come back? I'll have to clear it with DB.'

'Chris, I'll not let you down again. I promise.'

'Pete, you've got precious work to do, but you need to round out your personality shit. You'll never be any good if you don't.'

'I know, please let me come back, I'm lost out here. Nobody understands me. I'll go crazy or worse if I stay. Chris, I beg you, do something, please!'

'Leave it to me. I'll tell DB in a couple of days. I want you to really think about it, before you commit yourself to coming back.'

'Okay, but don't leave it too long. I don't know what I'll do.'

'Pete, we don't want any more losers here. Don't come back if you're just going to faff around and escape your responsibilities.'

'No, I'm ready to work. I'm ready to devote my life to His glory. I have what it takes; the Laud life confirms my commitment to the path.'

'I'll do my best, bye for now.' I turned to the others. 'Pete wants to come back. He's had a mystical experience; he's over the moon.'

'Are you going to give him another chance?' asked Roy. 'He let you down, what's stopping him doing it again?'

'It's not my decision, Roy. No doubt DB will consult me on it. Anyway, you almost betrayed me, didn't you? I gave you a second chance.' He shuffled around awkwardly and disappeared downstairs. 'I'm going to make a cuppa, anyone fancy one?'

In a week, Pete was back in camp. He waddled back humbly, with his tail between his legs. Roy was pleased to see him. It steadied his commitment to the path. They were like anchors for each other. I was content to have my lieutenants back. I needed people around me I could count on. I had organised 60 showings of *The Paracelsus* film preview and I needed them to support me.

Alana had kept in touch. She was my only true confidante. We were very close. I hadn't seen her for ages, but we were in tune. She was eager to help me, support me and prop me up when I was exhausted.

I came back one night, after a successful showing of the film. I was physically knackered, but mentally alert. I pulled out a horoscope in order to give it the final touches. Afterwards I sank into a light slumber where astrological glyphs fired their numinous energies in my consciousness. I was thrust into a dream vision; it was so vivid yet so surreal.

> *18th April, 2am, waking dream vision.*
> *I am dressed in Celtic warrior battle dress and armour. I am falling down a steep bank into a raging sea. With my Celtic broad sword in my hand and heavy shield on my back, I am hopelessly dragged into the searing, frothy currents. I thrust my sword into the rampant bowels of the sea shouting, '**the Chalice and the Sword are one**'. Suddenly, I merged with the ocean of life. It transformed into a sea of ethereal, multi-coloured mandalas. It was as if I was making love to the whole universe.*

I was heaving all over when I emerged from it. I could not comprehend its content at all. A Celtic warrior? The Chalice and the Sword? Fucking the whole ocean of life? The Chalice and Excalibur were mythical, a symbolic quest for spirituality. I had read Tennyson's *The Lady of Shalott* and *The Idylls of the King*. Surely it was all fantasy. It was linked to the chart I was doing. Yes, it had archetypal questing energies all through it. That was it; I dismissed the dream as merely a symbolic representation of archetypal elements. Quite a lot of unconscious material was just gibberish.

The tour was nearing completion, when DB called me for an impromptu meeting.

'Chris, sit down, I've got something important to discuss with you.'

'Is it about my spiritual experiences?' I asked. 'I'm overwhelmed with them at the moment.'

'No, just sit down and be quiet, for once in your life. Have you been following the media coverage of the AIDS epidemic?'

'AIDS epidemic? What's that got to do with me? I'm a healthy testosterone charged, heterosexual. Well I used to be. I don't know what I am nowadays.'

'Shut up, you silly sod. Sometimes I really wonder about you. You know I experimented with bio-magnetic healing, in my early days. I was part of a research team at the De La War Clinic. We constructed an electromagnetic device that sent high and low frequency pulses through the body. We cured all sorts of ailments: eczema, asthma, and rheumatoid arthritis. We were even treated mental disorders and experimented on leukaemia, though some of the results were inconclusive.'

'What's that got to do with the AIDS virus? No... DB, you're not are you?'

'Chris, I'm sure the virus would respond to electromagnetic stimulation, I'm sure of it. You see, the iron in the blood cells can be electro-magnetically charged. It would boost the immune system; give it extra energy to combat the virus. I'd have to cast the person's horoscope, analyse their karma and look how Mars is activating other planets. I've still got all my research notes and equipment. What do you think? Is it worth a go?'

'Fuck sake DB, you must be nuts. Blood cells, astrology, karma, Mars? Where do you propose to locate the treatment rooms? You've got no room here. No.. DB, you're not thinking of Claregate, are you? Tell me you're not.'

'It's the only place. There's the whole of the first floor. It can be easily converted. Pete's back, isn't he? He's a trained nurse, he's got his shit together.'

'How do you think the others will react? AIDS is a killer.'

'Chris, can you imagine if we could save lives using this type of therapy? We would vindicate the whole complementary medical field. Paracelsus fought the establishment in his day. He never gave up; we've got him to thank for many orthodox and complementary therapies. He was one of the first to use minute doses of poisonous substances to cure people of syphilis and all sorts of deadly illnesses. He was the father of homeopathy!'

'DB, I know of his achievements, but the AIDS virus is deadly?'

'It would be groundbreaking research. I'm not saying open Claregate's doors for all. Just a select few; It would only be for research, say three or four cases. Some early stages and some advanced.'

'DB, there are ethical and moral issues you have to think about. I don't think the group will agree to it, I don't.'

'They'll do as they are told or they are out. This is part of being on the front line. Are we to turn our backs on these poor, unfortunate souls? We are supposed to be healers, teachers and humanists. Where's the humanity in turning a blind eye?'

'You're right, but we'll have another mutiny in the ranks and guess who'll be at the head of it again.'

'I don't give a damn. They'll have to endure it. It's part of the process of detachment. If they can't adapt to circumstances, they'll have to go.'

'Let me talk to them first. I'll prime them up for the idea. I can win Pete and Roy over, it's the rest I'm worried about.'

'Do it. It's part of Claregate's program. We are frontiers people; we're here to tumble down barriers. This is New Age service at it's ultimate. Now off with you, I've got loads of work to do. Oh, before you run off, your progress is being noticed. They keep me informed. Your throat and brow centres have been energised. Your dreams are signposts of your spiritual progress. The fire, yes, 'My

God is an all consuming fire!' Chris, go with it, you're almost ready for *The Burning Ground*.'

'DB, I've had the most wonderful...'

'Multi-coloured mandalas, visions, energy transfers and super conscious experiences. I know Chris, I know. You don't have to tell me.'

'But, DB..'

'Oh, no, I'm not fucking you in the astral world. You are merging with my consciousness; The Nirmanakaya is overshadowing you. You have earned your spurs and won his respect. Keep up with your disciplines; you're almost ready. Focus your willpower, breed compassion and understanding; the mountaintops of initiation beckon you. It's there you'll encounter *The Burning Ground*.'

I trundled up the lane, thinking of my strategy. God, it was going to be difficult to get that sort of message out. What angle should I use? I had my reservations about the whole thing. Electro-magnetic fields? Bio magnetism? Solenoids? Pulses and frequencies?

All his gadgets were antiquated and in need of repair. It was all alien to me. Pete would be orgasming at the chance of being part of a research team. He loved the healing and therapeutic arm of the esoteric. As I pulled into the drive I bumped into Linda and Lance. They were coming back from a stroll up to the pub.

'Hi both, had a drink in the pub then?'

'Yes, we just couldn't resist it. Where have you been?'

'Oh, down at LE. DB's had a brainwave. It couldn't wait until the morning.'

'What's so important?'

'I'll share it with you in the morning, be prepared!'

They strolled in, muttering words of indignation. They knew something was amiss. They weren't stupid. I went to Roy and Pete's rooms, but they were deserted. It seemed they all had escaped for the night. I retired for the evening, bracing myself for the task ahead. I must admit, I wasn't confident of the outcome.

CHAPTER 41

I had an uneventful night; that was unexpected. My inner life was spilling over into my outer all the time. I welcomed the break in activity. How was I going to break the news of the AIDS clinic to them? I needed a personal angle. DB was right; this was the ultimate in service work to humanity. Christ wandered freely into leper camps, treating, healing and loving those unfortunate souls. I had to inspire them, make them realise the importance of the research. Imagine if DB came up with a cure? We would all be saints. I pulled on my patched up old jeans, threadbare red pullover and holey slippers, and trotted downstairs, where I bumped into Pete and Roy on the landing.

'Boys, am I glad to see you? Come in here, I need your support on something.' I proceeded to tell them about the idea. They just sat there, stunned into silence. Not a word, not one word of support or refusal.

'Well, what do you think? I know it's a tall order, but I'm willing to have a go.'

They just sat there shell-shocked, trembling at the thought of coming into contact with the killer virus. Pete sheepishly raised his head, heaved an almighty sigh and glanced at Roy for approval. Roy had shrunk into his shirt and trousers. I could hear their feeble, traumatised thoughts rattling in their vacant skulls.

'What? AIDS victims? No fucking chance! I don't want to die. They're filth; it's a gay man's virus; it's their own fault. It's their karma for thousands of years of abuse. I'm not putting my life on the line. Not for them, no way,' Roy blasted.

'What about you Pete? Give me some feedback. You've nursed psychiatric patients. It's just the same procedures, isn't it?' He wormed into the woodwork of the seat, squirming at the prospect.

'Well, err... yes; it's what we call barrier nursing. It's the same procedures all right, but we need every aid and protection. The whole ward must be immaculate and sterile.'

'But do you think it's possible? Look, it's your chance to shine, your chance to redeem yourself. You'll be heading research with DB. I know nothing about healing and treatments. You said you were into bio-magnetism, didn't you?'

'I suppose so, but...'

'So you'll give it a go then? Brilliant, I knew I could rely on your support. Roy, what about you? Are you for it?'

'Mmm, I don't know, the risks? AIDS, it scares the shit out of me.'

'Roy, you wouldn't be like that if your brother had contracted the virus, would you?'

'Well....'

'You bloody wouldn't! You'd want to do anything possible to find a cure, wouldn't you?'

'Well, yes of course I would, but I'm homophobic. They're the scum of the earth.'

'Roy, AIDS is not exclusively a homosexual disease; heterosexual men and women can catch it too. Isn't that a fact Pete?'

'Yes it is; it's not confined to any category, sex, race or colour. Men, women, children, the elderly, even nurses and doctors can contract it. It's the 20th century equivalent of the plague. It's an epidemic, a virus, just like the flu.'

He was getting all fired up; I could see his beady, little blue eyes, roll and light up. I had hit the jackpot with him. Roy was warming to it. I knew Pete would infect him with his enthusiasm.

'I'm off to put the kettle on, think about it. I'll be up with a brew for us.' I hopped downstairs; the rest of the group had assembled in the dining room. The atmosphere was charged with expectation. Heads dipped, lips whispered, eyes darted nervously as I pranced in.

'Good morning guys, what a good turnout. Are we expecting DB to arrive?' They weren't impressed with my jovial mood. They knew I had a message for them. 'I'll be back down in ten minutes to share our new project with you. DB called me over yesterday to give me the news. It's ground breaking, it's revolutionary, it's going to make impact.' I thought I'd fire them up and keep them guessing and I took a tray up to the office.

'Well, is it unanimous? Do I have your support?'

'Yes Chris, but only if it's done properly, in clinical conditions and strictly monitored.'

'Brilliant Roy, I've just primed that lot downstairs. Their ears are burning for information. Actually, you two can introduce the idea. Pete, you've got more knowledge and experience than I have on the matter. Roy, you've got to know them well, after all, you defected to them. You know their buttons.'

'Chris, they'll never listen to us, there will be an uproar. I can see it coming.'

'Don't try to shy out of it. I'll be in the background if you need my support. Oh, by the way, anyone who objects will be kicked out. It's all or nothing; there's no choice in the matter.'

'Is that it? An ultimatum?'

'Yep, that's it, on a plate. DB will take questions later. We have to steamroll them before he lays the final icing on the cake. Right off with you, it's your time to take some responsibility. If you're going to succeed in here you need to make your stand. I'll be down in a minute, get started, go on, beat it.'

My tactics worked a treat. The boys managed to convince the rest about the idea. Pete was fantastic; he knew his nursing stuff inside out. I didn't even have to intervene. DB came in and reassured them that it was important humanitarian service and it was inspired by *The Masters*.

We gutted the rooms, redecorated, serviced the equipment and created a clinical environment. Barry and John made contact with the national AIDS help-line and offered our services. In weeks we had our first two patients booked.

Claregate was spotless; a powerful healing aura flooded it. It was the day before the appointments. DB had gathered us together to demonstrate the treatment. He looked immaculate in his white, starched coat. Pete stood by him, with an air of authority, decked out in his nursing gear. They came across as very professional and convincing. We were all proud of our commitment to helping find a cure for the killer virus.

'Congratulations all around, the clinic looks marvellous. I don't want our approach to be too clinical though. By that I mean the environment must be relaxed, calming and homely. These kids need to be loved; they need to feel they're cared for and not treated as outcasts. I'll let Pete talk you through the necessary precautions you need to strictly adhere to.'

Pete was brilliant, clear and commanding. He had found his niche; he was buzzing with enthusiasm. What a far cry he was from his punch bag, suicidal days.

'Right Pete, sit down,' said DB. 'That was well presented; now it's my turn. Does anyone know how bio-magnetism works?'

Roy spoke up. 'It energises the pre-physical, etheric body and hence the aura. The aura is said to be electro-magnetic. It is the sum total of all man's bodies, from the etheric up to the spiritual. Primarily, electro-magnetic energy charges the chakras of the etheric body. As we know, the main chakras directly link to the endocrine glands.'

'Well done' Now. Who can tell me where the endocrine glands are situated and what their function is?'

'Endocrine glands secrete hormones and vitamins into the blood stream and central nervous system,' answered Linda. 'They are the natural valves and balancers; they vitalise the body; they are situated strategically, from the base of the spine to the head.'

'You know your esoteric anatomy, Linda.'

The praise encouraged Linda to further demonstrate her knowledge. 'The endocrine glands vitalise the whole spectrum of man's body and it is *prana*, the lifeforce that stimulates growth, regeneration and healing.'

As soon as she finished DB retook the floor. 'Now, let's get specific. According to our experts, the AIDS virus attacks the immune system, robbing the patient of vitality. It vampirises the blood, draining it's life-supporting nutrients and prevents them from being passed to the body. As a result, endocrinal organs such as the liver, pancreas, the thymus and the thyroid glands become agitated and ultimately starved of life. The central nervous system becomes severely stressed and affects the brain's intricate balance. Bang, the immune system is on overload, the patient progressively wastes away.' He turned to the group with a question. 'Can anyone tell me where to treat the patient? What organ is imperative?'

'It's the blood,' I put in.

'Yes, the blood, ladies and gents; what main element is found in human blood?'

'Iron.'

'Excellent Lance Iron! Which sign and planet rules the blood and iron?'

It was Griff's turn to answer. 'Mars rules iron, hence the blood. Scorpio is the sign ruled by Mars. Leo and the sun rule circulation.'

'You've got a brain after all, Griff. Scorpio and Mars rule short term, violent karma, let's not forget that. We cannot interfere if the illness is of karmic origin. That's going against cosmic law. Yes, we must always consider the person's karma. That's really important. Let's get back to practicalities. We are going to boost the patient with iron as well as a whole host of multi-vitamins. We are going to bathe them with love, teach them meditation, introduce them to concepts of ancient wisdom and blast them with bio-magnetic energy waves. Right, who can tell me how the bio magnetic waves work?'

'DB, we attach the devices on the surface of the body, strategically over the throat, heart and liver.'

'Yes, yes, we already know that Pete, come on think.'

'The iron supplements passing through the blood are charged and magnetised by the electro-magnetic current.'

'Awesome Chris, have you ever been into healing?'

'No, but it seems logical to me; Mars, iron, the blood and magnetism are linked to Scorpio. You don't have to be Einstein to see the link.'

'Don't get cocky boy, but that's right. I'm not sure about the frequencies, but that's part of our experiment. I'll need volunteers to keep my research notes, record feedback, set up the treatment rooms and organise meditations. Report to Pete, he'll be co-ordinating the program. Are there any questions? Pete can fill you in with details.'

'How long do you propose to treat them?' asked Linda. 'Would you use other healing aids, such as the Bach Flower Remedies?'

'Ha, ha, ha! The Flower Remedies? That's like putting a tiny plaster on a gaping open wound. I thought you had more sense than that, Linda. We could give them *Rescue Remedy,* but I don't want to mix and match approaches. The results would be of no consequence. We'll monitor them weekly, say three healing sessions a week, for a month. We'll continue for a three-month period. That would give us time to measure the effects.'

'You'll need their horoscopes cast, won't you?'

'Yes Linda, thanks for reminding me; you can organise that. Right, I'm off. Chris, make sure they're up bright and early. I want everything to run like clockwork.'

'Leave it to me DB. We won't let you down.'

That was that, the whole place was buzzing with excitement. I could see some of their faces reflected deep reservations. There was a lot of soul-searching going on. They all slowly petered away, leaving me pondering on this new project. I sat in the clinic and gaze around me. It was awesome just to be here whilst this extraordinary research was being initiated. But did I really want to be a part of it? I wasn't shirking my responsibilities, but my instincts were telling me it was time to expand my horizons. I had achieved a high degree of spiritual understanding and wisdom. I was being constantly guided by my *Daemon.* I was ready for *The Burning Ground.* Roy and Pete were coming on a treat, but they were still not ready to take the reigns.

I pottered around, completed my daily duties and retired for a meditation. Before seating myself I flicked open CW Leadbeaters' book, *The Chakras.* He was an extremely gifted clairvoyant and colleague of Alice Bailey. His research had formed the basis of our knowledge of energy fields, chakra centres, colour healing and man's true cosmic origins. He was a giant of his age, a visionary, a mystic and a member of the clergy. I settled down on my bed to review my future role at Claregate when suddenly I was bathed in gentle, rocking vibrations. I knew an experience was looming.

> *15th July, 4.35pm, fire experience.*
> *The force began to flow; first it was a trickle. My consciousness shifted to a higher plane. Then, from the base of my back, a torrent blasted through me. This time there was little pain and I withstood the fire as it shot upwards and inwards. Suddenly I am thrust into a dream vision. I am with Alana. She knows a previous life of mine. She gives me a clue.*
> *'You were a physician, alchemist, astrologer and advisor to William The Conqueror.' DB and Dick call me to confirm its validity.*
> *'Higginson, Higginson, Higginson.' The name hounded me as my consciousness thrashed back through the ethers and thudded back to my physical.*

Alchemist? Astrologer? Physician and advisor to William The Conqueror? I was on fire; I had no control over these experiences. They were frightening. Higginson? That was too contemporary a name for the 11th century, I thought. It must be a word play or something. Then I remembered that Higginson was DB's doctor. Why was I given his name? I wasn't sure anymore. The fire experience was so energising. Its spiritualising force penetrated the seals or webs protecting my chakras. That's what Leadbeater was on about; I had just read it.

Everything was happening very fast. It was as if I was being crammed full of wisdom. I couldn't understand it. It was overwhelming me; I needed a break; I needed to get back to grass roots and earth myself, otherwise I was convinced I'd go completely mad. Where was I to go? Who with? I was on my own. I couldn't go back to my old life. My uncles had moved on and I doubted they would have me back anyway. Elena, yes Elena, where was that scheming bitch? She had disappeared. That was probably the best place for her, as far as I was concerned. I could go back home, to Cyprus, for a while. Mum would be over the moon.

'Hey, Chris, it's for you, someone's on the phone.'

'Oh ta Lance. Do you know who it is?'

'She never said, but she sounds a wee bit Welsh. She your fancy lady then?'

'It's none of your business. She's just a friend, okay.'

'Well, there are friends and there are friends.' His eyes twinkled and he gave me a cheeky wink. I knew what would happen. It would be all over Claregate, like a virus, spreading to the ears of the plotters. Linda would have a field day. She'll make sure she uses it, like a stick to beat me with. She'll eventually feed it back to DB, after blackmailing me with it. Well I'll have to tell him first. Tell him what? Nothing's happened yet. But, every time I speak with her I go weak at the knees. I'm positive we're karmically linked.

'Hullo?'

'Hi Chris, it's me, Alana. I've got to talk to you.'

'What's up?'

'I've just come out of a deep meditation; the experience, oh the experience, it was so overwhelming.'

'What experience Alana? You're beginning to sound spaced out like Lance.'

'Chris, it was so vivid, so real. I'm still in shock.'

'Come on, tell me.'

'You were in my vision. It was so vibrant, so clear and oh, the feeling.'

'Feeling? Oo... I like the sound of that. I get those sorts of dreams too; oo... they're lovely; it's all to do with being celibate you know. The inner life compensates for the lack of emotional and sexual activity. I sometimes wake up all w...'

'Chris, shut up, stop babbling on. It wasn't like that at all. You were all dressed up in rich tunics, but you were not royalty. It was in medieval times; I felt you were a doctor, chemist or something. I saw you bent over an experiment, quill in one hand and a golden five-pointed star dangling from a neck chain. There were scrolls all over the place, bottles oozing vapours and jars of the weirdest things

I'd ever seen. Oh, the stench, sulphur, magnesium, mercury... Chris? Are you still there? Hullo?'

I was stunned. Tongue-tied, I flopped back in the chair. She's picked up on my vision. My god, we're telepathically linked. Pins and needles shot through my body and a cold sweat flushed through me.

'Hullo? Have we been cut off? Hullo?'

'Alana, no you've not been cut off, I'm in total shock.'

'Shock? Why? What's happened? You haven't fainted again?'

'No, go on, continue.'

'Well, I'm there, I'm really there, it's so clear. I scan the place and it's so spooky: mystical charts, astrological posters, all sorts of hieroglyphs of planets: strange alchemical drawings of demons, lizards and snakes. Suddenly, I'm blasted by a cloud of pungent smoke; before I'm shot back to the physical, I'm given the word *Conqueror! Conqueror!* What do you reckon it means?'

'I don't know. I just don't know anymore. Alana, I feel as if I'm cracking up. I'm going insane, I'm sure of it.'

'Why Chris? What is it? Tell me, don't bottle it all up inside.'

'Alana, I have dreams, visions, fire experiences, and now this.'

'What?'

'Alana, I experienced all you've said. I've just come out of a super-conscious experience. I was given almost exactly what you saw. We're telepathically linked, I can't believe it; it's all too much. I need to get away; I must get away. Now the AIDS clinic, I'm cracking up.'

'Wao telepathy, that's amazing. Do you think it's a past life connection. Hey, wait a minute, what did you say? AIDS clinic? What AIDS clinic?'

'We've set up a research facility at Claregate. We're going to receive our first patients tomorrow.'

'That's really interesting. Who is going to treat them?'

I proceeded to divulge the whole theory. She loved all that sort of thing, being a Virgo ascendant.

'That's so avant-garde; I'd love to be part of it. You should be privileged. To think DB may come up with a cure. That will put the seal of approval on complementary therapies. The establishment would have to take note and even endorse it. It's so wonderful.'

'Alana, I'm contemplating leaving. I need to spread my wings and explore new realities. I need to see if I can apply what I've learnt out there. Honestly, if I don't go soon, I'll crack up, I will!'

'Don't be silly; you've been through hell and back. You're too strong to falter; you've earned the right to wield your sword. You may need new battles to fight.'

'I think that's it. I feel as if my work is done here. I've been tried and tested; I've fought and won my battles here. My quest is opening out into a new direction. Tell me Alana, do you know anything about King Arthur and the Knights of the Round Table?'

'Well, as far as I know, there was an historic King Arthur.'

'Was there?'

'Yes, he was a 6th century, Romano-Celt, warlord and chieftain. He came from South Wales, not too far from my roots. There are lots of Celtic sites in the Gwent valleys and all around Wales.'

'Is that right? I thought the whole story was mythical?'

'Well, there is a mythical and spiritual dimension to it, but the real King Arthur Pendragon was a Silurian warlord. He inherited Roman culture as well as his Celtic roots. The whole of South Wales is littered with Celtic standing stones, burial mounds and hill forts. There's even one on the hill at Caerleon, just minutes away from Newport, my hometown. Why are you interested in him?'

'I had one of my surreal visions. I was a Celtic warrior. I tumbled into a raging sea with the words; the sword and the chalice are one! I dismissed it as a fragment of dream flotsam and jetsam. I linked it to an astrological chart I was interpreting. Could it be meaningful?'

'Possibly. Maybe you've got a link there.'

'I don't think so; I've no interest in Celtic history. Arthur, Excalibur, the Knights of the Round Table, it's all fantasy.'

'Don't be too sure, you never know. Listen, I must dash, I'm on an early tomorrow. Hope it all goes well, speak to you soon, bye.'

She left me lingering with loose ends tangled in a mass of knots.

Almost immediately I remembered Michael El Legion and the taped channelling. He mentioned a strong link with Merlin, King Arthur and the druids. I was completely confused. For the first time in ages I was unsure of my direction. My mettle was strong enough to withstand all the ravages of life here, but something was drawing me away. I needed to be tested in the big world out there. That I was sure of. I withdrew to my room and didn't even surface for dinner. I had to prepare myself for tomorrow.

CHAPTER 42

I had an unsettled night, but no dream recall. I woke with *Higginson, Higginson,* echoing in my ears. Maybe it was a previous life clue after all. Where did all that stuff come from when DB asked me about magnetic fields? It just flooded back from some mystic source in the pit of my unconscious. I pulled out my best shirt and trousers, 'bulled' my shoes and swished up my hair. I could hear a commotion in the hallway. Voices shouting, screaming, doors thudding and smash of glass. What was going on this time of the morning? I dashed downstairs to Linda's screams; Roy and Pete had Griff pinned to the wall. He was in a terrible; shirttails hanging out, jumper ripped. He was shouting obscenities and bleeding from face wounds.

'Chris, I think he's flipped,' shouted Pete. 'Look at him.' He was still lounging at them, trying to throw punches and head butts.

'Leave me alone! You're all a shower of bastards! That fucking whore, she's to blame. Bitch! Fucking bitch!' His eyes were rolling and his pupils were dilating; he was high on something.

'I'll fucking kill her; It's her fault!'

'Let's get him outside,' I shouted. We bundled him out onto the lawn and restrained him using a piece of old rope. 'Right, keep him here for now. Maybe he'll come to his senses. Does anyone know what happened? Pete?'

'Well, I heard Linda's screams and ran out from the kitchen. Griff had his hands around her throat and she was hitting him and kicking out. Then I saw the little brown bottle smashed on the floor.

It said it was Rescue Remedy but I sniffed it and it smelled of opium. You could definitely smell it.'

'Fuck sake, that's all we need, a raving maniac, high on opium, today of all days.' When I found Linda she was in a hell of a state, ghostly white, sobbing, trembling and delirious.

'I didn't mean it,' she cried. 'It wasn't my fault.'

'Calm down, its all right, calm down. What happened?'

'Griff came to me last night. He was in a hell of a state and stank of disinfectant. He was on tender hooks, pacing to and fro and rubbing his hands. I could see he was very agitated. When I did calm him down he admitted that he was terrified of the AIDS patients.

'He kept crying 'I can't do it. I can't do it. I've got to wash my hands. I need to wash! I need to wash!' I got him a cuppa and slipped in some Rescue Remedy Karen had left behind. That seemed to work, it settled his nerves. I gave him the bottle and told him to take a few drops every three hours. I didn't know it was going to send him berserk. How was I to know it wasn't Rescue Remedy? Karen must have mixed up a concoction. You know she was on opium, don't you!'

I told Linda to calm down and Pete would handle it. Then she admitted she was terrified of catching AIDS too.

'I've supported all of DB's mad schemes,' she said, in a pleading voice. 'I never questioned him, but this is beyond me. I don't want to put my life on the line, just in the name of research.'

'We'll be okay,' I told her. 'Pete knows all the procedures and precautions. Listen, you don't have to have contact with them. You could write up research notes. How about that?'

'I'm still scared. What if one of them goes ape-shit like Griff? He could bite or scratch us.'

'Linda, believe me, we'll be okay. Just rest for now; DB doesn't have to know about this.' I left her in a stable frame of mind. Hopefully, I had reassured her. It was a real test of character, certainly not for the faint-hearted to take on. By now Griff had come to his senses and was sitting up chatting to Roy while Pete gave him the once over.

'What's the diagnosis, will he live?'

'Yes, he'll be just fine. Won't you Griff?'

He turned to face me; his eyes were clear and alert. He grinned at me, flashing his greying, Welsh valley teeth.

'Yes 'butty', I'm feeling fine. I had some wicked experiences though,' he smiled, albeit faintly. 'I'll have to have a go of that again.'

'Fuck off Griff, we'll have a massacre on our hands next time and it will be you who'll be on the receiving end.' He was okay and back to normal. He apologised to Linda; they were mates again. The opium accentuated his paranoia, but he was quite looking forward to getting involved in the research.

The doors swung open. It was Barry, John and two frail looking lads in their 20s. One of them was seriously ill. He looked like a scarecrow, a bag of bones; his pale face stretched over his tiny skull like a transparent mesh. His eyes rolled around in his heavy, dark sockets; his skin was a patchwork of bruises and lacerations. He hobbled in on crutches, barely able to walk. The stench of death seethed from his mouth.

'This is Anthony and Nigel, Chris. We're going to be seeing a lot of them over the next few weeks, aren't we Anthony?'

'Yes indeed, nice to meet you, Chris. It's a beautiful, old place, very peaceful.' He stretched out a trembling, bony hand, bludgeoned with bulging blue veins and infested with clustered scabs.

'Don't worry, I'm in remission; it's okay, it's not rampant now.'

'Anthony welcome. Pleased to meet you and Nigel; we'll try to make your stay with us as comfortable as home.' I shook his hand, God it felt so brittle. I was afraid if I shook it any longer, it was going to fall off. He was in a really bad way. I supposed Claregate was his last hope.

'The garden is beautiful this time of year,' I added. 'Fancy a cuppa on the lawn?'

'Ooo, you are a darling, aren't you,' Nigel answered. 'That's really sweet. Isn't he gorgeous? I love the accent.' He was all eyes and gay innuendoes as he pirouetted into the garden. He looked very camp, sitting there, legs crossed, lips pouting and flicking back his long, blonde locks. He was full of life and buzzing with energy. He didn't look ill at all. In fact, he looked more alive than most of the Claregate mob.

'I'll introduce you to the boys and Linda later.'

'Boys, mm… you mean to say there are more hunks like you around?'

'Nigel, behave yourself,' chirped Anthony. 'You always show me up. Don't take him seriously, he's always a tease love.'

They were characters, never a dull moment when they were around. Nigel was hilarious, winking and nudging Anthony when he saw Pete and Roy walk by.

'Oo, look at that love, aren't they gorgeous? What do you need to stay here full time?'

'Shut up, Nigel, you'll be the death of me,' Anthony said coughing and spluttering. 'Don't make me laugh anymore, it really hurts.'

They had tea, we did the introductions and DB arrived looking very smart. He looked like he was just plucked out of Harley Street.

'Hi both, I'm Dr. Baker, I've already perused your files. Let's get down to business. Who is Anthony?'

'It's me the young, handsome one,' Anthony said trying to hold a straight face. 'Mm, ' D.B. frowned whilst peering over his spectacles. Well I suppose you are Nigel,' he said in an air of authority, pointing at him.

'Who me?' Nigel said in a sarcastic tone, turning his head behind him as if someone else was there.

'I'm glad you both have a sense of humour,' D.B. said in a sympathetic voice. 'Pete, come and take a diagnostic analysis, oh and don't forget to get their astrological details.' He swept out with a wave of his hand and added 'I'll leave you in the hands of my capable assistant. See you shortly.'

Pete looked immaculate in his white coat, notebook and stethoscope dangling from his neck. He'd trimmed his beard and oozed respect and professionalism. In an hour they were ready for their initial interview with DB. Pete attended for second opinions; after all, DB hadn't practiced in years. They had a short break, no food or water, before being led upstairs. The treatments lasted for an hour each. The day sped by and before long they were waving us goodbye, Nigel blowing kisses, swivelling his hips and strutting like a real catwalk queen.

DB shot back to LE, in exhaustion. He didn't even come in for dinner. Pete was all fired up. He was in his element, loving every minute of it: the respect, the control, and the self-importance. His Leo ascendant radiated like a blazing sun. I met him later, to update me on developments.

'So how did it go then?' I asked him.

'Hey, it's strictly confidential. I can't divulge any details.'

'Hey, Pete, just because you're the flavour of the month, it doesn't warrant that sort of bullshit. A few weeks ago you were a worn out old punch bag, ready for the tip.'

'Oh, all right, but it's strictly between you and me. Anthony is in a bad way; he's only got weeks to live, poor soul. I don't know why they sent him to us.'

'Maybe they're trying to discredit us, you know, put the boot in before we even start the treatments.'

'I don't know. Nigel is HIV positive; he's not got the full-blown virus yet. He's quite healthy, with no real symptoms.'

'So, do you think the treatments will work?'

'It's early days yet, but I'm optimistic.'

'Have you got copies of their charts?'

'Yes, there in my file.'

I studied them carefully. 'Mm, Anthony's not got much of a chance. He's Virgo ascendant; that's physical and soul purification through illness. His sun is intercepted in Scorpio in the third house. God, transiting Saturn is right over it now.'

'What does that mean?' Pete asked.

'The third house rules the nerves, lungs and the etheric body. Scorpio's influence is lethal. It rules death and rebirth. Saturn, the mythological Grim Reaper, is ready to scythe him clear of his diseased physical body. He's ready for purification, he'll need counselling.'

'What do you mean?'

'Look at him, he's decomposing, his life force is slowly vacating his body. It's like charging up a dud battery. No matter how hard you pump it up, it dies on you.'

'So you think we should prepare him for passing over?'

'Yes and no,' I replied. 'If we can enhance his quality of life, even for the remainder of his tortured existence, that would be something.'

'The electromagnetic blasts and vitamin injections will boost his immune system, but he can't retain the energy indefinitely.'

'Pete, his astro-mental and spiritual bodies are gradually withdrawing from the terminally tortured physical body.'

'So the soul is ready to withdraw it's anchor to the physical world. Why do you say he's being purified? AIDS is worse than all the other vile diseases thrust together. There's nothing pure about it.'

'Well, there's other ways of looking at it. From a soul viewpoint, AIDS casts out anything that is not self. It vomits the bile of years or life times of personality abuse, cleansing its vehicle. He's in preparation for a new vital system in his next life. He can't live in this energy field, here, now, on planet Earth.'

'What you're trying to say is, his immune system is being prepared to receive energy of a higher order?'

'Something like that; the soul will come back, trailing clouds of glory, say in 100 years. The physical-vital body it materialises will have been completely cleansed of impurities of its past lives. It will be ready to receive the life sustaining energy of planet Earth, 100 years from now.'

'I get it! That sounds logical. The way Earth's eco-system is going, we'll all need to mutate new organs to survive in our environment.'

'Yes, that's what the big seven, the League of Nations don't realise. They are bent on abusing Gaia's natural energies. She will fight back, she's a living, vital being, with consciousness and her own soul.'

Pete appeared thoughtful. 'You're right, just look at the dissipation of the ozone layer and the constant mining for oil. Toxic waste is being dumped all over the place; don't they know they're killing the planet?'

'The Earth is over heating,' I said quietly.

'What can we do Chris? It's out of our hands.'

'The planet's welfare is in our hands. We, as humanity, are responsible for all Earth's kingdoms: mineral, plant, animal, human and above. It's potentially another Atlantis waiting to explode.'

'So you think we're heading for self-destruction?'

'Pete, they draw millions of barrels of oil from the Earth's crust. You know what happens if you run your car without oil?'

'Boom!'

'Yes, boom! There are vast pockets of natural gas accumulating at potentially lethal levels. You see, oil is the natural cooling system of planet Earth. Rape it away and you've got a planet that is overheating and running out of time. Combine that with the depletion of the ozone layer and hey presto! A multi-dimensional explosive blast; another planet gobbled up in the universe's big black hole.'

'Mm, let's hope the Masters can influence the major players sufficiently. It's all in our hands.'

'Yes, let's get back to AIDS and it's spiritualising effect. You understand the need for preparing terminal cases like Anthony for transition to the other side?'

Pete smiled at me. 'Yes, thanks for the insight; I'll confer with DB tomorrow. I'm sure he'll be researching their esoteric case histories and charts.'

Needless to say, in a matter of weeks Anthony stopped coming. Laurence and Linda had sat with him after his treatments and prepared him for his transition into spirit. We all helped him to adjust his consciousness to embrace a new reality. We told him he would be released from his wrecked physical vehicle, the intense pain would subside and he would be purified in body, mind and soul. We meditated together, the whole group, united in the glory of his transition to the inner worlds. He was in his Master's hands, in his bosom, rejoicing in his aura. He had reached peace, bliss and harmony. His essence would rest and recuperate, waiting for its time to enter into a new terrestrial cycle.

The clinic slowly died a premature death, just as Anthony slipped into spirit. We all sighed with relief when it was over. We had tried, it did help, and it did work. Nigel was still living and he was healthy. He turned his life around, prayed, meditated, took doses of vitamins and studied the ancient wisdom. Even if we managed to give hope to one soul, that was enough. We helped the other fade into the spirit world, knowing he would come again, totally renewed; with stronger limbs and purified body, his old soul would take the road again. We had made impact; the results didn't matter.

I told DB about my plans of leaving. He was distraught at first, but he gave me his blessing in the end. I compromised, promising to stay three more months. I still didn't know where I was going, but that wasn't important. I knew my time to welcome a new phase had come. I was 28 years old, approaching my Saturn return. It was in Sagittarius, the sign of travel, philosophy, the Quest and publications. My destiny lay ahead of me, where it was going to lead, only God knew.

I had to wrap up loose ends, charts and projects for my exit. I woke one morning to a phenomenal waking dream experience.

> *28th August, 6.55am.*
>
> *A concentration camp packed with hundreds of young boys grouped together in a pen. A horse, tied up and bucking violently, is in with them. They are being thrust under the horse's hooves. Some are bleeding from severe head wounds as the horse bucks and kicks out.*
>
> *I am chained up in a dungeon. A torturer is playing with a thin, yellow snake. It's writhing all over his hands and arms. He points it at me; it shoots up inside of me. I feel it rushing around my body. Its tail is sticking out of my anus. I try to pull it out but I can't.*

I was overwhelmed with fear, anger, disgust, and despair. The horse tied up, mutilating those poor boys. It reflected my position I suppose. The horse is a symbol of Sagittarius. My Saturn return was in my second house, that rules being confined and thwarted. Lashing out, blood, wounding, that was Scorpio on the cusp. Yes, it was symbolic of my need to break free. If I didn't I would be so frustrated I would harm my chances of new potential growth. The new growth was the young boys, boxed in and being mutilated, that was quite clear. As to the rest of the dream and the snake - I felt like shit after it. Torture, that yellow snake shooting up inside of me, its tail hanging out of my anus. It was awful. I did care if it was the beginning of Kundalini fire; it was so dehumanising. However, it still proved I was on target; my decision to leave had been reinforced.

I got up and dressed and pottered around my room. The hall phone echoed in the background as a voice from above bellowed.

'Pick up the phone down there, you bunch of losers!'

A rumble of footsteps stopped in the corridor, just outside my room.

'Chris, it's for you, it's Alana.' Roy's voice thundered, like a foghorn. I jumped up and dashed downstairs to the office phone.

'Hi Alana, what's up?'

'I've been offered a post in Cyprus. I applied for a reps job with British Airways holidays. I've got it.'

'Brilliant, you kept that quiet.'

'I didn't want you to know unless I got the job. I'm just so excited.'

'When do you start?'

'Well, that's the problem; it's not till next season, March-April. But I've got two friends who'd love to come with me.'

'That's good. Where are you going to stay?'

'We're all chipping into buying a Volkswagen Camper. We're going to drive all the way. Isn't it exciting?'

'Wao, I'd love to do something like that. That's so adventurous.'

'It's a four berth.'

'What does that mean?' I asked hopefully.

'It means there's an extra bunk. Fancy a lift?'

'What, me? But I've got nothing: no money, no clothes and nowhere to live. Hey, hang on a minute; my grandmother's got a house in the village. I'm sure we could stay there; it's empty and my Mama wouldn't mind.'

369

'That's all sorted then. I'll tell the others. They'll be over the moon.'

'Hey wait a minute; you're so canny, aren't you. You planned this all along, didn't you?'

'Chris, you had decided to leave? That's what you told me. I just put two and two together. We can chill out in Cyprus until the spring. We've got the van for touring. It'll be absolutely brilliant.'

'God, I'm so excited. I had contemplated going home; but with you, it will be divine. I'll call my Mama later. When are you setting off?'

'Well, we've put an offer on a camper. That should be wrapped up soon. I think end of October, beginning of November.'

'That's only ten weeks away.'

'Yes, in ten weeks we'll be tooting our way through Europe. I can't wait to tell the girls.'

'Alana, give me a couple of days to sort it out with Mama. I'm sure she'll be thrilled to bits about having her prodigal son back. She'd thought all along that she'd lost me. God, just to see her face when I tell her; It will be the answer to her prayers.'

I clicked the phone down and sat there quite still and quiet. I was on my way out of here. I should have been elated, but I wasn't. I was going to leave all this behind, after it had been my home for five years. My spiritual brothers, DB, the work; I felt so guilty, so torn, but if that was my destiny, I had to follow it. My Soul's Purpose beckoned me to search out a new path. I had to follow my inner guide. The work would continue; he had plans for me.

I despatched my duties in mega-efficiency mode and bounded upstairs to my room. It was late afternoon, I burrowed into my hole, tired, elated, confused and drenched in guilt. The frenzied battle raged in my battered brain; thoughts collided with dreams and chimeras swamped my aspirations. The ghosts of my past and angels of my future swished me into a sweet slumber.

CHAPTER 43

I must have been exhausted; I slept through the call for dinner. It was 8.15pm. To tell the truth, I was so excited about the prospect of going to Cyprus, I hadn't thought of food. There was a knock at my door.

'Chris, are you in there?'

'What is it?'

'It's me Roy, you okay? You missed dinner?'

'I know I missed dinner, I'm not feeling that hungry.'

' I hear you're preparing to leave us: Is that true?'

'I don't want to talk about it tonight. We'll have a session tomorrow, okay? Get Pete to join us too. We'll meet in the office, say 8am.'

'Okay, goodnight.'

How did he know I was leaving? I didn't tell anyone apart from DB. I'm sure he wouldn't have spilled the beans. But Lance... yes, that bloodhound must have had his ears to the ground. He was sniffing around the place when I was talking to DB. Nothing was sacred in here. He just couldn't keep his scheming mouth closed. He had to tell everyone. I pictured him racing around like a rampant virus infecting everyone. I would soon know the extent of the damage.

I turned to a chart I had to complete. It embodied the myth of Prometheus, the Greek fire god. He was banished from Mount Olympus, chained to a rock face and tortured eternally. An eagle would feed from his liver, only for it to be restored the next day. That was his punishment for stealing fire from the gods and giving it to humanity. He was the original channel of spiritual fire; he sacrificed himself to share that fire with us. Hercules eventually released him from his torment. As I pondered on the significance of the myth, I was thrust into an awesome experience.

5th Sep. 10.30pm, previous life recall and Kundalini fire experience.

I lay on my side, with my thumb over Ajna. Suddenly a radiant flash zapped me, followed by the most intense point of light I'd ever seen. As I focused on it, my consciousness shot out of the physical, through the point into a totally new dimension. I was viewing a medieval scene through the eyes of a being. I was in a room; it felt like a chamber of some sort; thick castle walls and rich coloured tapestries hemmed in my vision. Massive candelabras decked the room, walls and ceiling. The stench of candle wax, old linen and antiquity, battled against a sweet, floral aroma from outside.

'Give me clues! Give me clues! Where am I?' I shouted.

My gaze led me towards a male leaning over a rostrum. He's dressed in heavy, red and golden robes. I sense he's in a position of authority, a lord or aristocrat. I'm still shouting and I peer over his shoulder to the rostrum. A manuscript is open; 1055 is flashed to me. The lettering is in medieval script, Latin, French or German; it wasn't English. I was getting really frustrated by now, so frustrated that I was tossed around in turbulence. I shot back in a blinding flash, back through the point of light into physical consciousness.

"Oh my god!' I shouted, as I was unceremoniously dumped back to physical reality. It took me minutes to centre myself; my heart pounded, my breath bellowed and my limbs were in a cataleptic cramp. The whole experience was highly energising, vivid and clear. I was fully conscious of all my actions.

What triggered it off? It must have been my focus on the Prometheus myth and the astrology. It couldn't have been anything else. I had found a way to access spiritual fire in the inner worlds; I was a fire god in the making.

I was on a high for hours; my whole body was buzzing with the aftermath. Who would believe me? They would all think I contrived the whole experience. Who could I talk to? This was the price I had to pay for entry into the realm of the gods.

The words *'to know, to will, to dare and to be silent,'* ricocheted around my tortured head like stray bullets, clearing debris of preconceived rational fragments. The words echoed into infinity. ***Be silent, be silent, be silent,*** beat a humming vibration on my eardrums. It resonated into that familiar, high-pitched, laser signal. I knew ***He*** was close. ***He*** was with me; ***He*** wanted me to savour the experience. I tucked myself in, flicked off the little, crooked bed lamp and sent the mossies into a blind frenzy. They mirrored the sparks of my esoteric mind stuff, igniting against the indigo backdrop of deep, unconscious sleep.

I woke with the early morning's warming rays reflecting me back to my super-conscious experience. It was past life recall again, but it didn't give me a lot to go on. After a moment I realised that 1055 linked with the last vision. William the Conqueror, his adviser!

'Chris, are you up? It's me, Pete.'

'What is it?'

'Nothing. Do you want a cup of tea? I'm going down.'

'Is Roy up?'

'I heard him pottering around.'

'Good, get him a cuppa too, we'll have an early morning meeting in the office.'

'Oh, alright.'

I ripped into my old, worn-out jeans, 'oh, not another hole,' I shouted. They were becoming more fashionable by the week. Patches here, holes there: kids paid a fortune for jeans like these in top designer stores. I plodded to the toilet. As I splashed my face with water I heard a grotesque blast of someone clearing his nose and throat; it was disgusting.

'Lance! For fuck sake, you sound like a filthy, old codger.'

'I feel like a filthy, old codger this morning. Christ, the gunge I've coughed up, it loo...'

'Spare me the details, please!'

'You ready Chris?' shouted Roy.

'Almost. See you in a minute.' I had a quick shave as Lance shoved past, giving me one of his, I wonder what pickings I can scavenge looks. He was always on the prowl for titbits of intrigue.

'Right, sit down guys, I've got something important to share with you. I have decided to move on.'

I felt their auras plummet to their heels. Their vibrant, fresh faces slowly leaked into pools of despair. They nervously glanced at each other sending out silent SOS signals.

'But, why Chris, why? You're on top of things here; DB will be so disappointed. Why?' Roy sounded completely distraught.

'DB knows already. I need to stand on my own two feet. If I stay I'll always be in DB's shadow. I don't want that; I want to win my right, I want to build my reputation and gain my own merits.'

'But who's going to take over?' asked Pete. 'Is someone going to come in? Someone new?'

'Whoever takes the reigns will come from inside the ranks. Only someone who has felt the *Dwellers* claws paw at the pit of their soul and experienced the *Solar Angel* in their heart will come close. You know the tests, commitment and dedication required.'

'Chris who's going to hold it all together, who?'

'Listen Roy, I'm not leaving just yet; I've given DB three months notice. I'll not just leave him in the shit. We're over the backbreaking hurdles now. We're not under much financial threat. The film is complete; we've had some solid interest. It will sell.'

'So Linda will step into your shoes then, I suppose?' said Pete.

'Linda? Why do you say that? Do you think she can handle all of the Claregate business? I doubt it.'

'There's no one else, is there?'

I paused for a moment and glanced into their eyes. They knew who would take the reigns; they saw it in their souls. They deflected my gaze; no exchange of words was necessary. An uneasy silence bled into the ethers. I heard their frantic thoughts collide in their shell-shocked craniums.

'What? Us? No not me, no chance! I'm used to crawling into the safe haven of my depressions. I'm not putting my neck on the block. I'll leave, if that's my way out. I'll leave before Roy does. Ha! Then he'll have to stay,' Pete blurted out in an emotional rupture.

'Well, it's up to you, both of you. You've shown you have the commitment, the loyalty and the responsibility.'

'Mm, well, I don't know, we'll have to discuss it,' Roy interjected in a more coherent way.

'Tell you what I'm famished. Pete, go and pop a loaf of toast in; I fancy some with butter and marmalade. Pete opened the door...'thud!' Lance's head cracked like a coconut. He lay there in a heap of bones, quite dazed.

'What the fuck are you doing out here Lance? You sneak. On the prowl again?' Pete shouted in anger.

'I was just passing by, honestly. I heard voices, I wasn't spying, honest I wasn't.'

'You might as well come in and hear it first hand, from the horses mouth.'

'Well, what's going on then Roy? What's so important?'

'It's Chris he's leaving us. He's going in three months.'

'What? He's joking, right? Chris, tell me Roy's joking.'

'No, it's true. Roy's not joking. I'm leaving in a couple of months.'

'So who's going to take over?'

'We don't know yet Lance. How about you? You've been here the longest.'

'Well, yes, but, I don't think I'm suited to the position; I'm more of a back room boy.'

'More like a back-stabber.'

'Shut up Roy. What do you know about it? You changed sides when the going got tough. You've got nothing to shout about, have you?'

'Oh, on yer bike, you hypocrite, all you do is hide under Linda's underskirts. She's got more balls than you.'

'Quit it, both of you,' I shouted as Pete came in with a tray brimming with tea, toast, cheese and marmalade.

'Oh that's so inviting, how cosy, the three of you tucking into breakfast in private,' Lance blurted as his senses went into a whirlwind of desire. 'Can I have some,' he said stretching over to the tray.

'No you bloody well can't! Get your grubby little fingers off...'Roy shouted, slapping him right on the back of his scrawny, expectant hand.

'Ouch, you shouldn't have done that, I'll have you!'

'Oh who's going to have me? You? You haven't got the balls,' Roy said in a defiant way.

'Enough, enough, give him some toast for God's sake, if that's going to keep his mouth shut. You'll have to pop some more in later Lance okay.'

'Okay, okay,' he said whilst stuffing his famished face.

Needless to say the toast disappeared into a vacuous void of hungry mouths in a few seconds. Licking his lips and slurping tea, Lance shouted, spraying us with breakfast debris, 'so where are you off to then? Somewhere nice?'

'Actually I'm going back home to my mother's in Cyprus. I haven't seen her in all the years I've been here. She's been worried sick about my involvement at Claregate. She thought it was a sect and I had been brainwashed.'

'Oh how nice for you, the sun, fresh sea air, the holiday atmosphere and Alana, your fancy woman, by your side on Agia Napa beach!'

My face exploded in a fiery rage. 'You fucking earwig, is there anything you don't know about? Can't I have a crap without you sniffing around my backside?' I launched myself at him, sending the tray up in the air. He fell backwards off his seat and crashed into the filling cabinets.

'Don't you touch me,' he shouted in desperation. Roy, Pete you are witnesses. If you lay one finger on me I'll have you for G.B.H.'

'G.B.H. my ass, get him the hell out of here, Pete. I don't want his stinking aura infecting me anymore.'

'Come on Lance, get going, before Chris does something he'll regret,' Pete said, picking him up and dusting him down.

'Get off of me, I'm not finished yet!' He hollered shrugging off Pete's arms. 'I suppose you'll meet up with your bosom buddy, that renegade worm Stellios. He pranced around thinking he was his past life, Rueben's. Ha! What a joke he hadn't an artistic hair on his head. What a looser!'

'Reuben's, Stellios was Reuben's? I never knew that!' I muttered under my voice, completely taken by surprise.

'And another thing, bet he's shacked up with your ex wife, that other drama queen. You must be on another planet if you didn't put two and two together.'

It felt as if he had hit me with a sledgehammer. I slumped back in my chair all confused and off balance. Images and thoughts frenetically raced around my head. Their convenient meeting at college, their spiritual interests, bloody hell it was set up. God I got rid of her, Stellios encouraged me; he said it was the right thing to do. Shit! She left and he followed her. That's why he left without saying goodbye. No, no, it can't be true, can it?'

The boys sat around in shock as I melted into a catatonic straightjacket.

'And another thing I know, your trusting and devoted ex wife was shagging that famous soap opera actor who starred in *Paracelsus*. You know who I mean don't you!' Lance shouted, rubbing salt into my wounds.

I had no reply; he silenced me. He knew all my dirty laundry and that meant everyone knew too! I had nor the energy nor will to retaliate. I was lost for words. I just sat there wallowing in a gapping, deep hole of self-pity. I felt my emotions swamp my aura as the life force slowly drained out of me. My eyes burned with intense, pent-up frustration, but I could not raise my heavy, hooded lids. He had completely demoralised me!

'Mm, well, I'll see you all later. I think I'll get down to some paperwork.' Lance squawked, as he glided out leaving the door yawning like a gaping, black hole in my soul.

'The fucking bitch: that bastard Stellios. I never really trusted him, 'growled Pete. 'He's just like that past life of his, that fucking, conspirator artist Reubens.'

I raised my sodden head, swiped my drenched nose and wiped my eyes on my tattered sleeve.

'No it's not true; I can't believe it. Not under my nose. I couldn't have been so stupid,' I muttered in a vacant drawl. 'Yes Reubens? Stellios was Reubens? I never knew. All these years I confided in him; he never gave me the slightest hint. Why did he keep me in the dark all these years.'

'I thought you knew. We all knew he was Reubens. Where were you? What were you doing?'

'What do you mean, Pete? I was working my balls off making sure this place didn't sink from under us,' I blasted in an almighty rage. I had lost the plot. I was shaking and shivering like a nervous wreck.

'Roy, get me some *Rescue Remedy*, it's in my room,' Pete said. 'Bring him a sugary cup of tea and a blanket. Come on Chris, lie down here on the couch, for a few minutes.'

'Reubens, Reubens, yes, yes,' I said in a feverish, frail voice. 'He set up The Flemish School with Van Dyke. He was given *carte blanche* to roam around the royal courts of Europe. He was an ambassador: more like a master spy, rather than a master painter. It all fits in; it all fits in. All the pieces fall into place.' I rambled on and on as if I was deranged.

'What do you mean Chris? You've lost me,' Pete said in deeply puzzling manner. 'There you are Chris. Here, sit up, said Roy, emerging from upstairs with the small wonder remedy in his hand.

'Take a few drops on your tongue and sip on this tea,' said Pete in a deeply soothing voice. 'There, there, that should calm you down. Here, wrap yourself with this and have a rest.'

They left me to relax alone for a while. I slowly slid into a soothing, soul restoring slumber. The morning's sordid secrets swished around in my head, like filthy laundry in a washing machine. Stellios....., Reubens; Roy....., King Charles; Pete....., Archbishop Laud; .... Earl Strafford, my past life; mind was in a mangle. Suddenly I was whooshed into a psychedelic spin. My consciousness spiralled into infinity. It all came to an abrupt halt. I opened my eyes to a phenomenal vision. It all made sense, all of it. All the group's faces manifested in front of me, revealing their past life identities. We were all connected to The English Civil War. We were thrust together in a cosmic melting pot to work out past life karma. We were all light workers to varying degrees. We all held positions of authority, but had abused our power. We had heavy burdens to deal with, as consequences of our past life actions. Karmic law would demand just penalties. There was always justice, *'an eye for an eye, and a tooth for a tooth'.*

Barry was my interrogator in the Strafford past life; he was the Parliamentarian leader Lord Pym responsible for his impeachment and subsequent beheading! Barry's first cousin was John Hampden, one of Strafford's prime enemies and one of the eight managers of his execution! I had met him once, purely by chance, with Barry in St Albans, before I knew of the past life connection. He gave me the shivers then, now I know why! Lance was George Herbert, a metaphysical poet at the time, drawn into court intrigue and I'm sure was involved in political plots. Cleary was an aggrieved Irish Lord, the Earl of Cork. Even Andrew had come back to haunt me. He was Lord Mountnorris, another Irish enemy of Strafford's. Linda, God! She was the infamous, power-hungry Cardinal Richelieu, chief minister and power behind the throne of Louis 13th of France. She was not connected to the English Civil War, but there were alliances and intrigues throughout the period. Roy was Strafford's cherished Lord, King Charles: Pete was his trusted friend and co-adviser to King Charles, Archbishop Laud. Ah, Elena, my dear Elena, her past life came waltzing back, trailing clouds of pomp and glory. She was Queen Henrietta Maria, King Charles French Catholic wife. She and Reubens could have been lovers then!

A whirlwind of images faded into each other; faces, names, titles and experiences ebbed and flowed. The final vision was of unity; all our souls merged together, to form one pulsating group soul, all loving, all understanding, and all knowing. We were the *Chosen Ones*, the few, working in the English Ashram under the Nirmanakaya, who was Socrates, Plato and the English Master Robert Browning in past lives. We had incarnated together, to rebalance karma and to strengthen and adapt the Ageless Wisdom. We had come back to hold the floodgates open for the New Age to flow through. It was our responsibility and our destiny to push the frontiers of human consciousness far beyond the confines of religion and science, on into the realm of spirituality. We worked endlessly, serving *The Will of God.* We had responded to the calling. We were sons of sacrifice, here to carry the mantle of the Aquarian Age. I knew my purpose. My destiny was clear; my questions had been answered.

I faded back to physical consciousness, totally content and humbled. I was privileged to have been shown the bigger picture. I was one with the Omni-present, Omni-potent, consciousness we call Christ and God.

CHAPTER 44

I slowly emerged from the mind-blowing experience. I eased up off the couch, promptly dusted myself down and sat in my desk again.

'Roy, come in, I want a word.'

'What the hell are you playing at? You were at death's door half an hour ago.'

'Get Pete up here; we need to talk.'

'Are you sure you're up to it Chris?'

'Just get him in here!'

He thudded upstairs and in minutes he returned with Pete.

'Right, come in, you both know the score; I'm leaving and that's final. It's up to you two. What you decide to do is on your shoulders. I'd like to think I could put Claregate's survival in your hands, but the ultimate decision is yours.'

'We haven't had much time to think about it. Give us a few days to mull it over.'

'All right, I want an answer in a week, one week. I'm off down to LE. Are you coming with me?'

'I'll come down Chris,' answered Roy. 'Dick wants to show me how to make printing plates.'

'What are you up to today Pete?'

'I'm collating a couple of books with Griff in the port-a-cabin.'

'Good, so you've both got projects you're working on. Roy meet me in half an hour in the hallway.'

I prepared myself for the backlash down at LE. Linda was there, settling final drafts of DB's next publication. Lance had sneaked off with his prized portion of gossip. He was going to do his dam best to spread it all around. I would have to face the fire and endure disgrace and dishonour. I was going to be goaded, especially now that they knew I was leaving with Alana to go to set up home in Cyprus.

'Come on Roy, let's get cracking,' I shouted as I marched outside into the drive. We squeezed into the oldest Claregate wreck. The bloody thing was falling apart. Gerald was informed of its condition, but he'd not had time to sort it or scrap it. It croaked into gear and shuddered as we trundled down to meet my destiny.

'You know the knives will be out, don't you?' asked Roy.

'Yes, I know they will. What's new? I've got to face the onslaught. I have no option.'

The old car croaked towards the cottage. Its tired, aching springs, squirming tires and screeching breaks alerted the cats and dogs. The dogs barked, bit and clawed at its flanks. Even they had ganged up on me. It came to one almighty termination. 'Bang!' Splutter!' Smoke bellowed and steam hissed from under the bonnet. The electrics fizzed and crackled on the dash. It was finished; it had died on me.

My entrance couldn't have been more dramatic, even if I had tried to stage it. Ghostly faces loomed out from the misty windows. The whole atmosphere was charged with expectancy. The dogs were in a rabid trance, barking violently as the cats snagged and scrammed each other. The stench of foul play smeared the heavy air with ghoulish past-life memories. Screams, scowls, crowds; bombast, blasts and brawls; anarchy, treason and conspiracy all mushroomed in my head. The toll of bells, chains and shackles, the henchman's blackened hood and glint of his expectant axe blade rushed past me, as my neck stiffened. I pushed the creaky, old door open. There was no reception, nothing but a rush of animals stampeding into the kitchen.

'Will you be okay Chris? I'm off down to the print works.'

'Yes Roy, I've got nothing to fear. I've done nothing wrong. My heart is pure and my conscience is clear. The lounge door thudded open to Lance's balding head. He squirmed past me, sneering and holding a tray full of used crockery. He had done his job well. I kicked the door in expecting a full inner circle gathering. The room felt like a mausoleum; echoes of heavy conversation saturated the air. Clumps of emotional debris lingered in the ethers, like clinging cobwebs trapping unsuspecting prey. There had been charged exchanges, they had been here all right, but now deadly silence reigned. I heard the ceiling shudder and the thump of slow, deliberate and determined feet thud monotonously across the room.

'Is that you Chris? I'm just getting dressed; I'll be down in a minute,' D.B. shouted.

'Yes, it's me, I need to talk to you, it's important.' His footsteps echoed like drums sounding my death knell, as his heavy, business boots creaked on the worn, old stairs.

'Well what is it? You know how valuable my time is,' he shouted in his arrogant, doctors drabble, as he marched past me wearing his favourite red, threadbare dressing down and hobnail boots.

' I just want you to know the truth about my...'

'Yes, yes I know,' he interjected in his customary manner, before I had a chance to finish my sentence.

'Chris, I've thrown everything at you. You've weathered every storm; you've truly won your spurs. Your mettle has been tested. I've prepared you well. Your heart is pure; your motives are of the highest. You've won the right to be at my side. The guardians of Esoteric Knowledge have also recognised your efforts. You are eligible to become a trusted member of the inner circle of the Master,' he said in a deeply philosophical tone.

' I've been waiting for a soul to incarnate, stabilise and integrate its personality and offer it to the Lord's work. Many have tried; many have failed to reach the mark. Look around you. Not that they are not devoted, able bodied and inspired, they are not ready for *The Burning Ground*. But they are all light workers; they have been with me, life after life, honouring my will, my teachings and my Master. You are special; you can inherit the mantle. It is in your hands.'

'I don't understand DB. *The Burning Ground*. Why me?'

'You will find out soon, be patient. You've got valuable spiritual work to do in Wales. You've got a lot of Karma to offload and harmonise there. You'll be going in 10 weeks.'

'What do you mean DB? Wales? Karma? I'm off to…

' Lance, bring in a cuppa for Chris and I,' he shouted, slicing my reply mid sentence.

'DB? Wales? I'm not planning to live there.'

'No, but *He* wants you there. *He's* made plans for you.'

'I'm off to Cyprus, back home to my Mama. You mean to say I'll set up home in Wales?'

'Yes, South Wales, with Alana.'

'So you know about her?' I said, sheepishly.'

'Oh yes, I knew even before you knew Chris. There's nothing that I don't know. It's all in here, in your chart. I know your Akashic record.'

'What about my karma with Wales? What's that all about?'

'You'll find out sooner or later. There are immense challenges ahead. I've prepared you for your future pathway; you are a Rainbow Warrior; I've worked out part of your Soul's Purpose.'

'Soul's Purpose? You mean to say you know why I'm here? My karma? My destiny?'

'Yes Chris, but as a first Ray personality, you've got to unravel it for yourself. I can only give you clues.'

'Well, then?'

'You are here to win heart consciousness. The heart centre is where Christ consciousness is hidden. It can only be accessed by expressing unconditional love. It is the centre of love-wisdom and the focal point of the heart of God.'

'Unconditional love? I've forgiven Elena. I understand why things had to happen the way they did. I know of our past life karma.'

'There's more. Your Leo is intercepted in the 10th house; Uranus is there retrograde. The pattern is related to your Soul's Purpose; Leo rules the heart centre, love, affairs and children. Neptune in Scorpio challenges; that is soul-wrenching karma.'

'What soul-wrenching karma? Haven't I gone through my tests? Haven't I overcome the ghosts of my past?'

384

'Chris, you'll have to struggle with honour, loyalty and betrayal. You will be dragged through hell and back. Your love and loyalty will be on the line.'

'How can you say that? Give me my chart. I've had enough tests, enough trials; all I want is a peaceful life.'

'Chris, you have taken up the work of the Lord. You've done it throughout history. You are a spiritual crusader. You have to take *The Word* with you. You can't deny your destiny.'

I snatched my chart from him and stormed out to the garden. My nerves were shot to smithereens. More stress, more challenges. Will there ever be an end to it all? I thought, as I sat and contemplated DB's words. What was I to do? What was I to think? He knew me intimately; he had never been wrong in the past. Wales? Karma? Unconditional love? Oh, yes the tape, Michael El Legion's channelling; it's all connected. I've got past life links to Wales. DB's also confirmed it. I sat for a while in the lush, quiet gardens, contemplating the events of the last few hours. D.B's creaky old window rattled in its frame as he lunged out.

'John, take Chris back with you. That old wreck he's driving is ready for the knacker's yard. Get Gerald to dump it!'

I caught a lift back to Claregate with Barry and John. They were going to make sure my duties were going to be covered. My work here had been done; I had passed my probation period; my destiny beckoned me. All would be revealed in time.

I called Mama, she was ecstatic; the adventure was set. I was on my way out. My tracks had been covered. Roy and Pete sighed with relief when they were absolved from their pending responsibilities. There was one final experience I was exposed to before I set off on my quest.

During a meditation I was flashed a five-pointed star. I had never used it before. He injected it into my consciousness; He wanted me to use it. What did it mean? What was its significance? It frightened me at first. I had only seen it in demonic horror movies. It symbolised Satan and devil worship. I got a hold of a copy of Gerald P Hall's *Teachings of the Ages*. It is an ancient wisdom encyclopaedia, crammed with mystery teachings, symbols and occult research. According to Hall, the five-pointed star symbolised man and the elements. It was an alchemical symbol of man's divinity and spiritual potential. However, if used in its inverted form it symbolised the dark lord, satanic rituals, possession and the black arts. I was given it to meditate upon. He wanted me to unite with its energies. I started to visualise it, concentrate on it and finally meditate on it.

One afternoon, over a full moon period, after a meditation on the symbol, I was thrust into the ultimate super conscious experience.

> *22nd Oct, super conscious experience.*
> *I lay in a semi conscious state after a meditation. Suddenly, I hear my mother's voice; she's reading the Tarot; the Ace of Pentacles is flashed to me. Out of the blue, the most intense vibrations began to pour through my body. The energy was so powerful it wracked me with excruciating pain. Suddenly, an electric current thrust through me, centring in my mouth and head. It shot around the fillings in my teeth and ricochets out through the top of my head. I endured the pain and power of the electric fire, but at one stage it became unbearable. I focussed my mind, concentrating on the Ajna centre. My consciousness shot through 'the Eye of the Needle', into a myriad of brilliant, multi-coloured, kaleidoscopic colours. My whole body was saturated with fire and colour. It was 'The Burning Ground'. I was surrounded by a torrential flow of purifying fire. I was the torrent! I was the fire! Tongues of fire from all the extremities of my body. I had become a flaming five-pointed star! The pain had become unbearable by now; I had to end the experience. I centred myself into my physical body. My heartbeat thumping, breathing bellowing, I regained consciousness as DB's voice echoed in the distance.*
> *'Christos, you have bathed in the fires of **The Burning Ground**. You have been baptised in the fire of God. My God is an all-consuming fire! You are ready, you are the chosen one!'*

My physical body remained in a cataleptic trance for minutes. God, what an experience! I was drained, elated, confused and inspired. My whole body had been transformed with the fire of divinity. This was **The Burning Ground** and I had survived it; I had become a fire God, a blazing five-pointed star, prepared to carry the torch of the Lord. My Soul's Purpose lay in front of me. I now knew what I was here to express. I was here to feed the masses with spiritual food. I had come back to de-mystify the ancient teachings. I had to unveil the ancient wisdom. Humanity needed to understand how to become divine. I had to prepare them for Christ consciousness, the Second Coming of the Lord of light, love and compassion, Jesus the Christ.

My initiation was complete; I was ready to fulfil my quest; I was fully equipped, tested and tried. I was a graduate of Claregate's elite inner circle. My *daemon* beckoned me into a dance with destiny. Within days I was ready to make the epic journey back again to Cyprus, the Isle of Aphrodite and then to Wales, the hub of Britain's Celtic civilisation. I had a date with my destiny. What adventures lay ahead? Were the gods going to honour me? I had five hard years of experience behind me. Was it going to be enough?

ABOUT THE AUTHOR

Tak Paris is a professional astrologer with 25 years experience. In 1980 he studied at Claregate College under Dr. Douglas Baker, the eminent master astrologer and metaphysician. He gained Bachelor of Astrology and Metaphysics. He has lectured extensively and taught Esoteric Science and Astrology.

In 1990 he edited and published Chalice New Age Magazine for 5 years in Wales. In 1998 he joined British Airways where he became BA's Contact magazine astrologer. He is preparing the sequel to *The Burning Ground* at present. He is happily married and lives in Worthing, West Sussex, UK.

Lightning Source UK Ltd.
Milton Keynes UK
UKOW052148300312

189918UK00001B/37/A